NOT BY BREAD ALONE

BY VILHJALMUR STEFANSSON

My Life with the Eskimo, 1913

Anthropological Papers (American Museum of Natural History), 1914

The Friendly Arctic, 1921

Hunters of the Great North, 1922

The Northward Course of Empire, 1922

The Adventure of Wrangel Island, 1925

My Life with the Eskimos (abridged), 1927

The Standardization of Error, 1927

Adventures in Error, 1936

The Three Voyages of Martin Frobisher, 1938
(With collaboration of Eloise McCaskill)

Unsolved Mysteries of the Arctic, 1938

Iceland: The First American Republic, 1939

The Problem of Meighen Island, 1939

Ultima Thule, 1940

Greenland, 1942

The Friendly Arctic (new edition), 1943

Arctic Manual, 1944

Compass of the World, 1944
(With Hans Weigert)

BOOKS FOR YOUNGER READERS
(In collaboration with Violet Irwin)

Kak, the Copper Eskimo, 1924

The Shaman's Revenge, 1925

The Mountain of Jade, 1926

Northward Ho!, 1925
(In collaboration with Julia Schwartz)

NOT
BY BREAD ALONE

BY

VILHJALMUR STEFANSSON

ECHO POINT BOOKS & MEDIA, LLC
BRATTLEBORO, VERMONT

Published in 2017 by Echo Point Books & Media
Brattleboro, Vermont
www.EchoPointBooks.com

Originally published in 1946 by The MacMillan Company

Not By Bread Alone
ISBN: 978-1-63561-078-9 (casebound)

Cover design by Adrienne Núñez
Cover image by longtaildog, courtesy of Shutterstock

TO

OLIVE RATHBUN WILCOX

Collaborator on fourteen previous books
and on this one

Contents

Introduction: The Physiological Side

BY EUGENE F. DU BOIS, M.D.

Medical Director Russell Sage Institute of Pathology,
Professor of Physiology, Cornell University Medical College

HERE is a book that should be read by everyone who eats meat. It will relieve unnecessary apprehension regarding the food we most enjoy. Of course it should be read by, or read to, everyone who does not eat meat.

The most intensive consideration should come from all those who are working in the fields of nutrition and its allied science, dietetics. Vilhjalmur Stefansson states clearly the fact that men can remain in good health on a diet of meat alone. The evidence is ample and incontrovertible.

This message was brought to us by Stefansson a good many years ago but its implications have been neglected. The text books on nutrition are still narrow in their viewpoints. They do not seem to realize the great adaptability of the human organism and the wide extremes in diet that are compatible with health. The modern tendency is to encourage a wide selection of foods and this seems to be sensible and economical for the great bulk of our population. The propaganda is strong and on the whole excellent. Take for example the government pamphlet on the so-called "Basic Seven."

FOR HEALTH

Eat Some Food From Each Group Every Day

Group 1: Green and yellow vegetables: some raw, some cooked, frozen or canned.

Group 2: Oranges, tomatoes, grapefruit, or raw cabbage or salad greens.

Group 3: Potatoes and other vegetables and fruits: Raw, dried, cooked, frozen or canned.

Group 4: Milk and milk products fluid, evaporated, dried milk, or cheese.

Group 5: Meat, poultry, fish or eggs or dried beans, peas, nuts, or peanut butter.

Group 6: Bread, flour and cereals, natural or whole grain or enriched or restored.

Group 7: Butter and fortified margarine (with added Vitamin A).

IN ADDITION TO THE BASIC 7 . . . EAT ANY OTHER FOODS YOU WANT.

(U. S. Government Chart)

It is startling when we learn that large groups of active hunters in many parts of the world subsist on nothing but a small subdivision of Group 5. It is not quite as startling when we consider that the vegetarians live comfortably on all the groups except this very part of No. 5. The strictest vegetarians exclude also Group 4 and butter in Group 7.

Physicians will note that those who live on meat alone metabolize a mixture of protein and fat that corresponds exactly to the materials that were metabolized by patients with "moderately severe" diabetes in the days before insulin was available. Evidently the danger lay not in the mixture ordinarily metabolized but in the exacerbations of the disease that changed the "moderately severe" to the "very severe" type. The normal hunters and explorers were entirely without this danger.

The student of vitamin deficiencies will find in *Not By Bread Alone* much food for thought and very little that will conform to his previous ideas. Quite evidently we must revise some of our text book statements. According to the books, Stefansson and his companions should have died of scurvy. One can think of half a dozen different explanations for their striking lack of symptoms. Each one of the half dozen is merely a possibility, as yet entirely unproved. Some day someone will find the right answer and it may very well be a combination or a balance of several factors.

Those who are interested in the techniques of studies in nutrition will be interested in the combination of field and laboratory investigations. Stefansson's field study had been completed and preliminary reports published several years before he requested supplementary work by the Russell Sage Institute of Pathology, a small research laboratory affiliated with Cornell University Medical College and Bellevue Hospital.

In 1926 when this part of the work was planned our country was passing through a phase in nutrition work when there was a concerted effort on the part of a small but very articulate group to prove that meat was harmful. It was supposed to cause high blood pressure, kidney disease, hardening of the arteries, arthritis and other similar ailments. The old bogey of ptomaine poisoning had faded but the newer work on allergy over-emphasized the rare sensitizations to specific meats. In addition there was, as always, the host of vague prejudices of religious, humanitarian or esthetic nature. In the background, subconscious but none the less potent, lurked the old Puritanical certainty that anything we enjoyed was bad for us either physically or morally. All these combined against meat and particularly against a liberal meat ration. It required a good deal of writing on the part of Stefansson and some of the nutritionists before the intelligent citizen was able to consume without fear as much lean and fat meat as he wanted.

When Stefansson first came to us with his problems we were concerned regarding the attacks on meat and anxious to secure impartial, reliable information. We were asked to find out what happened if two men in New York lived on nothing but meat for a year. This was a good problem in itself and best of all there were two experimental subjects available. Those who work in the field of nutrition have plenty of problems, but great difficulty in securing good subjects for unusual diets over long periods.

The results of the extensive work in the Sage metabolism ward of Bellevue Hospital, the calorimeter room and the chemical laboratories have been published in a dozen scientific articles which are well summarized in this book. The only dramatic part of the study was the surprisingly undramatic nature of the findings.

This did not disappoint us. In a long study of orthodox and unorthodox diets in disease we had become accustomed to the undramatic. When observations were carefully planned and most exact technique employed the results on each individual were surprisingly uniform. A great many dire predictions and brilliant theories faded into nothingness.

In spite of the fact that there were no striking departures from normal when Stefansson and his companion, Andersen, lived on meat, the scientific results were of considerable value. They furnished data in a long study which will be almost impossible to repeat and various parts of the work supplemented investigations in related fields. Even our errors of judgment in trying extreme diets on Stefansson in the first month were fortunate. They may have been tough on Stefansson and a source of anxiety to those responsible but they added materially to our practical and scientific knowledge of diets.

At the time of the Bellevue episode there were not available the modern exact methods of vitamin assay in human subjects. It would be helpful if the experiment were repeated using these modern methods. Clinical observations cannot detect minor deficiencies in vitamins. The work must be done with great care and common sense or it will be misleading. Some of the early enthusiasts in vitamins published surveys implying that the great majority of healthy people in our country were far below the average in their vitamin consumption. Apparently the "average" was confused with a so-called optimal supply purposely made liberal to include a large factor of safety. The reader who is interested in the newer methods of vitamin assay and nutrition surveys will find them well described in the proceedings of a recent meeting of the American Institute of Nutrition.* The various papers at this symposium were prepared by authorities on vitamin research. In the light of this book of Stefansson's the one italicized remark of the Chairman, Dr. Charles Glenn King, is worth quoting: "Perhaps the most seriously needed type of related study in America is to find, through long periods of time, the degree of correlation that exists between the health records of individuals and their dietary habits."

March 7, 1946.

---

* Symposium on Nutrition Surveys, Federation Proceedings, *Federation of American Societies for Experimental Biology*, September, 1945, *4*:252-281.

Introduction: The Anthropological Side

BY EARNEST A. HOOTON, PH.D., SC.D.

Curator of Somatology of the Peabody Museum, Professor of Physical Anthropology in Harvard University

ABOUT 1912, when I was studying anthropology at Oxford, my teacher, Dr. R. R. Marett, told me that Vilhjalmur Stefansson had written him inquiring for a young anthropologist to accompany him on an expedition to the Arctic. Marett asked me whether I would like to go, but I replied that I was having a hard enough time surviving the English winters. The next year I took a job at Harvard.

Among the human skeletons housed in the Peabody Museum of Harvard University, I found a sizeable lot of remains dug up by Stefansson and Hastings in 1905 from certain mediaeval cemeteries in Iceland. I was immediately fascinated by these Icelandic skulls, because of the perfection of their teeth and because they showed certain other features —palatine and mandibular tori, thickened tympanic plates, gable-shaped vaults—that were strongly reminiscent of Eskimo crania. Were these "Eskimoid" features the effect of a meat diet, of the Icelandic environment in general, or of an adulteration of Icelandic blood with that of Eskimo through the colonization of Greenland? I wrote an article on that subject in 1918, but even now I do not know the answer. Soon after this Stefansson returned from his explorations and we began to correspond about the teeth of Eskimos, Icelanders, and Arctic diets.

Before I met him, I was slightly wary of Stefansson, because he was the center of controversies that lit up the northern skies like the aurora borealis, because he was alleged to have discovered "blond Eskimos," and because he said that nothing in the diet of the Eskimo required the development of massive jaws and enormous chewing muscles. Stefansson seemed to me to be an anthropological heretic who denied everything I had been taught about the Eskimo. However, as soon as I met him personally, I was immediately and permanently convinced of his sincerity, his honesty, and of the really tremendous scope of his knowledge of Arctic life and of the habits of the Eskimo. My experience with Stefansson was like his with a boiled fish diet—having at length brought himself to try it, he at once found it superior to all other preparations of fish. Thus began an intermittent professional association and an uninterrupted friendship.

I have found Stefansson neither unsound in his ideas nor inaccurate in his statements. I have never met a man who, in both public and private utterance, displays less rancor against those who have attacked him, or who is more willing to give credit to his adversaries for scientific accomplishments and good intentions. He is a severe critic of his own theories— quite ready to change his mind when his views are conclusively refuted. I have gone to the mat with Stefansson about all of his facts and theories that seemed to me questionable. He has always come out on top. What he says in this book about the jaws and teeth of Icelanders and Eskimos, is, to my knowledge, correct. What he says about meat diet is convincing to me. I saw Stefansson at various times during his experiment of living for twelve months exclusively upon that diet and he seemed to me to be in good health (although not perceptibly better than usual).

This book is a fair and honest presentation of a powerful case. Stefansson seems to me to have established most of his contentions. I doubt that my judgment is seriously biased because I like meat and have little faith in dietitians.

February 14, 1946.

NOT BY BREAD ALONE

1

Preliminaries and Speculation

THE saying that a man is what he eats derives an expanded significance from the theory that development from ape-hood to humanity was caused by a change in diet. The school of scientists which believes that food made men of apes pictures a remote age when the climate of the Old World was so rainy that forests were spread over most or all the tropic and sub-tropic lands of Europe, Asia and Africa. In this humid forest lived many anthropoids, among them the gorilla, orang, chimpanzee and that cousin of theirs from whom mankind is descended. They were all vegetarian, about to the extent that the apes are now, meaning that they lived principally on tubers, nuts, fruits, buds and tender shoots. Like the present apes, they would catch and eat a few small animals. Living among the branches, or at least able to climb a tree when in danger or in want of a food which grew aloft, these ancestors of man flourished—as long as the woodland remained damp, hot and substantially unbroken.

But, according to the hypothesis, there came a change in Old World climate such that areas here and there became too dry to support a forest, and turned into prairie. This would not matter at first, while the glades were small; the forest population withdrew from or scampered across the patches of grassland. But if the change in climate was progressive and of continental scope it would come to pass that islands of forest were surrounded by wide stretches of meadow and treeless plain. As the drying cycle progressed, through centuries and millenniums, the anthropoid tree dwellers would become more and more crowded into their limited asylums.

As the forest islands shrank the prairie grew and the living space of the grazing animals—horse and cow, antelope and sheep—which starve in woodlands but thrive on grasslands, expanded.

The anthropoids as we see them today, and as we know them from remote ages through their teeth and other revealing bone formations, are vegetarians but not grazing animals; they cannot manage on timothy and bluegrass, but they can live on the flesh of the grass eaters.*

The first men had to learn to hunt, if they wanted to live. Like the anthropoids of today, our remote ancestors doubtless combined rudimentary hunting with gathering—they searched habitually for nests, and ate the birdlings as well as the eggs, and the mother bird, too, if they could catch her. The anthropoid manner of search for rodents and grubs combines hunting and gathering methods.

The theory pictures those of the anthropoids which found themselves on the grasslands as facing a new environment with about the mental equipment of a chimpanzee, equal to that of a four-year-old child. In the service of a childlike brain they had the most marvelous tools that nature ever gave to an animal, a pair of hands.

At first the prairie-stranded anthropoids were chiefly gatherers, finding dead fish along a stream as the partly vegetarian grizzly bears do in Alaska, finding a ground-squirrel in its burrow as the chiefly vegetarian grizzlies do in Arctic Canada, finding honey in a bees' nest as the black bears do

---

* The animals that can live on flesh foods, or at least can exist on them for considerable periods, are more numerous than most of us realize. What we think of as strict carnivora, like the eagle, the wolf and the seal, are but a small segment of the actual and potential flesh-eaters. For animals which by choice eat grass will turn to meat when necessity arises. Of these the best known, perhaps, are the horses of Iceland which, in certain districts at certain times, live on fish. The lean meat of whales, dried and ground into a flour, is a standard cattle feed in parts of Europe. It is well known that rats and similar rodents can live on the bodies of other animals. Most species of fish live mainly or exclusively on other fish. The carnivorous habits of reptiles are notorious; little snakes swallow mice, a python will swallow a dog.

in New England, finding grubs in decaying trees as the native Blackfellows do in Australia, gathering snails as the French do, digging clams as New Englanders do, bird-nesting like youngsters all over the world, sucking eggs like a Huck Finn or a modern chimp.

Of these habits there would be gradual and natural expansion among those apes who found themselves unable to discover a forest in which to gather what had been their main food and was still the chief food of their ape cousins in regions of more rain. The prairie ape would have the ingenuity, as many other animals have, to lie motionless in the grass till some small grazing animal, perhaps a lamb or kid, came near enough to be seized. Troops of these pre-humans would work together as troops of baboons still do, for defense and offense.

In short, as this theory holds, the apes found it necessary, in the grassland that swarmed with grazing animals, to become ingenious in order to live; while the ancestors of the chimpanzee and gorilla, at home in their accustomed tropical forest, required no more than apish industry and perseverance in the search for roots, shoots and fruits. What had been good enough for their fathers was good enough for them—served them well in a familiar environment and kept them what they were, anthropoids.

On the grasslands there was now in play a rigorous process of natural selection. Those apes that kept searching for tubers and fruits, in a region that no longer contained many of them, had less and less chance for survival as the islands of tree growth along rivers or lakes became increasingly scarce with the progressive change from a heavy forest to a uniform prairie. As the grasses spread to replace the trees, there was more and more food to support more and more antelope, sheep, horses and buffalo, and thus more and more survival opportunity for those slowly evolving forebears of man whose brains guided their hands toward the use of clubs, the throwing of stones and finally to the development of knife, spear and bow.

In this transition period the death rate must have been heavy not only among those slower of brain and lacking ingenuity, but surely also throughout the prairie communities. There must have been serious trouble in adapting the old vegetarian digestive functions to the new food—just as it seems clear that the Iceland pony which lives on fish is not quite so well off as his hay-fed brother. There must have been new derangements, producing many an early death; and dietetic lacks, causing deficiency diseases.

All these things, if they happened, must have taken place millions of years, or at least a million years, before the present era. During the eons of time since then the forest-dwelling anthropoids have changed little, so far as can be judged from their preserved bones. In the same space the near-humans changed to human so effectively that some anthropologists assert that Cro-Magnon man of 20,000 or 30,000 years ago in France was in his physique if anything more ideally human than the present day European, if humanness is measured in terms of difference from the anthropoid.

This book, although written by a part-time anthropologist, is not a work of anthropology; although written by a part-time geographer, it is not a geographic treatise. So I do no more in this introductory chapter than touch upon the facts and theorizing that back up the view of man's origin upon which, as a peg, the twelve chapters that follow are hung.

The anthropologists through their archaeology, and the geologists through their paleontology, find themselves in agreement that agriculture is a recent development in the evolution of man, for its existence is not provable in any part of the world more than 20,000 years back. Professor Ellsworth Huntington, distinguished authority on man's relation to land and climate, says in his *Mainsprings of Civilization,* published in 1945, that the first agriculture, which he thinks consisted merely in such operations as gathering and storing the kernels of self-sown grains, does not even in that primitive form go back farther than the New Stone Age, thus much less than 20,000 years, perhaps only 10,000; and this, he thinks, will have been in some such country as Egypt. He considers that those of us who are descended from North Europeans have had agricultural forebears through only two, three or four thousand years.

During the period before agriculture, it is chiefly in the tropics, and not everywhere there, that men could, as some do at present, live like their anthropoid predecessors and cousins by digging roots and tubers, collecting shoots, bulbs, buds, fruits and nuts, and by catching a few small creatures. Outside the tropics pre-farming man was necessarily in the main a hunter; secondarily he was the gatherer of such animal foods as worms, grubs and insects (e.g., locusts), shellfish and fish thrown up along the beach, stranded seals and whales. He scouted around, no doubt, and competed with the hyena and vulture for the bodies of animals that had died of illness, accident or old age.

This necessarily almost complete dependence of pre-agricultural man on animal food is not confined to the grasslands of the world, tropic, temperate or arctic; it applies nearly as much to some temperate-zone and most arctic woodlands, even to many tropic forests. Carl Lumholtz reports, for instance, that when he was with the tropical forest-dwelling natives of northern Australia they lived mainly on animal food, and never ate anything of vegetal nature if flesh foods were available.

So from the time when our ancestors ceased being apelike gatherers of monkey food down to the substantial growth of agriculture, mankind lived through one or several millions of years chiefly on the lean and fat of animals. The exception to this would be some groups which drifted back into subtropical and tropic forests of that humid type which enabled the chimpanzee and gorilla to remain anthropoid.

Animal husbandry, true enough, developed before agriculture; or, at least, there is evidence that it was extensive and widespread throughout Asia, Africa and Europe when thoroughgoing agriculture was as yet restricted to special regions, like Egypt and the Fertile Crescent. But, dietetically, the herdsman and the hunter are practically at one. There is the difference of the extensive use of milk and its products by the owners of herds. But this difference is superficial; for milk is only a slightly modified form of blood, and blood was always a considerable element in the food of the hunter, in so far as ancient hunters can be judged from those with whom we have come in contact through the history of the last two or three thousand years, since records began to be kept on the progress of geographic discovery by European explorers.

As I have said, there must have been a lot of digestive and other physical troubles when the anthropoid was changing to man through the rigors of natural selection in a country that had vegetation on which cattle flourished but apes did not. The few who survived that grueling process to become the first men were, however, of necessity well adapted to the huntsman's diet, content with it and healthy on it—else they would not have survived. This suitability of organs was naturally inherited by their descendants, or at least by those of them who were healthy, and thus successful, on the meat diet of the hunter or on its slight modification, the meat-and-milk diet of the herdsman.

There is, however, the fundamental drawback to living by means of hunting that no small area can support a large population. This difficulty is mitigated rather than solved by the domestication of animals, which, for instance, enables a man both to ride a horse for hunting buffalo and also to eat the horse when it is not needed for further use as a mount. The basic difficulty with both hunting and herding is that, by varying estimates, something between five and ten men can live on a given amount of what hogs eat for every one who can live by eating the hogs. So there is a powerful economic pressure for returning to the food habits of our apelike ancestors—with the modification that, instead of hunting for things to dig from the ground or to pick off trees, we till the ground for cereals and plant trees that bear fruit.

Since we all have an urge to live, and since parents desire that their children shall not go hungry, the development of agriculture followed necessarily as soon as men found out that more of them could live on wheat from plowed soil than could possibly get along by hunting the animals that grazed over the same land.

But there are few gains without pains. Just as there must have been ill health and difficult adaptation when the ape-man was changing from the diet of the gathering ape to that of the hunting man, so there would be similar trouble when people who had been hunters began to change gradually from a nearly or quite exclusive flesh diet to one that contained more and more of rice, wheat and corn. The million or so years which had intervened since the ape turned into man had eliminated, by natural selection, those that were best suited for digesting vegetables, since they would have been least suited for digesting meat. Besides, the roots-and-shoots diet of the ape-man in the humid forest is markedly different from that of the grain-fed farmer.

In this introductory chapter I shall not go deeply into the difficulties encountered by man in making the necessary adjustments when he turned, after ages of hunting and herding, to a diet which, although largely from the vegetable kingdom, was nevertheless strikingly different from that of his prehuman ancestors—a diet not mainly of roots and shoots, nuts and fruits, but of cereals. I rest with quotation and paraphase of a section from Professor Huntington's *Mainsprings of Civilization* in which he discusses the medley of advantages and troubles, some of them definitely known and the rest inferred, that came upon hunting man when he began to try to support large numbers of his kind on small areas through the cultivation of beans, lentils, rice, wheat, oats, and the rest of the cereals.

In his chapter "Agriculture, Disease and Diet" Huntington says: "The ideal diet, it would seem, must be essentially that to which man becomes adjusted during his long, slow evolution. Among most of the ancestors of modern Europeans and Americans an agricultural diet has prevailed less than two thousand years. There is no reliable evidence that in that brief span any appreciable change has occurred in the inherited dietary requirements which had become established during a preceding period perhaps a thousand times longer." Huntington, then, believes about 2,000,000 years intervened between the time when early man, or preman, ceased depending mainly on the food of apes and the time when, as an agriculturist, he returned to a diet which, although similar to that of apes in containing a relatively small percentage of flesh foods, is unlike any previous diet of ape or man in its high percentage of cereals.

Huntington thinks, it would appear, that the change in diet brought on through the cultivation of fields introduces a reciprocal relation. For he believes that as agriculture raises the quantity it lowers the quality of food, the quality being judged by its healthfulness to men who have been living for 2,000,000 years on something else. He says:

"The most important effect of agriculture on efficiency probably results from malnutrition. . . . One of the main reasons for poor nutrition is that agriculture has lowered the quality of man's diet and at the same time made it possible for more people to subsist. Mechanical methods of preparing food have gone still further along this same sad path until the typical 'modernized' diet has become appallingly poor. By 'modernized' we do not mean the diet now eaten by the more intelligent and prosperous people of Europe and America, but the kind that is still eaten by people at the lower economic levels and in many other countries by the majority of the population. In such a diet, bread, cereals, potatoes and other forms of starchy food play a dominant part; the rest is largely composed of [vegetable] protein foods, such as beans, together with carbohydrates in the form of sugar."

Huntington summarizes: "Agriculture has been a powerful factor in lowering human efficiency as well as in advancing civilization. . . . Practically every step of progress is accompanied by drawbacks which are not rectified for a long time."

Humanity may have needed most of Huntington's 2,000,-000 years for evolving from the largely vegetarian habit of the anthropoid to where it could make the best use of the diet of a hunter. We should not feel discouraged, then, if in a mere five or ten thousand years of agriculture we have not as yet grown fully reconciled, biologically, to the intrusion of large quantities of sugars, starches, vegetable proteins and vegetable fats, into a regimen which had so long consisted in the main of animal proteins and animal fats.

Following the line of Weston Price in his *Nutrition and Physical Degeneration,* Huntington believes that among the effects of the transfer from previous diets to those of the agriculturist are the difficulties that our women have in childbirth, contrasted with the ease of this function among those who live the pre-agriculture type of life. Another effect is the tendency to malformed jaws and bad teeth among grain-fed peoples.

As to the ease of childbirth under pre-agricultural conditions, it seems to support Price's reasoning, but I shall not here analyze the evidence. Neither do I pursue further the question of whether the common recession of the lower jaw among the Japanese, which gives them a physiognomy made to order for our cartoonists, is due to the large percentage of cereals in their food; nor do I examine in detail the uselessness of wisdom teeth among us caused by a shrinking of the lower jaw to where there is not room left for them, this being allegedly a result of our large dependence on starch and sugar.

I do, however, anticipate my chapter "And Visit Your Dentist Twice a Year" to the extent of pointing out that Price and Huntington have had many predecessors, as well as followers, with regard to the effect of starches and sugars on the teeth themselves. For instance, Henry B. Collins, Jr., Director of the Wartime Ethnogeographic Board, and ethnologist on the staff of the Smithsonian Institution, considers that if archaeologists discover anywhere a group of several skeletons, of no matter what probable antiquity, they may be sure that if the teeth have cavities in them, signs of dental caries, then those are the skeletons of a people who had lived under a fairly well developed agriculture.

Practically the whole world is now agricultural in its diet, for even the Eskimos of parts like the north coast of Alaska have succumbed to our food fashions. There are left, however, a few places where men still use the diets that preceded agriculture, and we possess books of the last three thousand years that tell a good deal of the lives of hunters and herdsmen.

It would seem, then, that if the speculative study of our forebears is begun at the stage when they first deserve the name of anthropoid, or Ape-Human, their dietetic history will fall into three main stages—gathering, hunting, and farming.

According to the geologists, the gathering stage, or apeman period, lasted several million years. During this time man ate roots and tubers, shoots and succulent leaves, fruits and yams and nuts, worms and snails and rodents, eggs and fledgling birds. This period was long enough for us to become well adapted to digesting and assimilating the diet, to be healthy on it. We can be healthy on it now, as is demonstrated by those vegetarians, like Bernard Shaw, who have money enough to buy these at-present rather costly foods. The deficiency group of diseases, malformed bones, difficult childbirth, they seemingly do not trouble those humid-forest natives, and those high-income vegetarians, who can manage to get enough of the sort of food on which monkeys do well.

After the largely vegetarian gathering stage came the hunting stage, during which the ape turned definitely human. This will have lasted between one and three million years. The period was long enough to enable digestion and assimilation to adapt themselves to a largely carnivorous diet.

To judge from present knowledge of so-called savages, the foods of the hunting period ranged from the entirely carnivorous, in lands where grass was plenty and humid forests rare or absent, to a partly carnivorous regimen in places where it was convenient to supplement the flesh diet with a certain amount of monkey food. So far as can now be known, those men who during this stage lived wholly on the new diet, that of the hunter, and those who supplemented the new with the old, were in equally good health. In both cases the deficiency group of diseases was absent—certainly from the exclusively carnivorous and probably from those who combined the methods of gathering and hunting.

The pastoral way of life does not constitute a separate stage in the history of human diet; for, as we have pointed out, the change was not fundamental. It was only the substitution of milk for blood as an element in the diet—or rather the supplementing of the blood part with a milk part, the milk being a slightly modified form of blood.

The third or agricultural stage of diet marks a profound change from either of the two previous diets, those of the gathering ape and of the hunting or herding man. For hitherto, as exclusive gatherers in the anthropoid stage and as occasional gatherers in the hunting stage, men cannot have had any high percentage of cereal food. A little gathering of wild rice or wild wheat now and then, by small groups here and there, cannot have given the people of ten or twenty thousand years ago much evolutionary preparation for the drastic change that came in when our recent ancestors, in some such place as Egypt, India or China, discovered that they could support great numbers on small areas by planting crops—which, in practice, were chiefly cereals, at least over great stretches of several continents.

Ten or even twenty thousand years is a short spell, in terms of biologic evolution. So the human mechanism for digesting and assimilating must still be much like what it was when agriculture thrust upon the human race a change in diet that was nearly as profound as the one which had been forced on the anthropoid long ago when he faced the choice of hunting or perishing.

I have suggested that there must have been a cycle of malnutrition, discomfort and early deaths that lasted many tens of thousands of years, while the mechanism of the body for handling monkey food was being adapted to handling considerable and at length very high percentages of flesh foods. It is doubtful that mankind is as yet through biologically with the worst of the corresponding period of change from the hunting and pastoral to the agricultural way of life.

Much has been printed on the general state of the public health in the Americas and Europe, and it, at any rate, can be judged absolutely. Relatively we are not so clear on facts and views, those of us who read the newspapers and supplement them with books on medicine, dietetics, physiology. It is practically the anthropologists alone, the students of pre-history and of modern primitives, who seem aware that broad conditions of health, as influenced by food, were ever fundamentally different from what they now are.

For most branches of the sciences which deal with health never have been jolted from a nearly unquestioning acceptance of the predominantly agricultural civilization into which we were born and in which we and our neighbors, and nearly all the people we ever heard of, have lived.

On the agricultural diets now taken for granted this nation, like most or all other civilized nations, is having a deal of trouble with malnutrition. Except among those who can afford a lot of hunting man's food, like beef steaks and chicken, or a lot of monkey food, like fresh fruit and raw vegetables—except for these fortunates, we suffer on our usual diets with endemic deficiency troubles, among them pellagra, beri-beri, scurvy, rickets, contracted lower jaws and poor teeth.

Even the prosperous among us do not quite escape, for not all their forethought and care will prevent such records as a 95 per cent incidence of tooth decay in the high school senior class of a fashionable suburb, and a 98 per cent decay ratio for the senior class of any college.

Things like dental caries and rickets are the commonplaces of the only way of life known to most of us, whether by trial or by vivid hearsay. Such troubles have been with us since agriculture began; thus from prehistoric times. Most of us conceive of nothing different, take as inevitable, as the common lot of man, the pains and derangements which we suppose to have been universal at all times and in all places. If we discuss general health problems, it is usually with regard to details, perhaps whether the caries incidence among high school seniors is 95 per cent or only 90 per cent, and whether some way could not be found to reduce it by five or ten per cent. No one thinks of the decay ratio being reduced to anything like 20 per cent, and certainly no one would talk of reducing it to zero, at least unless some revolutionary discovery were to be made.

However, we are accustomed to comparing the results of changes in diet and to discussing the health consequences of various dietary systems. Much has been published, for instance, about questions of health that involve comparisons between agricultural diets and those vegetarian regimens which are of the monkey-food type—green vegetables, yellow vegetables, nuts, fruits, sprouts, shoots, roots and the juices of fruits and vegetables. Bernard Shaw has been along this line an education in himself.

Thus we are posted on comparing the foods of our prehuman ancestors with those of farming man. In contrast, relatively little that has been printed is available for a comparison of the diets of agricultural man with those of the hunters whose lives spanned the million or so years between ape and farmer. This comparative lack started me, twenty years ago, gathering material for what I hoped would be a substantial contribution to a relatively neglected branch of knowledge. The results of the study were to be described in a series of books which would carry the over-all title, *The Lives of Hunters.*

Of that work this volume, *Not By Bread Alone,* is the first instalment. In it, as in the rest of the study, I draw upon my training as an anthropologist, my experience of living exclusively on meat among exclusive meat eaters, and a lifetime of studying books and other records that deal with hunting and pastoral man. I draw, too, upon manuscript and verbal contributions from numerous personal friends and scientific colleagues among explorers, geographers, anthropologists and physiologists.

In this introductory volume, but naturally more so in the work as a whole, I am trying to furnish material for a sounder comparison than has hitherto been practicable between our lives as an agricultural people and the lives of those others whom I have known directly or vicariously and who still live by hunting, much as our forefathers presumably did through the rather considerable stretch of time, whether it be two million or only two hundred thousand, years, from the period when their ancestors and ours became human to the time when the ancestors of some of us became farmers.

2

The Home Life of Stone-Age Man

THOSE who speculate on prehistoric man usually think he lived on meat, and particularly so in the northern lands of the world during the ice ages. They go on to say, in books and journals, that fat meat is a good diet for strenuous living in cold weather, and to specify that in low temperatures one needs to stoke the internal fires with fuel of high caloric value, meaning fat.

These theorizers frequently go on to say that paleolithic man, who hunted the reindeer and musk ox in middle Europe thousands of years ago, was in a stage of culture similar to that of the Eskimos who have been found in the Arctic during modern times, hunting the same animals, using stone implements like those of prehistoric man, and dressing in skins .

Seemingly, then, nutritionists who reason as I have sketched believe that the modern stone-age Eskimo fights the cold through burning up physiologically a lot of protein and, especially, a lot of fat. The evidence will show, however, that the Eskimo requires no more food than a Scotsman, or at least not through living where the weather is colder.

Perhaps the best-phrased solution to this problem is that of the late Archdeacon Hudson Stuck of the Protestant Episcopal mission, Fort Yukon, Alaska. That post has nearly or quite the lowest temperature record for Alaska, 79° or perhaps 80° below zero, and this was known to an audience whom the missionary addressed during what proved to be his last lecture tour through the States, in 1919. A woman rose to question him: "Archdeacon, we simply cannot understand how you manage to endure the terrible cold at Fort Yukon."

Stuck replied: "Madam, we do not *endure* any cold at Fort Yukon. We live in houses, we burn fuel, and when we go outdoors we put on clothing."

This correct answer has within it the right solution to the problem whether ice-age man required a diet specially high in calories with which to fight the cold. Biologically speaking, he could not have fought it and still survived to become our ancestor.

For the human animal seems incapable of more than insignificant biologic adaptation to cold. He does not have feathers as grouse do, he does not have fur as rabbits do; he would freeze to death long before he could develop through evolutionary process either of these forms of protection. The little hair he has on his body is not well distributed for keeping him warm, nor does he grow fur at the roots of the hairs, as with many dogs. His fat has a tendency to gather in certain restricted localities and does not spread over his whole body as a shield beneath the skin, like the blubber of a seal.

Indeed, few things are more nearly self-evident than the complete biologic failure of man to adapt himself to a climate of chill winters. This means that African, European and Greenlander are on equal footing here. Admiral Peary is on frequent record that his best traveling companion was Matthew A. Henson, a Negro; Cape Verde Islanders, Canary Islanders and Hawaiians were favored personnel of the Yankee whaling fleet when it used to winter in the northwestern Canadian Arctic; one of the best men of my third Arctic expedition was a Samoa Islander; an Italian polar expedition under a member of the royal family, the Duke of the Abruzzi, took the farthest-north record away from the Norwegians; and did it, as the narrative of the expedition shows, less through skill than brute endurance.

But I need not labor a point that is now generally conceded. Either man has not been away from his ancestral tropics long enough for evolutionary adaptation, or else his trend of change is not in the direction of bodily adjustment to sub-zero cold. Why should it be, when all he needs in order to be safe and comfortable in the Arctic is to adapt his mind, his ideas? As for us Europeans, we do not even have to make new discoveries, if only we have the humility to borrow the technique of the Eskimos, and not to start trying to improve on it until we have first learned to grasp its principles and to apply its practice.

It is doubtful that man has anywhere else on earth managed an adjustment to environment so nearly perfect as that of the Eskimo to his Arctic.

Going from Mexico toward northern and wooded Canada, the amount of caloric energy from food required by the Indian contest with environment does increase with fair regularity; for there is not evident a satisfactorily progressive adjustment of clothes and housing to the increased length and chill of the winter. But at the northern edge of the forest the process is abruptly reversed; for on the Arctic prairies one meets a culture which ceases to fight environment and instead deals with it by adaptation. No caloric energy is then needed for a struggle with the cold, because there is no such struggle.

The difference between a Scotsman and an Eskimo dealing with cold resembles the difference between a human swimmer, who comes up when necessary for air, and a fish, which does not need to come up for air at all. Johnny Weissmuller is tense, active, burns a lot of fuel in a struggle; a codfish lets the water cover him and is relaxed under conditions of biological economy.

I take for an example the case of the Eskimos of the Mackenzie and of Coronation Gulf, before Europeans interfered. "Changing what should be changed," as the scholastic reasoners used to say in Latin, the picture applies, likely enough, at least in considerable part, to the living conditions . of our stone-age and ice-age forebears.

Eskimo ways of living as the first explorers found them, and probably those of Northern Hemisphere man in the ice ages, when glaciers covered large parts of North America and Eurasia, were badly adapted to warm weather. Ice-age man endured summer, no doubt, as Australians and Italians now endure winter.

When continental Eskimos go inland they meet terrific heat, humid temperatures running toward 100° F. in the shade, with the nights almost as hot as the days, the unsetting sun beating upon them the twenty-four hours through. The best they can do for cool garments is to use nearly worn out skin clothes, full of holes. Through every hole the mosquitoes sting; the sand-flies get in and crawl around, biting like fleas. The only protection from the insects is smoke, and the insects can stand more smoke than the Eskimos can.

In old-fashioned language, summer is hell on earth, as long as the wind blows off the land. When the summer wind blows off the sea it brings fogs and chill rains to men who live near the shore. Skin clothes, then, are of little protection. Garments of mammal intestine shed rain, and so does the hide of the seal when rightly prepared, but even then stone-age clothes do not approach the moisture-resistant qualities of our waterproofs and umbrellas. The houses of last winter leak, and no one remains in them during summer. The skin tents in which people live get soggy, and rot if the damp weather lasts.

With the Eskimo summer and the Italian winter the condition is one—in both cases people just endure, and long for the change of season. In Texas summer brings the normal conditions of the year; in Arctic Canada winter brings them. The Canadian Eskimo has been nearly a prisoner from May to September. It is impractical for him to cross rivers by swimming, and in any case most Eskimos have no idea how to swim. The lakes, which in his country cover half the surface of the earth, must be detoured. The ground is boggy and one's feet sink in; the clay is sticky and one's boots are clogged with it. The insects make life a torment. One is wretched part of the time because he is wet, and if not wet he is sweltering with the heat.

All this the frosts of autumn change. The insects die or go to sleep; the lakes and rivers freeze over and one can walk across them; the snow arrives and the whole land becomes a sledge road which leads in every direction. Winter clothes and winter houses, which have been developed to meet the normal weather of the year, bring an average of comfort that seems to the stone-age Eskimo as pleasant as the usual comfort of Park Avenue does to a New Yorker.

In a discussion that considers everything from the dietetic point of view, there is not time to explain fully the Eskimos' clothes, how the materials are prepared and how the garments are made. Many books, however, including some written by me, have covered this subject in detail.* I simply state, then, that the clothes the Eskimos wear in the Arctic during the coldest month of the year, January or February, weigh under ten pounds, which is a good deal less than the winter equipment of the average New York business man. These clothes are soft as velvet, and it is only a slight exaggeration to say that the wearers have to use a test to find out whether the day is cold. At —40° F., a Mackenzie Eskimo, or a white man dressed in their style, sits outdoors and chats almost as comfortably as one does in a thermostat-regulated room. The cold, about which the polar explorer can read upon the scale of his thermometer, will touch only those parts of his body which are exposed, the face and the inside

* See especially the author's *Arctic Manual;* but also *Hunters of the Great North, My Life with the Eskimo,* and *The Friendly Arctic.*

of the breathing apparatus, a small fraction of the body, needing little fuel for counterbalance. Warm and completely protected elsewhere, he can sit comfortably even with bare hands. Indeed, the ears, particularly liable to frost, seem to be about the only parts likely to freeze if exposed at 40° below zero while most of the rest of the body is warm.

This holds only during calm weather. A strong wind at —20° F. or —30° F. will freeze almost any exposed part of the body, if given time. But Eskimo clothes are nearly wind-proof, as part of being nearly coldproof, so that, even in a wind, little caloric energy is needed for counterbalancing a low temperature.

The houses of Mackenzie River, typical in their warmth of the dwellings of most Eskimos, have frames of wood, with a covering of earth so thick that, practically speaking, no chill enters except as planned ventilation, for which a diving-bell principle of control is used. A room filled with warm air can lose no great amount of it through an opening in the floor, while the cold air below that opening is not able to rise into the house appreciably faster than the warm air escapes at the top.

The roof ventilator of a dwelling that shelters twenty or thirty people is likely to resemble our stovepipes in diameter. This makes fairly good ventilation, for there may be a temperature difference of from 100° to 150° between indoors and out. With that gradient the house air is so much lighter than the general atmosphere that the difference produces a terrific pressure and the warm air rushes out as a forced draft. Air for replacement enters at floor level by a trap with an area of from fifteen to thirty square feet, so slowly that there is no draft appreciable to the inmates.

Through this diving-bell control of ventilation there develop several temperature levels within the house, or rather an upward gradation of warmth. Lying on the floor you might be cool at 60°; sitting on the floor, the upper part of your body would be warmish at 70° or 80°; sitting on the bed platform three feet above the floor you could reach up with your hand to a temperature of 90° or 100°. These temperatures, in the Mackenzie district and in many other places, are produced by lamps which burn animal fat, odorless, smokeless and giving a soft, yellowish light.

During my first Mackenzie winter, described hereafter, there were enough lamps extinguished at bedtime, say 10 o'clock, to bring the room temperature down to 50° or 60°. Both sexes and all ages slept completely naked, under light robes.

Before white men's influence spread over the North American Arctic, the typical Eskimo house in the afternoon and evening resembled a sweat bath rather than a warm room. When garments are made of fur, as they probably were among our northerly stone-age ancestors and as they are with the Eskimos, nakedness at such house temperatures is the only thing possible; for, with constant perspiration, the skin clothes would decay so rapidly that, to say nothing of the smell, they would fall to pieces in a few weeks.

There were, accordingly, before the whites interfered, only two Eskimo styles within doors. For these, West Greenland and Northern Alaska (including Mackenzie River) are typical. In Greenland, by the accounts of early travelers, men, women, and children were completely naked within doors. In Northern Alaska, children up to six or seven years of age were naked, but grown people wore breeches, outworn garments from a previous year, old and full of holes, which covered them from just above the hips to just above the knee. These might get wet with perspiration during the evening but would not be worn more than a few hours. Whoever put on regular clothes for outdoors would hang his indoor breeches up to dry.

For the stone-age Eskimo realized that drying prevents decay. One person might have two or three pairs of trunks, being careful that at least once every three days each of these would get thoroughly dry. They did not have any theory about germs that flourish in warmth and moisture, but they prevented decay by a method which killed the germs.

In the Mackenzie house, then, we used to sit stripped, except for the breeches, from around four in the afternoon, when the outdoor work was done, to around ten or eleven, when it was bedtime. There were streams of perspiration running down our bodies constantly, and the children were occupied in carrying around dippers of ice water from which we drank great quantities.

Pausing for dietetic emphasis, note is made of two important conditions under which we ate our meals that were 100 percent meat:

(1) While indoors we were living in a humid, tropical environment; when outdoors we carried the tropics around with us inside our clothes. Neither indoors nor out were we using any considerable part of the caloric value of our food in a biologic struggle against chill.

(2) We drank with our evening meal (four o'clock dinner) some warm broth in which our meat had been boiled. However, by native custom, we never alternated bites of food and sips of drink. We might eat a whole meal without a drink, following sometimes with a dipper of warm broth and perhaps a little later taking a good round draught of cold water. At the cold meals, or after them, our drinks were also cold.

If inexperienced in primitive cultures, one is likely to misinterpret general statements about food. I might tell you, correctly, that the chief food of a certain group of Eskimos with whom I lived was caribou meat, with perhaps 30 per cent fish, 10 per cent seal meat, and 5 or 10 per cent made up of polar bear, rabbits, birds, and eggs. This might lead one to visualize meals where there would be a fish course followed by a meat course, and where we would breakfast at least occasionally on eggs. Such is most unlikely to be the case, with primitive peoples. If 50 per cent of the year's food is caribou meat, the primitive likely eats practically nothing but caribou during approximately half the year, seldom tasting this meat the rest of the twelve months. His fish percentages will come in similarly restricted periods, and they are likely to be fish exclusively. The eggs, far from being breakfasts distributed through several months, would be occasional days of nothing but eggs during only one month of the year, in the spring.

The Eskimo situation varies from ours still more when it comes to vegetables. In the Mackenzie district these were eaten under three conditions:

(1) The chief occasion for vegetables here, as with most Eskimos, was a famine. There were several kinds of vegetable things known to be edible and they were resorted to in a definite succession, as prejudices were overborne by the pangs of hunger. (True famines seldom, if ever, occurred in the Mackenzie, but small groups would get short of food through some accident and then famine practice in eating would result).

(2) Some vegetable foods were eaten because the Mackenzie River people liked them. These were chiefly berries; and among berries chiefly the salmon berry or cloudberry (*Rubus chamaemorus*). The Mackenzie River people ate these only during the season; but in Western Alaska, and elsewhere, berries and some other vegetable foods were preserved in oil for winter use—sometimes as delicacies, sometimes to guard against famine, and no doubt frequently with a mixture of both motives.

(3) One form of vegetable dish is eaten strictly in connection with another that is non-vegetable—the moss, twigs and grass from a caribou's stomach are used as a base for oil. In my experience the commonest reason for this use was that someone from a distance arrived with a bag of oil that was either in a particularly delectable state of fermentation (cor-

responding to Camembert cheese that is just soft enough),
or else this was an oil from a favored animal not common
in the district, say white whale brought into a sealing community. The question would then arise, how shall we eat this
oil? Most likely there would be on hand boiled lean meat, or
perhaps wind-dried fish, and the matter was simple—you cut
or broke the lean meat or the fish into bite-size pieces, dipping each into the fat. But if no lean happened to be available there was perhaps the suggestion that a caribou had
been killed recently, the paunch was likely still in fair condition, and why not use that to make a salad? Usually the
suggestion had an uneven reception, the majority perhaps
agreeing and eating the oil that way, while the remainder
just dipped their fingers into the oil a few times and licked
them off.

Nobody drinks large swigs of oil, or at least this habit is
not known among Eskimos. There are European districts
where certain oils are drunk in limited quantities. For instance, Scandinavian fishermen often have a belief in the
nearly magical value of cod or halibut liver oil, and some of
them will toss off, most likely in the morning, the equivalent
of a wineglassful.

I have never seen a similar custom among Eskimos. The
nearest to it was during one famine period where there were
six Eskimos with me, five of whom ate oil soaked up with
feathers or caribou hair, moss or tea leaves, to make a kind
of salad. But one member of our party, an aged Eskimo man,
wanted his ration of oil in a teacup, about half a cup. He
took longer to sip it than the other Eskimos and I did to eat
our salad, perhaps requiring half an hour.

A white man's preferences in cuts of meat will change
when he switches from the average European or American
diet, where meat is less than the combined quantity of the
rest of the food, to a diet that is mainly or wholly meat.

It seems that in the good old days, when teeth were presumably better, the people of England judged meat not by its tenderness, by ease of chewing, but by its juiciness and flavor. They condemned their meat by saying it was tasteless or dry; we disparage by calling it tough. The difference of our attitude from theirs is no doubt in part a reflection of the change to where more than ninety per cent of even our high school children have cavities in their teeth.

Quite as much, no doubt, the difference may be traced to the increased prevalence of what we think of as French cooking, where the ideal seems to be to season and otherwise handle any food so that it shall taste like something else. For that sort of cooking, and for weak teeth, the ideal piece of meat is the tenderloin. Having no flavor of its own, it will readily take on whatever flavor the cook desires to confer upon it, by a sauce or other device, and it is never hard to chew.

The teeth of exclusive meat eaters are good, at least it is so with those who have been brought up on meat; they use no sauce and want their meat to have a flavor of its own. So they usually feed tenderloins to dogs.

When first I lived with Eskimos I was inclined to favor the cuts I had preferred in "civilization"; but the facilities for roasting were poor, and often the only available fat to fry in was seal oil, which I never liked for frying meat even though I grew to like it for other uses. In any case, it was not long till I came to agree with the Eskimos on preferences between different cuts of meat, and these favor mostly parts not adapted to roasting or frying.

Among the Mackenzie River Eskimos, the head was considered the best part of the caribou—not just the tongue and brain, though both were relished, but the head as a whole. Among the best parts of it were the fat behind the eye and the meat, a blend of lean and fat, inside the angle of the lower jaw. As to this group of tastes, I have found no difference among other Eskimos, Indians of the northern forest or white men who have lived for any considerable time exclusively on meat. Indeed, a preference for heads is met with here and there all over the world, even among people who do not live wholly on meat. In New England, for instance, chowder from fish heads is considered better than if made from other parts.

After the head come, in descending order of preference, brisket, ribs, pelvis and backbone. The principle applies that "the sweetest meat is nearest the bone"; excess outside meat is frequently peeled off from the backbone for dog feed, and sometimes from the ribs.*

If there are four in a family and if they have a team of eight dogs, they divide the caribou nearly half and half, for two well-furred fifty-pound dogs that sleep outdoors in the cold eat about as much as one man who is well dressed and housed.

Beginning with what is least desired by the family, the dogs get the tenderloin, lungs, liver, sweetbreads, and everything else from within the body except the kidney and intestinal fat, the kidneys themselves and the heart. Most of the meat is peeled off the hams for dog feed. Humerus and femur are saved for boiling, with what meat remains on them, and these bones are broken for marrow while hot. The other long bones of fore and hind legs are cleaned of all meat and are saved up to crack for the raw marrow, which may be used with a meal, or, in small quantity, eaten raw between meals, somewhat as we eat candy.

---

* The substantial equivalent of this discussion was read, as it appeared in an article I published some years ago, by Dr. G. W. Harley, who is quoted at some length in the chapter "Living on the Fat of the Land." On the basis of eighteen years as a medical missionary in tropical Africa, Dr. Harley writes under date of September 25, 1944: "The preference of Eskimos and (other northern) hunters for head, brisket and ribs is of particular interest to me personally because they are also the favorite cuts not only among the natives of Liberia but also among both Negroes and whites in North and South Carolina." (Dr. Harley is a North Carolinian by birth and is a graduate of Duke University in that state.)

When the Hebrews praised "fat things full of marrow," they knew what they were talking about; for a skinny beast does not have marrow, at least not the fat kind that our ancestors loved. When a marrow-bearing animal gets so thin that the eyes begin to recede, because of the gradual disappearance of the fat behind the eye, practically all fat has disappeared from the marrow; so that, instead of the expected firm stick of white, you find when you crack the raw marrowbone, a liquid of blood color. Cooked, whether boiled or roasted, this liquid develops the consistency and somewhat the taste of the white of a hard-boiled egg.

Hunting man is a connoisseur of fats, and has a definite sequence of preferences in the different fats according to their origination in different parts of the body. The marrows are the best, and range in excellence from the hip and shoulder joints down—the farther down the better. The marrow of humerus and femur is hard and tallowy at "room temperatures," harder at the upper end. These bones are sometimes broken and the marrow eaten raw; but usually the bone, with what remains on it after the dog meat has been peeled off, is boiled and the cooked marrow is eaten warm.

Passing down the leg the marrow is softer and softer, more and more like a particularly delicious cream in flavor, and is in each bone softer at the lower end than at the upper, so that if one is given a small piece in the dark he can tell, by the feel when he crushes it with his tongue against his palate, and by the taste, from which bone it is and from which end of that bone. To hunting man, the marrow of the long bones is the greatest delicacy he knows, except perhaps boiled moose nose or the boiled liver of the loche.* Nose and liver are improved by cooking, in his opinion; but to

---

*The loche, or ling, is a fresh-water fish that, although nowhere taken in large numbers, is perhaps the favorite food fish of the Eskimos of northern Canada and Alaska. It is especially prized for its large, fatty liver.

him the cooking of marrows, other than those of humerus and femur, is a spoiling of good food, or rather the turning of a great delicacy into mere ordinary food.

To the hunter all caribou fats, except the marrows of the long bones, are better cooked than raw. The ratings, in descending order, are: the fat from behind the eye, the kidney fat, the fat on the brisket near the bone, the fat of ribs and other parts where it is mixed with the lean. Last comes the back fat, which is a separate layer that begins to appear when the animal already has fat in its marrow, and gets thicker as the fatness cycle advances.

The Eskimos, like the Homeric Greeks, prefer the flesh of older animals to that of calves, yearlings and two-year-olds. In the chapter "Living on the Fat of the Land" Homer is quoted to the effect that the Greeks preferred the meat of bulls five years old. It is approximately so with those northern forest Indians with whom I have hunted, and probably with all caribou-eaters. Caribou bulls probably seldom live more than five or six years; for the older the beast the slower it runs, and the wolves catch up with the slowest when they pursue a band.

In the Natural History appendix to *My Life with the Eskimo*, Dr. R. M. Anderson, who was naturalist and second in command of our 1908-1912 expedition, says: "The largest slab of back fat which I have seen taken from a caribou on the Arctic coast was from a bull killed near Langton Bay early in September, the fat weighing thirty-nine pounds. A large bull killed by Mr. Stefansson on Dease River in October had back fat 72 mm. in thickness (2⅞ inches). Comparing the thickness of this with the Langton Bay specimen, the back fat of the Dease River bull must have weighed at least fifty pounds. The thicker the back fat of a caribou is, the richer it is in proportion—the amount of connective tissue remaining the same, and the additional weight consisting of interstitial fat."

The slab of back fat is thickest a little in front of the roots of the tail and goes down about half way to the hock joint, thinning rapidly. Forward it extends well out along the neck, thinning gradually from the hips forward. On the sides it goes a third of the way down over the ribs. When a caribou is killed the back fat is peeled off and laid out on the grass or snow to harden. As Dr. Anderson says, it may run to fifty pounds on a bull that dresses 250-300 pounds. The slab is thinner the younger the animal, and for the same age is thinner with females than males.

The fat cycle with caribou differs in timing with age and sex. The bulls are leanest in November, begin picking up flesh before Christmas, enough to make good eating of the marrow, and fatten steadily thereafter. (For those who think cold weather has a bearing, I note that, in the Arctic, January and February are usually the coldest months of the year, with March likely to be as cold as December.) The mosquitoes, usually worst in June, evidently delay and lessen the fat accumulation; for there are some grassy northerly islands in the Canadian archipelago so small that they are swept throughout by sea breezes chilly enough to keep the mosquitoes down, and we found in these islands that the caribou fattened earlier in the season and grew fatter, in proportion to size, than in the mosquito-plagued larger islands or on the still worse infested mainland. Old bulls are fattest in early September, just before the rutting season.

The cows are thinnest in May, when the old bulls have picked up a fifth or a sixth of the fat they are going to have. During the mosquito season the cows begin to fatten—much more rapidly in the described islands where the flies are not bad—and are at their fattest in November, at the end of the rutting season, when the old bulls have lost all their fat. Thereafter, as the bulls get fatter the cows get thinner, until they are thinnest just after fawning.

The fawns, born in May or early June, have a barely perceptible back fat in September, the males slightly more than the females. Yearling and two-year-old bulls have a cycle like that of the older bulls, except that they do not grow quite so fat, and that there is a time lag, the younger bulls reaching a given stage somewhat later than the old.

The fat of the blubber animals varies a little in quality by age and sex. With these the fat of the younger is slightly preferred—which is not the case with the marrow-bearing animals, which differ also a little by age and sex but in the reverse direction, the fat of the older being considered just a shade better. In eating seals there may be a slight preference for the fat on the flipper, or rather the fat which there blends into a sort of gristle that is very agreeable when medium-boiled.

Seals do not have fatty marrow in their bones. Seal marrow, when raw, has the consistency and color of blood; when cooked it resembles the white of hard-boiled egg, as does the marrow of emaciated caribou. In fact, the blubber animals have fat in only one place, the layer that separates the skin from the red flesh underneath. There is no streak-of-fat-and-streak-of-lean in their rib meat, nor, indeed, any fat anywhere mixed with the lean that is perceptible to eye or palate; nor do they have kidney or intestinal fat.

Being entirely lean, the flesh of the seal is very dry as it is eaten, and this fact explains a difference in Eskimo food habits. With caribou they usually eat each piece of meat as is; with seal they like to dip each piece of lean into oil before placing it in the mouth.

The groups that depend on the blubber animals are the most fortunate, in the hunting way of life, for they never suffer from fat-hunger. This trouble is worst, so far as North America is concerned, among those forest Indians who depend at times on rabbits, the leanest animal in the North, and who develop the extreme fat-hunger known as rabbit-starvation.

Rabbit eaters, if they have no fat from another source—beaver, moose, fish—will develop diarrhoea in about a week, with headache, lassitude, a vague discomfort. If there are enough rabbits, the people eat till their stomachs are distended; but no matter how much they eat they feel unsatisfied. Some think a man will die sooner if he eats continually of fat-free meat than if he eats nothing, but this is a belief on which sufficient evidence for a decision has not been gathered in the north. Deaths from rabbit-starvation, or from the eating of other skinny meat, are rare; for everyone understands the principle, and any possible preventive steps are naturally taken.

It is practically impossible for a hunter of seals and whales to run short of fat. Like all meat eaters, the sealers use about six pounds of lean for each pound of fat, when both are available. Therefore, in calories, the meat eater gets about eighty per cent of his energy from fat, the remainder from lean. Now the make-up of the seal is such that if one secures enough of them to supply the needed lean meat, he has thereby secured at least three times the amount of fat needed for food; and the same ratio of fat to lean applies in the feeding of dogs. This means that, when the Eskimo has used for family and dog team what they require, he has plenty left over to burn in his lamps for light, for cooking and for the heating of the house.

If caribou hunters could kill in August and September all the animals they need, and if they could preserve this meat to last them through the year, they would have enough fat to eat with their lean, but even then not enough left over for fuel. In practice most caribou hunters burn something else than fat, but they use a little tallow for lighting their houses in winter; in summer they have the midnight sun for light, and before and after that the bright nights. But, with the greatest economy of lighting, they do not have enough fat to go with their lean, since they are seldom able to kill

enough bulls and fat cows in autumn to last more than half
or two-thirds of the winter. For this reason most caribou
Eskimos go to the sea coast each year to hunt the blubber
animals; or else they purchase bags of blubber from the coast
dwellers. These bags are made by casing a seal, and each will
contain from 150 to 250 pounds of seal, walrus, or whale
blubber.

So much for preferences in fat and the need for fat. I
return to preferences in cuts of caribou lean meat, stipulating
that there is considerable dependence on the varying
amounts of fat mixed in with the lean.

About halfway in quality are shoulder blades and neck,
in which both dogs and family are interested. Often there is
a compromise; the outside meat is peeled off these pieces
for the dogs and the inside meat is boiled on the bones for
the family. Usually, the humans get the best of it. The uncivilized Eskimo, where I have known him, is very considerate of his dogs, but even more so of his family. In any case,
he makes between them the difference that he does not give
the dogs more than he thinks good for them, but he coun-
tenances, and is even pleased with, gorging by members of
the family, and by visitors.

The preferences are not the same with all animals. Moose,
of which the Mackenzie Eskimos get some and the Arctic
forest Indians many, are divided up the same as caribou,
except that there is a special tidbit, the nose, which is rich
with a particularly delectable fat and is favored in Alaska
and northern Canada about as the tail of the fat-tail sheep
was by the ancient Hebrews and still is by the modern Arab.
Eskimos do not rate the head of the mountain sheep quite
as high as that of moose or caribou; apart from this, the order
of precedence is the same as with caribou, except that sheep
livers are more favored than those of caribou. This is, no
doubt, because sheep have a gall bladder that can be removed; in the family to which the caribou belongs there is

no gall bladder and the gall is distributed throughout the liver, giving it a peculiar, bitterish taste.

In the case of sea mammals, the order is very different. With the polar bear the kidneys are preferred, and then the paws, if there is enough fuel to cook them, for they take a lot of boiling. Ribs usually come next, but there is no such strong feeling as with caribou that one part is better than another. The head is seldom eaten by the family; the tongue is eaten, but not as a tidbit; the brain is liked, as with all animals.

Polar bear liver is never eaten by the Eskimos, for they believe it to be poisonous. Trying out a dozen livers, to test the belief, we found that about one in five or six makes the eater ill. The symptoms are anything from a mild to an excruciating headache, in the latter case with vomiting. It is believed that dogs which have been severely "poisoned" lose their hair. There appears to be no record that either a man or a dog ever died from eating bear liver.

The cause of the trouble with bear liver is unknown, but there have been many theories. One of these is that the symptoms are produced by an overdose of vitamins, in which these livers are known to be rich. There is in them, no doubt, as in other vitamin-bearing livers, a great variation in amounts contained, which has been offered as an explanation of why one may eat half a dozen livers with complete satisfaction and become violently ill at the seventh. There would be a greater danger if a second liver were eaten immediately after the first: the danger of vitamin overdosage.

The liver of caribou and moose is eaten by the family occasionally; that of mountain sheep frequently, and that of the seal nearly always, for it is the favored part. The flipper is liked, too, and the leg above the flipper, fore and aft. Apart from this, there seem to be no strong preferences; and that is probably true also for the walrus, but I have never lived where they were hunted. Walrus are found only where the ice is in motion all winter and where it keeps breaking into small floes; for, unlike the seal, they are unable to gnaw for themselves breathing holes through solid ice. Therefore they are, in the North American Arctic, found only in the west around Alaska and in the east around the more easterly Canadian islands, Hudson Bay, Labrador and Greenland.

In the whales, from the huge bowhead that may be seventy-five feet long to the beluga, or white whale, that is no bigger than a walrus, the liking is strong for only one part, the skin. It is so removed from the beast that half an inch of blubber still clings to the inside of the hide. This is the renowned *maktak,* which has been a favorite with many whites who, unlike me, have not taken to other delicacies of the Eskimos. In Charlie Brower's famous station at Barrow, a few miles from the northernmost tip of Alaska, which has been visited by every traveler in that region since he first went there in 1884, the hospitality has always been famous. A special part of it is that the guest is served a spiced pickle which he likely will say is about the best he ever tasted—maktak done up by a secret recipe brought there, or devised, by Brower's colleague Fred Hopson.

The Mackenzie people did not get many birds, and seemed to have no marked preference as to parts. In fish they considered the head best and the tail next best. In some fishes they were especially fond of the liver. Fish heads and fish livers were always eaten boiled, which was, indeed, the usual form of cooking.

But the tastes described seem to apply only when one is living mainly or wholly on meat. If, like most people in our cities, and even on the farms, a man eats just a little meat along with a lot of other things; then, even if he has eaten by the tastes of hunting man for a continuous decade, as I once did, he will likely come back again, in city or on farm, to the preferences of his former years, before he became a hunter. At any rate, that is the way it has been with me, though I do think wistfully of the delights of northern meals and do have still a doubtless greater inclination toward boiled meat than I would have had otherwise.

But I want my meat boiled northern style, which I learn was also the style of the heavily meat-eating Plains Indians. I want it boiled so that the outside of each piece is cooked but the inside is pink. It is hard for me to see how anybody can like meat boiled to pieces, our fashion, and I am not surprised to notice that few do.

Among the Eskimos with whom I lived, perhaps 90 per cent of the animal food was eaten fresh. There were several kinds of preservation. One of these, freezing, was available only in winter; it kept the food fresh, as the other methods did not.

Quick freezing keeps a fish fresh, irrespective of whether it is cleaned or not. Small birds freeze so fast in cold weather that they do not taste appreciably strong, even with entrails, and there are no big birds that can be killed in cold weather, unless a rare owl or raven. Seals, too, freeze quickly enough to retain freshness of taste. Caribou must have the entrails removed immediately, no matter how cold the weather, and will then freeze fresh even though the skin remains on. Unskinned grizzly bears taint considerably even with entrails removed, and polar bears may taint slightly. Musk oxen taint seriously unless the hide is removed as well as the entrails. All of this, of course, depends on the rapidity of freezing and varies with the temperature and with the insulating quali-ties of the coats of different animals.

By reason of these causes and precautions, surely less than 5 per cent of the winter-killed food of the pre-white Eskimo became tainted. Summer foods were quite another thing.

In many districts fish were caught throughout the summer in larger quantities than could be consumed. There were two methods of preservation.

I saw a typical instance of one method during my first year in the North. Fish, ranging from one to three or four pounds in weight, were caught in great numbers. They were immediately slit and the entrails removed, and were then piled in long windrows just back from the sea beach, and covered with piles of driftwood for protection from dogs and wolves. If there had been June fishing at this place, the fish would have been nearly liquid by fall. Late July catches grew so rotten that a fish might fall to pieces if you tried to handle it. The August catch was pretty high; but toward the end of September there was so much frost at night and so little thaw during the day that putrefaction ceased.

Decayed fish were not eaten during the warm weather; they were not considered good until frozen. As soon as the freeze-up came, they began to be used as delicacies, sometimes as whole meals. The only way of serving decayed fish was to allow them to thaw in the house until they were as soft as hard ice cream, when they were eaten somewhat as a child would consume an ice cream cone. The taste is similar to that of our strong cheeses. The attitude of the Mackenzie Eskimos toward decayed fish was about that of our fashionable diners toward Camembert or Limburger.

When fish are caught rapidly there is nothing to do but pile them in windrows. But if the catch is slower, the few not eaten are likely to be split and hung up to dry. Commonly, the backbone is removed and used for dog feed, either then or later—indeed, fish bones, no matter what the condition of the fish or the method of eating, are mainly dog feed.

The mentioned second Eskimo way of preserving fish is wind-drying. This is seldom carried to such an extent that the flesh becomes as hard as in Scandinavian practice. Usually an Eskimo dried fish is about as soft as our salted cod. When they get to that hardness they are taken down, piled, and covered from rain by water-shedding skins.

In some districts a good deal of sand gets into fish that is being dried, and the teeth of those who eat it are worn down much more rapidly than in other communities. But it seems that no matter how great the wearing of teeth by sand in food, dentine is replaced so rapidly on a carnivorous diet that the teeth never get worn down quite to a pulp, and no alveolar abscesses are produced.

When caribou or other animals are killed in summer there are again two methods of preservation. Sometimes the meat, after cooling, is placed in pits below the perpetual frost line, and covered with grass, loose earth, or sod. Under such conditions there will be a very slow decay. Meat buried in August, chilled through a month or so, and then frozen in September or October, will be only slightly tainted—not nearly so much as properly "hung" English venison.

Caribou meat which cannot be eaten at once is somewhat more likely than fish to be wind-dried. The process is the same—the flesh is sliced, hung up, and taken down when the outside has formed a dry skin, with the inside still soft. This partial drying completely prevents the development of the taste or odor of decay. Some pieces that are exceptionally thin become quite hard, but normally the flesh is intended to be only partially dehydrated.*

In isolated instances, both fish and caribou were sometimes smoke-dried. Eskimo smoking was never systematic, as with some Indians. It might be, for instance, that if ten caribou were killed the meat of nine would be hung in the open and that of the tenth would be hung within the tent. But this happened only where the people lived in tepee-shaped camps, and there were few of these.

* Thus the Eskimos did not produce true jerky, since only occasional pieces were hard enough to be made into pounded meat, which was therefore unknown to the Eskimos except as produced by the neighboring forest Indians. Nor did they have pemmican, although their *akutok*, a mixture of boiled meat and rendered fat, has been so miscalled by some writers.

The meat of bears and other large animals might be preserved in either of the two ways described for caribou, although drying would be less probable.

Some Eskimo communities, where eggs were plentiful, never used them at all—for example, the Mackenzie district where geese nest in thousands.* Western Eskimos who use eggs eat them fresh, unless, as sometimes happens, they have been partly incubated. If there were any western districts in which eggs were preserved till they became "high," these were on the fringes of the Eskimo world where outside fashions prevailed. The eating of eggs in all states is common in Greenland, and elsewhere in the east.

If we compare the whole diet of a strictly carnivorous group of Eskimos with the carnivorous portion of our diet, they would be found to eat, on the average, a higher percentage of raw or rare meat than we do. But if we compare our whole diet with theirs, remembering that our milk and cream are sometimes raw, our fruit and vegetables frequently raw, our eggs usually soft-cooked while Eskimos invariably cook theirs hard, and that our roasts are more rare than theirs though their boiled meat is more rare than ours— if we consider the whole picture, we doubtless use nowadays a far higher percentage of uncooked food than did the pre-white Eskimo world.

The Eskimos cooked whenever convenient. If they breakfasted on raw food it was either because the group did not want to waste time in cooking or else because they awoke with too keen an appetite—pre-white cooking was usually slow, requiring two or three hours. The same would be true for lunch. At dinner time, in the Eskimo way of life, there was ample leisure, and this meal was seldom eaten raw. The

---

* This is as of the period before Alaska Eskimos came in with the Yankee whalers and popularized egg eating in the Mackenzie district. The first of these whalers wintered at Herschel Island in 1889. In 1906, my first time in the Arctic, few if any of the local people were fond of eggs; but it was common knowledge that Alaska Eskimos and white men liked them.

fourth meal of the day, just before going to bed, normally consisted of cold boiled food left over from dinner.

Some Eskimos eat a good deal of dried food and others never taste it for years or decades; there are also pronounced variations of diet in other ways. Some groups, for instance, hardly ever have any appreciable amount of food except fish, while others seldom taste fish, living chiefly on the flesh of mammals.

No frying was ever practiced before Europeans came— apparently frying is a rare form of cooking among primitive people everywhere. Roasting was occasional, and usually by Eskimos who lived in forested districts. Even in the woods, boiling is the normal method, while on sea coasts or at sea it is practically the only form.

3

The Field Experience

IN 1906 I went to the Arctic, with the food tastes and beliefs of the average American. During the following twelve years I spent ten winters and the intervening summers as an Eskimo among Eskimos, as a hunter among a hunting people. By necessity at first, later by choice, I followed the rule of doing in Rome as the Romans do, which included living on Eskimo foods prepared in the Eskimo way. In that process my tastes underwent a gradual change, and I came also to realize that many of my former beliefs about the wholesomeness of food and about "normal likes and dislikes" were due to the locale of my birth and upbringing; that they were matters of social and not of biological inheritance.

In 1919 I decided that my field work in exploration was over. I have kept to that, excepting one journey in the middle twenties to the tropics of central Australia where, incidentally, I met a few white men, among them the famous Sir Baldwin Spencer, who were as fond of certain delicacies of the Australian native as I am of corresponding Eskimo tidbits.

The conflict between my experience and orthodox dietetics, which is also a conflict between the usual teachings of anthropologists and those of nutritionists, has been subject matter for a number of papers which I published in the decade 1918–28 through medical and other journals. The same conflict was dealt with upon occasion in the first three books I published. As a result, year by year an increasing number of physicians, dietitians and physiologists became interested, leading finally to the Bellevue Hospital studies that are described hereafter.

At the start of the Bellevue tests, in 1928, the following were among the common dietetic beliefs: To be healthy one needed a varied diet, composed of elements from both animal and vegetable sources. One tired of and eventually felt a revulsion against things which he had to eat frequently. This latter belief was supported by stories of persons who through force of circumstances had been compelled, for instance, to eat during two weeks nothing but sardines and crackers and who, according to the stories, had sworn that so long as they lived they never would touch sardines again. Southerners commonly maintained that nobody could eat a quail a day for thirty days.

It was strongly and widely held that the less meat one ate the better it would be for him. If one ate a good deal of it he was supposed to develop rheumatism, hardening of the arteries, high blood pressure, with a tendency to breakdown of the kidneys—in short, premature old age. An extreme variant had it that one would live more healthily, more happily, and longer if he became a vegetarian.

Specifically it was believed that without vegetables in the diet one would develop scurvy. It was a "known fact" that sailors, miners, and explorers frequently died of scurvy "because they did not have vegetables and fruits."

The addition of salt to food was considered either to promote health or to be necessary for health. This was "proved" by various allegations, such as that African tribes make war on other tribes to get salt; that minor campaigns of the War Between the States were focused on salt mines; and that "all herbivorous animals are ravenous for salt." I do not remember seeing a critical appendix to any of these views, suggesting, for instance, that Negro tribes also make war about things which no one ever said were biological essentials of life; that tobacco was a factor in Civil War campaigns without being a dietetic essential; and that members of the deer family in Maine, which never have salt, and are not known to show a hankering for it, are about as healthy as those of Montana which devour quantities of it in salt licks and are forever seeking more.

A belief I found crucial in my Arctic work, making the difference between success and failure, life and death, was the view that men cannot live on meat alone. The few doctors and nutritionists who thought it could be done were considered unorthodox, if not charlatans. The arguments ranged from metaphysics to chemistry: Man was not intended to be carnivorous; this was known from examining his teeth and his stomach, and from the account of him in the Bible. As mentioned, he would get scurvy if he had no vegetables, and there are no vegetables in meat. On a diet of nothing but meat, kidneys would be ruined by overwork; there would be protein poisoning and, in general, hell to pay.

With these views in my head and, deplorably, a number of others like them, I resigned my position as teaching fellow in anthropology at Harvard in the spring of 1906 to become anthropologist of a polar expedition. Through circumstances and accidents which are not a part of this story, I found myself that autumn separated from the rest of the expedition and living as a guest of the Mackenzie River Eskimos.*

The Hudson's Bay Company, whose most northerly post was at Fort McPherson two hundred miles to the south, had had little influence on the Eskimos during more than half a century; for it was only some of them who made annual visits to the trading post, and then they purchased no food but only tea, tobacco, ammunition, and things of that sort. But in 1889 the Yankee whaling fleet had begun to cultivate the waters off the north coasts of Alaska and Canada, and for fifteen years there had been close association, with some-

* For a narrative of the year's experiences, see *Hunters of the Great North,* New York, 1922.

times as many as a dozen ships and four to five hundred men wintering at Herschel Island, just to the west of the Mackenzie delta. During this time a few of the Eskimos had learned some English, and perhaps one in ten of them had grown to a certain extent fond of white men's foods.

Now the whaling fleet was gone because the bottom had dropped out of the whalebone market, and the district faced an old-time winter of living on fish and water. The game, which might have supplemented the fish some years earlier, had been exterminated or driven away by the intensive hunting that had supplied meat to the ships. There was a little tea, the only element of the white man's dietary of which the Eskimos were really fond, but not nearly enough to see them through the winter. The lack of it would worry them, so I was facing a winter of fish without tea; for the least I, an unvited guest, could do was to pretend a dislike for this delicacy.

The issue of fish-and-water against fish-and-tea was, in any case, six against half a dozen. For I had had a prejudice against fish since I could first remember. I had nibbled at it perhaps once or twice a year in course dinners, always deciding that it was as bad as I had thought. This was pure imagination, of course, but I did not realize it.

I was in a measure adopted into an Eskimo family at Shingle Point, just west of the Mackenzie delta. The head of this family knew English, for he had grown up as a cabin boy on a whaling ship, where they called him Roxy though his name was Memoranna. It was early September and we were living in tents; the days were hot, but it had begun to freeze during the nights, which were now dark for six or eight hours.

The community of three or four families, fifteen or twenty persons, was engaged in fishing. With long poles, three or four nets were shoved out from the beach about one hundred yards apart. When the last net was out the first would be pulled in, with anything from dozens to hundreds of fish, mostly ranging in weight from one to three pounds, and including some beautiful salmon trout. From knowledge of other white men, the Eskimos considered the trout most suitable for me and would cook them specially, roasting them against a fire. They themselves ate boiled fish.

Trying to develop an appetite, my habit was to get up soon after daylight, say four o'clock, shoulder my rifle, and go off breakfastless on a hunt south across the rolling prairie, though I scarcely expected to find any game. About the middle of the afternoon I would return to camp. Children at play usually saw me coming and reported to Roxy's wife, who then put a fresh salmon trout to roast. When I got home I would nibble at it, and write in my diary what a terrible time I was having.

Against my expectation, and almost against my will, I was beginning to like the baked salmon trout when one day of perhaps the second week I arrived home without the children having seen me coming. There was no baked fish ready but the camp was sitting around troughs of boiled fish. I joined them and, to my surprise, liked it better than the baked. Thereafter the special cooking ceased and I ate boiled fish with the rest.

By midwinter I had left my cabin-boy host and, for purposes of anthropological study, was living with a less sophisticated family a hundred miles from Shingle Point at the eastern edge of the Mackenzie delta. Our dwelling was a house of wood and earth, heated and lighted by Eskimo-style lamps, burning seal or whale oil. Mostly we burned the oil of white whale secured during a hunt of the previous summer, when the fat had been stored in bags and preserved, although the lean had been eaten. Our winter cooking, however, was not done over the lamps but on a driftwood burning, sheet-iron stove which had been obtained from whalers. There were twenty-three of us living in one room, and there were sometimes as many as ten visitors. The floor was then so completely covered with sleepers that the stove had to be suspended from the ceiling. The temperature at night was around 60° F. The ventilation was excellent through cold air coming up slowly from below by way of a trap door that was never closed, the heated air going out by a ventilator in the roof.

Everyone slept completely naked—no pajamas or night-shirts. For bedclothes we used cotton or woolen blankets which had been obtained from the whalers and from the Hudson's Bay Company.

In the morning, about seven o'clock, winter-caught fish, frozen so hard that they would break like glass, were brought in to lie on the floor till they began to soften a little. One of the women would pinch them every now and then. When she found her finger indented them slightly she would begin preparations for breakfast. First she would cut off the heads and put them aside to be boiled for the children in the afternoon; Eskimos are fond of their children, and heads are considered the best part of the fish. Next best are the tails, which were cut off and also saved for the youngsters. The woman would then slit the skin along the back and also along the belly and, taking hold with her teeth, would strip the fish somewhat as we peel a banana, only sideways where we peel bananas endways.

Thus prepared, the fish were put on dishes and passed around. Each of us took one and gnawed it, about as one does with corn on the cob. We leave the cob; similarly, my housemates taught me to eat the flesh from the outside of the fish, not touching the entrails which were to be used as dog feed.

After breakfast all the men and about half the women would go fishing, the rest of the women staying at home to keep house. About eleven o'clock we came back for a second meal of frozen fish just like the breakfast. Around four in

the afternoon the working day was over and we came home
to a meal of hot boiled fish.

Also we came home to a dwelling so heated by the cooking
that it was more like a Turkish bath than a warm room.
Within the house we would sit stripped except for the customary knee breeches, perspiring copiously and drinking
great quantities of ice water.

Dinner over around five or five-thirty, we sat through the
evening listening to stories, singing songs, and occasionally
playing indoor games. Because there was so much work to
do, the ordinary entertainment was story-telling, where even
the narrator could usually work at the same time, as women
in the States knit while talking. The rest worked quietly,
pausing occasionally to ask the narrator questions. Some
evenings there was general conversation, to which everyone
listened so carefully that even with as many as thirty people
in a single room only one spoke at a time, except, perhaps,
that a woman might admonish a child. So whatever anyone
said was heard by everybody; or, if it was not heard, the
speaker was asked to repeat.

The latter part of the evening the temperature of the
house would gradually go down. About nine-thirty or ten
o'clock the larger part of the flame of each lamp was put out
—a lamp that had been burning with, say, a twelve or fifteen-
inch flame had the wick shoved into the oil and doused so
that only two or three inches were left burning. There was
no odor and no smoke. Seal and whale oil lamps are like
kerosene lamps in that the flame is odorless if the wick is
properly trimmed; there is a disagreeable smell, whether
from kerosene or whale, if combustion is incomplete and the
lamp smokes.

Just before going to sleep we would have a cold snack of
fish that had been left over from dinner. Then we slept
seven or eight hours and the routine of the day began once
more.

After some three months as a guest of the Eskimos I had acquired most of their food tastes. I had come to agree that fish is better boiled than cooked any other way, and that the heads (which we occasionally shared with the children) are the best part of the fish. I no longer desired variety in the cooking, such as occasional baking—I preferred it always boiled if it was cooked. I had become as fond of raw fish as though I were a Japanese. I liked fermented (therefore slightly acid) whale oil with my fish as well as ever I liked a dressing of vinegar and olive oil with a salad. But I still had two reservations against Eskimo practice: I did not eat high fish, and I longed for salt with my meals.

There was some fish stored from the previous summer, and it was high in several gradations. The August catch, which had been protected by logs from animals but not from the heat, was outright rotten; the September catch was mildly decayed; the October and later catches had been frozen immediately and were fresh. We had less of the August fish than of any other, for which reason among the rest it was a delicacy, to be eaten sometimes as a snack between meals, sometimes as a dessert, or rather as what the English would call a savory, and always frozen, raw.

About midwinter it occurred to me to philosophize that in our own and foreign lands a taste for mild cheese is considered somewhat plebeian; it is at least a semi-truth that connoisseurs rise in station as gourmets when the cheeses they prefer grow progressively stronger. This grading can apply to meats, as in England where it is common among nobility and gentry to relish game so high that the average Midwestern American, or even an Englishman of a lower class, would think it unfit for food.

I knew of course that, while it is good form to eat fetid milk products and rotting game, it is very bad form to eat high fish. I knew also the view of our populace that there are likely to be "ptomaines" in decaying fish and in the plebeian meats, though not in decaying pheasant or venison; but it struck me as an improbable extension of class-consciousness that ptomaine would avoid the gentleman's food and lurk in that of the commoner.

This led to a summarizing query: If it is almost a mark of social distinction to be able to eat strong cheese with a straight face, and to relish smelly birds, why is it necessarily a low practice to eat pungent fish? On the basis of such philosophizing, though with qualms, I tried the rotten fish one day, and, if memory serves, liked it better than my first taste of Camembert. During the next weeks I became fond of high fish.

It is not easy to resist the feeling that things one likes are intrinsically better. My initial prejudice against tainted fish was no doubt greater than my objection to tainted red meat, for I had never heard of anyone who relished high fish but I knew that many, particularly those of lofty social station, were fond of tainted birds and other game. Yet I have sampled tainted red meat a good many hundreds of times without acquiring a taste for it, and I did acquire a taste for high fish.

One finds in books about the North, now and then, testimony similar to mine. There was, for instance, John R. Jewitt, an Englishman who later became a New Englander. He was captured by the Indians of British Columbia in 1803 and held by them until 1805, living the while on their food, prepared in their manner. He testifies in the "Narrative" as published, New York, 1815:

". . . it is not a little singular, that these people will eat no kind of meat that is in the least tainted, or not perfectly fresh, while, on the contrary, it is hardly possible for fish to be in too putrid a state for them."

There may not be in this, however, much support for the intrinsic superiority of high fish over high red meat; for Jewitt's testimony goes on to say or imply, in this connection and elsewhere in his book, that by fish he meant animals that live in the sea, including mammals. He says, for instance, "I have frequently known them when a whale has been driven ashore, bring pieces of it home with them in a state of offensiveness insupportable to anything but a crow, and devour it with high relish, considering it as preferable to that which is fresh."

The key to my own tastes is, no doubt, that smelly birds and venison have been presented to me upon rare and scattered occasions, usually as a course in a meal that was sufficient if the rest of it were eaten; or else I have fallen in with such decayed things as summer-killed caribou in the Arctic when a choice of other meats was available and when my companions ate the putrescent red meat only for a few meals or at most a few days. I probably owe my conversion to gamy fish to the circumstance that during my first northern winter it was a daily practice with my housemates for months on end to eat rotten fish, and to eat it with a particular gusto which impressed upon me their liking for it. Still further, it was eaten as a sort of dessert and thus fell into that one of my mental grooves which predisposed me to thinking that a meal ought to have more than one course.

By the fourth month of my first Eskimo winter I was looking forward to every meal (fresh or high), enjoying them all, and feeling comfortable between times. But I kept thinking the cooked fish would taste better if only I had salt to use with it.

From the beginning of my northern residence I had suffered from the lack of salt. On one of the first few days, with the resourcefulness of a Crusoe, I had decided to make myself a little salt, and had boiled sea water down to where only a brown scum remained. If I had remembered as vividly my freshman chemistry as I did the books about shipwrecked adventurers, I should have known in advance that the sea contains many chemicals other than sodium chloride, among them iodine. The scum tasted bitter rather than salty. A more resourceful chemist could no doubt have refined the product. I gave it up, partly through the persuasion of my host, the English-speaking Roxy.

The Mackenzie Eskimos, Roxy told me, believe that what is good for grown people is good for children and enjoyed by them as soon as they get used to it. Accordingly, they teach the use of tobacco when a child is very young. It then grows to maturity with the idea that it can not get along without tobacco. But, said Roxy, the whalers have told that many whites get along without tobacco, and he had himself seen white men who never used it, while of the few white women who had been in this part of the Arctic, wives of captains, none used tobacco. (This, remember, was in 1906.)

Now Roxy had heard that white people believe salt is good, and even necessary for children; so they begin early to add salt to the baby's food. The white child then would grow up with the same attitude toward salt that an Eskimo child has toward tobacco. However, said Roxy, since the Eskimos were mistaken in thinking tobacco so necessary, may it not be that the white men are equally mistaken about salt? Pursuing the argument, he concluded that the reason why all Eskimos dislike salted food, though all white men like it, is not racial but due to custom. You could, then, break the salt habit with about the same difficulty as the tobacco habit, and you would suffer no ill result beyond the mental discomfort of the first few days or weeks.

Roxy did not know, but I did as an anthropologist, that in pre-Columbian times salt was unknown, or the taste of it disliked and the use of it avoided, through much of North and South America. It may possibly be true that the carnivorous Eskimos, in whose language the word *mamaitok*, meaning "salty," is synonymous with "evil-tasting," disliked salt more intensely than those Indians who were partly herbivorous. Nevertheless, it is clear that the salt habit spread more slowly through the New World from the Europeans than the tobacco habit through Europe from the Americans. Even today there are considerable areas, for instance in the Amazon basin, where the natives still abhor salt. Not believing that the races differ in their basic natures, I felt inclined to agree with Roxy that the practice of salting food is with us a social inheritance and the belief in its merits, at least to some extent, a mere part of our folklore.

Through this philosophizing I was somewhat reconciled to going without salt; but I was, nevertheless, overjoyed when one day Ovayuak, my new host in the eastern delta, came indoors to say that a dog team was approaching which he believed to be that of Ilavinirk, a man who had worked with whalers and who possessed a can of salt. We went out to receive the visitor and, sure enough, it was Ilavinirk. He was delighted to give me the salt, a half-pound baking-powder can about half full, which he said he had been carrying around for two or three years, hoping sometime to meet someone who would like it for a present. He seemed almost as pleased to find that I wanted the salt as I was to get it. I sprinkled some on my boiled fish, enjoyed it tremendously, and wrote in my diary that it was the best meal I had had all winter. Then I put the can under my pillow, in the Eskimo way of keeping small and treasured things. But at the next meal I had almost finished eating before I remembered the salt. Apparently, then, my longing for it had been what might be called imaginary. I finished that meal without salt, tried it once or twice during the next few days, and thereafter left it untouched. When we moved camp the salt remained behind.

After the return of the sun, I made a journey of several hundred miles to the whaling ship *Narwhal*, which was wintering at Herschel Island. The captain was George P. Leavitt, of Portland, Maine. For the few days of my visit I enjoyed his steward's good New England cooking, but when I left

Herschel I returned without reluctance to the Eskimo meals of fish to eat and warm fish broth or cold water to drink. It seemed to me that, mentally and physically, I had never been in better form in my life.

So, during the first few months of my first year in the Arctic, I acquired, though I did not at the time fully realize it, the munitions of fact and experience that have within my own mind defeated those theories of dietetics which were reviewed at the beginning of this chapter. I could be healthy on a diet of fish and water. The longer I followed it the better I liked it, which established in my mind one of the first principles of dietetics: You never become tired of your food if you have only one thing to eat.

I did not get scurvy on the fish diet, nor did I learn that any of my fish-eating friends ever had had it. Nor was the freedom from scurvy due to the fish being eaten·raw—we proved that later. There were certainly no immediate signs of hardening of the arteries and high blood pressure, of breakdown of the kidneys or of rheumatism.

These months on fish were the beginning of several years during which I lived on an exclusive meat diet. For I include fish when I speak of living on meat, using "meat" and "meat diet" as if I were a teacher of anthropology rather than as the editor of a housekeeping magazine. The term in this book, and in like scientific discussions based on my work, refers to a diet from which all things of the vegetable kingdom are absent.

To the best of my estimate, then, I lived in the Arctic for more than five years exclusively on meat and water. This was not, of course, one five-year stretch, but an aggregate of time within a period of ten years. One member of my expeditions, Storker Storkerson, lived on meat alone for about the same length of time. There were a dozen who lived on meat from one to three years. They were of several nationalities and of three races—ordinary whites; Cape Verde Islanders who had a high percentage of Negro blood; and South Sea Islanders, from Hawaii and Samoa. Neither from experience with my own men nor from what I have heard of similar cases do I find any racial dietetic difference, but there are marked individual differences.

Our typical method of breaking a party in to a meat diet is that three to five of us leave, in midwinter, a base camp which has, according to conventional theories, nearly or quite the best type of mixed diet that money and forethought can provide. The novices have been told that it is possible to live on meat alone. We warn them that a wholly unvaried diet is hard to get used to for the first few weeks, but assure them that eventually they will grow to like it and that any difficulties in changing diets will be due to their imagination.

The men will believe these assertions in varying degrees. I have a feeling that, in the course of breaking in something like twenty individuals, two or three young men believed me completely, and that this belief collaborated strongly with their youthful adaptability in making them take readily to the meat.

Usually, I think, the men feel that what I tell of myself is no doubt true for me personally, but that I am peculiar, a freak—that a normal person will not react similarly, and that they are going to be normal and have an awful time. Their past experience seems to tell them that if a person eats one thing every day he is bound to tire of it. In the back of their minds there is also what they have read and heard about the necessity for a varied diet. They have specific fears of developing the ailments which they have heard of as being caused by meat or prevented by vegetables.

In the Arctic we secure our food by hunting, and in midwinter, at which time most of our long journeys begin, there is not enough good hunting light. Accordingly, we carry with us on our dog sledges from the base camp provisions for several weeks, enough to take us into the long days. During this time, as we travel away from shore over the moving pack ice, we occasionally kill a seal or a polar bear and eat them along with our groceries. Our men like these meats as an element of a mixed diet as well as people in the States like beef or mutton.

We are not on rations. We eat all we want, and we feed the dogs what we think is good for them. When the traveling conditions are right we usually have two big meals a day, morning and evening; if we are stormbound or delayed by open water we eat every few hours, to help pass the time away. At the end of four, six, or eight weeks at sea we have used up all our food.

We do not try to save a few delicacies to eat later with the seal and bear, for experience has proved that such things are only tantalizing. Beginning the meat diet gradually, trying to make the change less painful, would be about as considerate as chopping a dog's tail off gradually, by inches. It is true (and does not conflict with what is being said) that we have sometimes yielded to the persuasion of men who wanted to save a little malted milk in case of illness or a few raisins to celebrate a birthday or a holiday. I have seen to it, irrespective of this token hoarding, that the men changed abruptly from the mixed to the straight meat diet, the saved-up delicacies being strictly saved, never used in any tapering-off process.

Suddenly, then, we are on nothing but seal; for while our food at sea does average ten per cent polar bear, there may be months in which we do not see a bear. The men go at the seal loyally; they are volunteers and, whatever the suffering, they have bargained for it and intend to grin and bear it. For a day or two they eat square meals. Then the appetite begins to flag and they discover, as they had more than half expected, that for them personally it is going to be a hard pull or a failure. Some own up that they can't eat, while others pretend to have good appetites, enlisting the surreptitious help of a dog to dispose of their share. In extreme cases, which are usually those of the middle-aged and conservative, they go two or three days practically or entirely without eating. We had no weighing apparatus; but I take it that some have lost anything from ten to twenty pounds, what with the hard work on empty stomachs. They become gloomy and grouchy and, as I once wrote, "They begin to say to each other, and sometimes to me, things about their judgment in joining a polar expedition that I cannot print."

But after a few days even the conservatives begin to nibble at the seal meat; after a few more they are eating a good deal of it, rather under protest; at the end of three or four weeks they are eating square meals, though still talking about their willingness to give a soul or a right arm for this or that. Amusingly, and perhaps instructively, they often long for ham and eggs or corned beef when, according to theory, they ought to be longing for vegetables and fruits. Some of them have mentioned hankering for things like sauerkraut or orange juice; but more usually it is hot cakes and syrup or bread and butter.

In the years of our long sledge journeys, when we used to live for six months or more on meat, and when we customarily broke in a new man or two at the beginning of each journey, I felt certain that in changing from a varied to an unvaried diet, from groceries and meat to meat alone, the difficulty was wholly psychological, thus depending on the conservatism of the individual, the strength of his prejudices. I still think of this as the main factor.

But I came to believe there might be subsidiary factors of consequence when the studies at Bellevue, to be described a few pages ahead, showed that in about the same number of days as are required by the novice to reach a square-meal appetite, on the exclusive meat, there takes place within the digestive tract a profound change of the organisms which live there.

It is a common belief that the bulk of human feces depends mainly on the quantity of undigested material that is passed along through the intestine; the roughage. The fact seems to be that the larger part of the bulk is accounted for by the bodies of microorganisms that inhabit the digestive tract; bacteria, the so-called intestinal flora. On a mixed diet these are very numerous, and great quantities of them are carried along with the food in its passage, they meantime playing their part in the digestive process.

Two things seem to be true, that the bacteria which flourish on a mixed diet cannot live on exclusive meat, and that their help is not needed in the digestion of meat. These bacteria die off when they cannot get starches and sugars to feed on and are no longer there to furnish bulk; so that meat eaters who take in little undigestible material, like those living on pemmican, find themselves on a diet that has only a fifth or a sixth the residue they are used to.

In the digestive process as it is on a mixed diet, and no doubt on a vegetarian regimen, gases are generated in considerable amount, particularly with those whose elimination is slow. These gases, and the feces, have an unpleasant odor. We noticed in the Arctic, and this was later confirmed at Bellevue, that when we had been for several days on meat alone all trouble with gas ceased and the feces became practically odorless—the Bellevue report, years later, described a slight acid odor, somewhat as from vinegar.

It is the Bellevue confirmation of the character of these changes, and my having noticed in the North that they take place in about the length of time needed by the novice to attain full appetite, which makes me recede from the earlier view that the difficulty in shifting from a mixed to a meat diet (or the opposite shift in the case of a meat eater) is wholly psychological, one of conservatism. I now feel that a part of the trouble is connected in some way with the change in intestinal flora which follows a shift from a mixed diet to meat or from a meat diet to mixed.* And then there are the current views about enzyme adjustment.**

Two of the main questions about an abrupt change of diet are: How difficult is it to get used to what you must eat? How hard is it to be deprived of the things to which you are used and of which you are fond? From the second angle, I take it to be physiologically significant that we have found our people, when deprived, to hanker equally for unnecessary things which have been considered necessities of health, like salt; for things where a drug addiction is considered to be involved, like tobacco; and for items of staple food, like bread.

In my early northern days, and indeed until toward the end of my field career, I kept thinking that salt might be one of the predisposing or activating causes of scurvy, and therefore did not carry it on long sledge journeys. During one of my earliest trips I had a strike on my hands because some of the party (Eskimos) would not go without tobacco, so thenceforth I steadfastly refused to take along men who were unwilling to leave their tobacco behind. It is not feasible to carry bread or other white men's foods, for we plan our journeys to be so long, and frequently do make them so long, that it is physically impossible to transport provisions of any kind in quantity that will not give out. Moreover, accidents

* See "The Influence of an Exclusive Meat Diet on the Flora of the Human Colon" by John C. Torrey and Elizabeth Montu, *The Journal of Infectious Diseases*, August, 1931, pp. 141-176.
** In reply to a letter on this general subject Dr. George O. Burr, Department of Physiology, University of Minnesota Medical School, wrote July 27, 1944: " . . . there is plenty of evidence in the literature to substantiate your second conclusion, i.e., that the body builds enzymes to take care of habitual dietary ingredients. When a sudden change is made in the diet, as from fat to carbohydrates or vice versa, the enzyme system is lacking and the tolerance for the new ingredient will be low." However, the adjustment period would be only a few days.

may happen to lengthen the most carefully planned itinerary; starvation is then upon the explorer unless he can discover and secure food locally. Therefore, as has been said, we depended on game and usually did not try to carry salt, tobacco or provisions for more than the first few weeks of a trip.

As was implied a page or two back, it has happened on several trips, and with an aggregate of perhaps twenty men, that they have had to break at one time their salt, tobacco, and bread habits. I have frequently tried the experiment of asking, a week or two later, which they would prefer: salt for their meat, bread with it, or tobacco for an after-dinner smoke. In nearly every case the men have stopped to consider, nor do I recall that they were ever unanimous.

When we are returning to the ship from a sledge journey, after several months on meat and water, I usually tell the members of the party that the steward will have orders to cook separately for each man all he wants of whatever he wants. Especially during the last two or three days before reaching the ship there is likely to be a great deal of talk among the novices about what they are going to ask for. One man wants a big dish of mashed potatoes and gravy; another a pot of coffee and bread and butter; a third perhaps wants a stack of hot cakes with syrup and butter. On one occasion a sailor, who had spent many years before the mast, wanted corned beef, which he called "salt horse," and an Eskimo brought up at Nome, Alaska, wanted canned sardines.

On reaching the ship each does get all he wants of what he wants. The food tastes good, although not quite so superlative as the men had imagined. They have said they were going to eat a lot, and they do. Then they get indigestion and headache, feel miserable, and within a week, in nine cases out of ten of those who have been on meat six months or over, they are willing to go back to meat again. If a man does not want to take part in a second sledge journey it is usually for a reason other than dislike of exclusive meat.

Still, as just implied, the verdict depends on how long one has been on the diet. If at the end of the first five or ten days our men could have been miraculously rescued from the exclusive seal and brought back to their varied foods, most of them would have sworn forever after that they were about to die when rescued, and they would have vowed never to taste seal again—vows which would have been easy to keep, for no doubt in such cases the thought of seal, even years later, would have been accompanied by a feeling of revulsion. If a man has been on meat exclusively for only two or three months he may or may not be reluctant to go back to it again. But when the period has been six months or over, I remember no one who was unwilling to go back to meat. Moreover, those who have done without vegetables for an aggregate of several years usually thereafter eat a larger percentage of meat than the average citizen.

4

The Laboratory Check

NOW THAT the conclusions of the experiments in diet which Karsten Andersen and I undertook at Bellevue Hospital have been accepted by the medical world, it is difficult to realize that there could have been such a storm of excitement about the announcement of the plan, such a violent clash of opinion, such near unanimity in the prediction of dire results.

The feeling that decisive controlled tests were needed began to spread after I told one of the scientific heads of the Food Administration in 1918 that I had lived for an aggregate of more than five years, with enjoyment, on just meat and water. A turning point came in 1920 when I had an hour for explaining a meat regimen to the physicians and staff of the Mayo Clinic. The concluding phase began in 1928 when Mr. Andersen and I entered the Dietetic Ward of Bellevue Hospital to give modern science what appeared to have been the first chance in its history to observe human subjects while they lived through the chill of winter and the heat of summer, for twelve months, on an exclusive meat diet. We were to do it under conditions of ordinary city life.

At the beginning of our northern work in 1906, as was said a few pages back, it was the accepted view among doctors and dietitians that man cannot live on meat alone. They believed specifically that a group of serious diseases were either caused directly by meat or preventable only by vegetables. Those views were still being held when, in the autumn of 1918, an old friend, Frederic C. Walcott (later Senator from Connecticut), decided that my experiences and the resulting opinions were revolutionary in certain fields, and introduced me to Professor Raymond Pearl of Johns Hopkins, who was then with the United States Food Administration in Washington. Pearl considered several of the things I told him upsetting to views then held; he questioned me before a stenographer, and sent the mimeographed results to a number of dietitians. Their replies varied from concurrence with him to agreement with David Hume that you are more likely to encounter a thousand liars than one miracle.

Pearl was convinced that neither fibs nor miracles were involved and proposed that we write together a book on dietetics. I agreed. But cares intervened and things dragged.

In 1920 I had the above-mentioned chance to speak at the Mayo Clinic, Rochester, Minnesota. One of the Mayo brothers suggested that I spend two or three weeks there to have a check-over and see whether they could not find somewhere in my carcass evidence of the supposed bad effects of meat. I wanted to do this, but commitments in New York prevented.

Then one day in the hearing of the gastroenterologist Dr. Clarence W. Lieb I told of my regret that I had not been able to take advantage of the Mayo check-over. Lieb spoke up, saying that there were good doctors in New York, too, and volunteered to gather a committee of specialists who would put me through an examination as rigid as anything I could get from the Mayos.

The committee was organized, I went through the mill, and Lieb reported the findings in the *Journal* of the American Medical Association for July 3, 1926, "The Effects of an Exclusive Long-Continued Meat Diet." The committee had failed to discover any trace of even one of the supposed harmful effects.

With this publication the Lieb and Pearl events merge. For when the American Meat Institute wrote asking permission to reprint a large number of copies for distribution to the medical profession and to dietitians, Lieb, Pearl and I

went into a huddle. The result was a letter to the Institute
saying that we refused permission to reprint, but suggesting
that they might get something much better worth publishing,
and with right to publish it, if they placed an adequate fund
at the disposal of a research institution for a series of experiments designed to check, under conditions of average city
life, the problems which had arisen out of my experiences
and views. For it was contended by many that an all-meat
diet might work in a cold climate though not in a warm,
and under the strenuous conditions of the frontier though
not in common American sedentary business life.

We gave warning that, if anything, the institution chosen
would lean backward to make sure that nothing in the results
could even be suspected of having been influenced by the
source of the money.

After long negotiating, the Institute agreed to furnish the
necessary funds. The research organization selected for conducting the tests was the Russell Sage Institute of Pathology,
which was housed in Bellevue Hospital and was then, as now,
affiliated with the Medical College of Cornell University.
The committee in charge consisted of leaders in the most
important sciences that appeared related to the problem,
and represented seven institutions:

American Meat Institute: Dr. C. Robert Moulton.

American Museum of Natural History: Dr. Clark Wissler.

Cornell University Medical College: Dr. Walter L. Niles.

Harvard University: Drs. Lawrence J. Henderson, Earnest
A. Hooton, and Percy R. Howe.

Johns Hopkins University: Drs. William G. McCallum
and Raymond Pearl.

Russell Sage Institute of Pathology: Drs. Eugene F.
DuBois and Graham Lusk.

University of Chicago: Dr. Edwin O. Jordan.

Unattached: Dr. Clarence W. Lieb (private practice) and
Vilhjalmur Stefansson.

The Chairman of the committee was Dr. Pearl. The main research work of the experiment was headed by Dr. DuBois, who was then Medical Director of the Russell Sage Institute, who has since been Chief Physician of New York Hospital, and who is now (1945) Professor of Physiology in the Medical College of Cornell University. Among his collaborators were Dr. Walter S. McClellan, Dr. Henry B. Richardson, Mr. V. R. Rupp, Mr. G. F. Soderstrom, Dr. Henry J. Spencer, Dr. Edward Tolstoi, Dr. John C. Torrey, and Mr. Vincent Toscani. The clinical supervision was in charge of Dr. Lieb.

After meetings of the supervising committee, the election of a smaller executive committee, and much discussion, it was decided that, while the experiment would be directed at strictly scientific problems, there might be side glances now and then toward common folk beliefs and the propaganda of certain groups. For instance, our definition of a meat diet as "a diet from which all vegetable elements are excluded" would logically permit us to use milk and eggs, for they are not vegetables. But some vegetarians are illogical enough to allow milk and eggs; we agreed to be correspondingly illogical and exclude them. This forestalled the possible cry that we were being saved by the eggs and milk from the ill effects of a diet that excluded vegetables.

The aim of the project was not, as the press claimed at the time, to "prove" something or other. We were not trying to prove or disprove anything; we merely wanted to get at the facts. Every aspect of the results would be studied, but special attention would be paid to certain common views, such as that scurvy will result from the absence of vegetable elements, that other deficiency diseases may be produced, that the effect on the circulatory system and on the kidneys will be bad, that certain harmful microorganisms will flourish in the intestinal tract, and that there will be insufficient minerals, in particular calcium. The broad question was, of course, the effect upon the general health as judged by the observations of the supervising doctors and by the testimony of the subjects themselves.

The test was originally planned for me alone; but I might get run over by a truck, and that would be construed, by mixed-dieters and vegetarians, as showing impairment of mental alertness and bodily vigor through the monotony and poison of meat. It was difficult to find me a colleague, for the sort of test we planned cannot be made on just anybody. That appears if two elementary cases are considered:

Assume that the news of a ruinous stock market crash is conveyed to a number of victims after they have eaten a good meal. Digestion may stop almost at the point of the mental shock. Obviously the sickness which follows that meal should not be construed as a reflection upon the quality of the food.

Or ask some impressionable friends to dine. Serve them veal, of good quality and well cooked. When dinner is over you inquire about the veal; they will answer with the usual compliments. Then you say that your case has been proved. Rover died and they have eaten him. If the stage setting and the acting have been adequate, some at least of the company will make a dive from the room. What has sickened them is not the meat of a dog but the idea that they have eaten dog.

The Russell Sage experiment, then, could not be made upon anybody controlled by strong dietetic beliefs, such as that meat is harmful, that abstinence from vegetables brings trouble, that one tires of a food if he has to eat the same thing often. But almost everyone holds these or similar beliefs. So we were practically compelled to choose subjects from members of one of my expeditions; they were the only living Europeans we knew who had used exclusive meat long enough to eliminate completely the mental hazards.

One man fortunately was available. He was Karsten Andersen, a young Dane who had been a member of my third expedition. During that time he had lived an aggregate of more than a year on strictly meat and water, suffering no ill result and, in fact, being on one occasion cured by an exclusive meat regimen from scurvy, which he had contracted on a mixed diet. Moreover, he knew from the experience of a dozen of his colleagues on the expedition that his healthful enjoyment of the exclusive meat diet was not peculiar to himself but common to all those who had tried it, including members of three races—as has been said, ordinary whites, Cape Verde Islanders, and South Sea Islanders.

But there were other things which made Andersen particularly suitable. Through several years he had been working his own Florida orange grove, spending most of practically every day outdoors, lightly clad and enjoying the benefits (such as they are) of sub-tropical sunlight. In that mental and physical environment he had naturally been on a diet heavy in vegetable elements, and had suffered constantly from head colds, his hair was thinning steadily, and he had developed a condition involving intestinal toxemia such as would ordinarily cause a doctor to look serious and pronounce: "You must go light on meat" or "I am afraid you'll have to cut out meat entirely."

We could find no one but Andersen whose mind would leave his body unhandicapped. So, in January of 1928 the test began with the two of us. It was under the direct charge of Dr. DuBois and his staff in the Dietetic Ward of Bellevue Hospital, New York City.

A storm of protests from friends broke upon us when the press announced that we were entering Bellevue. These were based mainly upon the newspaper report that we were going to eat our meat raw~and the belief that we were using lean meat exclusively. The first was just a false rumor; the trouble under the second head was linguistic.

Eating meat raw, our friends chorused, would make us social outcasts. It is proper to serve oysters raw, and clams, in the United States; herring raw in Norway; several kinds of fish raw in Japan; and beef raw almost anywhere in the world if only you change the name and call it rare. The fashion of giving raw meat to infants was spreading; but we were babes neither in years nor stature and could not take advantage of that dispensation.

The answer to the raw-meat scare was an explanation of a basic procedure of our test—Andersen and I were to select our food by palate (so long as it was meat) and we were to decide for ourselves how far each meal was to be cooked. It proved that usually he leaned to medium cooking and I to well-done.

The linguistic trouble came from a recent change of American usage. In Elizabethan English meat was any kind of food, as in the expression "meat and drink." In modern England this has narrowed down to what is implied in the rhyme about Jack Sprat eating no fat and his wife no lean, although they both ate meat. In the United States "meat," in the last few years, has become a synonym for "lean." The meaning can become even narrower, as when somebody, usually a woman, tells you that she is strictly forbidden by her physician to touch meat, but that she is permitted all the chicken she wants, with an occasional lamb chop. To that woman "meat" signifies lean beef.

Linguistically, then, we pacified our friends by references to Mr. and Mrs. Sprat. Our diet would be of meat in the English sense. We were just going to live under modern conditions on the food of our more or less remote ancestors; the food, too, of certain contemporary "primitive" hunters.

During our first three weeks in Bellevue Hospital we were fed measured quantities of what might be called a standard mixed diet: fruits, cereals, bacon and eggs, that sort of thing for breakfast; meats, vegetables, including fruits, for lunch and dinner. During this time various specialists examined us from practically every angle that seemed pertinent.

Most tedious, and let us hope correspondingly valuable, were the calorimeter studies. With no food since the evening before, we would go in the late morning to the calorimeter room and sit quiet for an hour to get over the physiological effect of having perhaps walked up a single flight of stairs. Then we slid into calorimeters which were like big coffins with glass sides, and everybody waited around an hour or so until we were over the disturbance of having slid in.

The box was now closed up, and for three hours we lay there as nearly motionless as we could well be while a corps of scientists, visible through the glass, puttered about and studied our physiological processes. We were not allowed to read; we were cautioned even against thinking about anything particularly pleasant or particularly disagreeable, for thoughts and feelings heat or cool you, speed things up or slow them down, play hob generally with "normal" processes.

(Dr. DuBois told of a calorimeter test ruined by mental disturbance. A nervous Rumanian had developed an intense dislike for a fellow-patient named Kelly. During the second hour of an experiment that had been going very well, Max caught a glimpse of the hated Kelly through the window. This raised his metabolism ten per cent during that whole hour.)

With the air we breathed and the rest of our intakes and excretions carefully analyzed, with our blood chemistry determined and a check on such things as the billions of living bacteria which inhabit the human intestinal tract, we were ready for the meat.

During the three weeks of the Bellevue mixed diet and preliminary check-up, we had been free to come and go. Now we were placed under lock and key. Neither of us was permitted at any time, day or night, to be out of sight of a doctor or a nurse. This was in part the ordinary rigidity of a controlled scientific experiment, but it was in some part a bow to the skepticism of the mixed-diet advocates and to the emotional storms which were sweeping the vegetarian realms.

Nor was the skepticism and excitement all newspaper talk. One of the leading European authorities, Dr. M. Hindhede, was touring the United States. He called on us during the preliminary three weeks and assured the presiding physicians most solemnly that we should be unable to go more than four or five days on meat. He had tried it out himself on experimental human subjects who usually broke down in about three days. (The breakdowns, I thought, were of psychological antecedents; but Dr. Hindhede insisted they were strictly physiogolical—quite independent of the emotions.)

This European did take an extreme position, but many American nutritionists and physiologists were like-minded. One of the most distinguished, Dr. Francis Gano Benedict, Director of the Nutrition Laboratory of the Carnegie Institution, gave an outside of three weeks before the test would have to cease. It was he, in fact, who had written Dr. Pearl it was easier to believe that I, and all the members of our expedition, were lying than to concede that we had remained in good health for several years on an exclusive meat regimen.

The experiment started smoothly with Andersen, who was permitted to eat in such quantity as he liked such things as he liked, provided only that they came under our definition of meat.

In my case there was a hitch, in a way foreseen. For I had published in 1913, on pages 140-142 of *My Life with the Eskimo*, an account of how some natives and I became ill when we were forced to go two or three weeks on lean meat. So I forecast trouble when DuBois suggested that I start the test by eating as large quantities as I possibly could of chopped fatless muscle. But he countered by citing my own experience where illness had not come until after more than a week, and he now proposed lean for only two or three days. So I gave in.

The chief purpose of placing me abruptly on exclusively lean was that there would be a sharp contrast with Andersen, who was going to be on a normal meat diet, consisting of such proportions of lean and fat as his own taste determined.

In the Arctic we had become ill during the second or third fatless week. I now became ill on the second day. The time difference between Bellevue and the Arctic was due no doubt mainly to the existence of a little fat, here and there, in our northern caribou—we had eaten the tissue from behind the eyes, we had broken the bones for marrow, and in doing everything we could to get fat we had evidently secured more than we realized. At Bellevue the meat, carefully scrutinized, was as lean as such muscle tissue well can be. Then, in the Arctic we had eaten tendons and other indigestible matter, we had chewed the soft ends of bones, getting a deal of bulk that way when we were trying to secure fat. What we ate at Bellevue contained no bulk material of this kind, so that my stomach could be compelled to hold a much larger amount of lean. Moreover, I had in New York a much larger stomach than in the Arctic; there it had been constricted in accord with the small bulk of a lean-fat diet; here in "civilization" it had been expanded through the needs of a bulky mixed diet.

The symptoms brought on at Bellevue by an incomplete meat diet (this ration of lean without fat) were exactly the same as in the Arctic, except that they came on faster—diarrhoea and a feeling of general baffling discomfort.

Up North the Eskimos and I had been cured immediately when we got some fat. Dr. DuBois now cured me the same way, by giving me fat sirloin steaks, brains fried in bacon fat, and things of that sort. In two or three days I was all right, but I had lost considerable weight.

A second upset was a result of the first, and a result, too, of carelessness. As has been said, my cure from the lean-meat difficulty was in part the eating of brains fried in bacon fat. The brains tasted delicious, partly no doubt on their own merits but also partly on account of the bacon fat through which we were compensating for the previous excess of lean; so I ate too much. This produced a mild indigestion, with attendant discomforts, and reminded me that the only recurrent digestive upsets I had had on our exclusive meat up North were those produced by eating large meals which contained too high a percentage of fat, which was most likely to occur just after we had been living on meat that was too lean.

There is no tendency to overeat of fat if you have fat every day (not necessarily at every meal); but there is danger of it after a shortage of fat. So far as memory serves and my records go, there is no corresponding tendency to overeat of lean to an injurious extent after one has been on an excessively fat regimen.

If the diet has been too lean, one is likely to overindulge in fat to a degree which causes vomiting within the next hour or two. This single gorging and its violent reaction apparently leave no bad effect; but a persistent overindulgence can produce discomforts and difficulties that may last a day, or even several days. The best practice, in such case, would seem to be eating for two or three meals somewhat less than the appetite dictates, and of a meat that is chiefly or entirely lean. Another good way might be to go without a meal or two.

For the first three weeks of the Russell Sage test, the outside endurance limit set by Dr. Benedict, I was watched day and night by the Institute staff. My exercise was supposed to be about that of an average businessman. I went out for walks, but always under guard. If I telephoned, the attendant stood at the door of the booth; if I went into a shop, he was never more than a few feet away; and he was always vigilant.

As DuBois explained, and as I knew in advance, this was not because the staff were suspicious of me but rather because they wanted to be able to say that they knew of their own knowledge my complete abstinence from all solids and liquids except those which I received in Bellevue and which I ate and drank under the watch of attendants.

But my affairs this year demanded that I travel widely through the United States and Canada. This was an added reason why Andersen had been secured for the experiment. When, after three weeks, they had to put me on a kind of parole, they retained him under lock and key, for a total of something more than ninety days. Thus, in a way, the supreme test, or at least the one best certified, was made on Andersen, not on me.

Those who had believed that a meat diet would lead to death had set at anything from four to fifteen days the point where Dr. Lieb, as clinical supervisor, would have to call a halt in view of danger to the subjects. Even those who expected only a slow breakdown, an impaired health merely, had placed the appearance of the dread symptoms well before thirty days. In any case, Andersen reported back to the hospital constantly after he left it, and I whenever I was in town.

After my three weeks and Andersen's thirteen, and with the constant analyses of excretions and blood when we came back to the hospital for check-ups, the doctors felt certain they would catch us at it if we broke diet. Moreover, long before the thirteen weeks ended they had satisfied themselves that Andersen had no longing for fruits or other vegetable materials and, therefore, no motive for breach of contract.

During the early summer, toward the middle of our experiment, both of us were living in New York City and eating mainly in restaurants, though there were a few home-cooked meals. At the restaurants we looked over the menu each time, in the way of a regular customer, and selected whatever appealed to us. Our belief was that no theory of what to select would be as safe a guide to health as our unbiased cravings.

We sometimes had difficulty, however, in getting what we wanted in restaurants. I remember, for instance, a meal at the Commodore Hotel one day when I had a strong feeling that I would rather have mutton fat than bacon. I told the waiter, in words of one syllable and with pauses between them, that I wanted chops from-which-the-fat-had-*not*-been-trimmed. He assured me that my chops would come just as I had ordered them. But when they came they had been "frenched"—there was scarcely a visible trace of fat.

Now I called a head waiter, or captain, and was assured that next time the chops would be right. He may have given the corect orders to a waiter, but I got the same kind of "frenched" chops once more. My time was up, and I had to eat bacon with those chops, after all.

A philosophic steward of a railway diner gave me his theory on why I had so much trouble getting the fat I ordered with my lean. He said that when a customer speaks of fat to a waiter it is nearly always to specify that it must be removed; or, in the case of bacon, that it should be fried to a crisp. There was, he considered, at least a twenty-five per cent chance that all the waiter would remember when he got back to the kitchen was that the customer said something about fat, and naturally this would be that it should be removed. Then there was another twenty-five per cent chance that, even if the waiter said the right thing, the cook would get it wrong, for he is used to no commandments on fat except those of prohibition.

Occasionally when I was in a hotel that prided itself on serving anything that a customer wanted in the style which he desired, I would inquire whether I could get beef or other meat broth free from vegetable contamination. In most cases this proved impossible, except upon a very long wait or an order in advance. In a few cases they tried to put over on me broth which I found on investigation really had one sort or other of vegetable taint.

Our regimen permitted ordering broiled chicken in a restaurant, but not fried; because the frying might be in butter or even in olive oil. The oil would have been a major pollution of our diet, being of vegetable origin; the butter would have been only a technical infringement. For, as has been said, we were really within our rights if we ate butter; it is not directly a vegetable product, and was omitted from our diet merely because we did not want to give a foothold to those vegetarians who exempt milk and its products from their damnation.

Naturally chicken Maryland was forbidden, along with breaded chops, and things of that sort.

Something near to an exemption in the class of "milk, milk products and eggs" was arrived at by our authorities in view of my need for extensive traveling. It would happen in a small town that I had to get off a train at, say, two in the morning and wait around the station till five or six o'clock for my connection. Usually there would be in the neighborhood a restaurant of the wagon type. They would have puffed rice and corn flakes and many other things that were strictly forbidden to me; there might remain only such mildly taboo things as bacon and eggs. In such case, perhaps a dozen times during the year, and in a few analogous cases, I did eat eggs. But there were periods of several months at a time during which I did not touch an egg or anything under that classification.

My colleague Andersen was immaculate. He did not have to travel and was never under the necessity, any more than he was under the inclination, of using eggs or butter. He never tasted eggs, milk or milk products the whole year.

Meals that were amusing to me and difficult for my hostess came now and then when I was invited out to dinner. I told

them always that what I really preferred was just one thing
to a meal—a big sirloin steak, several lamb chops with the
fat on them, a dish of boiled mutton ribs, or something of
that sort. I preferred the meat boiled, partly for its own taste
but largely because then I could have the hot broth for drink
instead of just cold water.

But I found that a plain meal of one article gave many a
hostess such distress that it seemed worth while to devise a
plan of alleviation. Finally we arrived at a course dinner
which might go something like this:

Hors d'oeuvres
Caviar served on slices of white chicken breast each
about the size and thickness of a fifty-cent piece.

Soup
Broth made by boiling meat—in some cases bone.

Fish
Any kind of fish boiled or baked; if fried, then in
bacon fat.

Entree
Lamb chops. Most hostesses preferred to garnish with
bacon.

Dessert
Gelatin, solely of meat origin and made according to
a recipe which I got hold of somewhere.

Demi-tasse

It seemed to please hostesses that I was permitted to drink
black coffee. The permission was given by our supervising
committee because there had been carried through some
time before an extensive research, I think at the University

of Rochester, which showed that black coffee and black tea contained no appreciable Vitamin C, and those who expected our experiment to fail were counting heavily on our developing scurvy—the simple formula then current (1928-29) being that "meat is deficient in the Vitamin C needed to prevent scurvy."

It happens, however, that I never liked coffee without sugar, which was forbidden; nor did I ever get used to saccharine. I don't think I often drank more at these formal dinners than half of a small after-dinner cup. The coffee was there primarily for the sake of my hostess; as long as they could serve it they did not usually seem to mind whether I drank it or not.

Both Andersen and I, on rare occasions, took advantage of the permission to use black tea, but only in restaurants, where we drank water certainly more than ninety per cent of the time. For the summer Andersen and I took a small house near Croton, New York, and did our own cooking. Our chief motive for home cooking was to get a mutton, beef or chicken broth in which we had confidence and which we liked after many years of having used caribou and seal broth in the Arctic. During those several months we lived mainly on boiled meats, including fish. A practice that amused or horrified our friends, according to their predilections, was that we ate bones.

The Eskimos, from whom we had learned our meat eating, have no theories about diet; at least, none that remotely resemble ours. They chew a lot of bones of a certain kind; other bones which are just as chewably soft they do not use at all. They eat the ones that taste good.

The bones not chewed by Eskimos are those of the blubber-carrying sea mammals—seal, walrus, whale, polar bear. Theoreticians will say that there you are!—that the Eskimos don't chew those bones because they are getting plenty of fat from the blubber direct. So far, so good. They do certainly get plenty of fat. We have found in traveling over the sea ice on our exploratory journeys and living entirely by hunting, Eskimo fashion, that when we kill seals enough to supply the lean desired we necessarily secure so much fat that, after men and dogs have eaten all they want, and after we have burned all that is necessary for cooking our meals and heating our dwellings, we still have left over fully a third of the blubber. If you were to follow our trail, as polar bears sometimes do, you would find a little heap of blubber at every third or fourth camp site; or, if you didn't, Sherlock Holmes methods would tell you that the hunting was not going well and that we were on short rations.

Perhaps the reason why the ends of bones from sea mammals do not taste particularly good is that there is little or no fat in them; but all we ever think of, and still more certainly all the Eskimos ever think of, is just that they do not taste good. (The bones of the blubber mammals do not have marrow, in the sense that human or beef bones do. Apparently there is corresponding absence of fat from the cavities in the spongy ends of the bones. In the typical herbivorous mammal, bone ends usually carry much fat.)

With sea mammals, as with those of the land, we eat cartilage when we find it. If the beast is young there is more cartilage, and in that sense we do eat a certain amount of the bones of blubber mammals.

From all animals, we eat the sinew, unless it has been removed because the women need it for sewing thread. The tendon of Achilles in northern animals, from the gigantic moose down, is eaten as something of a delicacy, either cooked or raw. In neither case is it chewed; it is cut into bits that slide down easily and are swallowed one after the other, each getting just a few bites and rolls around to cover them with saliva. These tendons have little taste, but still one feels inclined to eat them.

When fat-hungry we eat not only the soft ends of all bones

of grazing mammals and birds but the whole of each bone which is readily chewable. About all that would not be eaten from a ptarmigan would be the shafts of the long bones. The neck and backbone are particularly good, if your teeth are good; and, as explained elsewhere, the teeth of all uncivilized Eskimos are always good, at least from the caries point of view.

In New York City during the Russell Sage tests, and at Croton, we ate a lot of bones. We cleaned up a broiled spring chicken as completely as an Eskimo would a ptarmigan, and we selected portions of other animals at butcher shops somewhat with reference to the chewability of the bones, which tasted as good in New York as they ever had up North. I feel sure I would have eaten practically the identical bone proportions had there been no theory; but, even in the North, I rationalized the desire for bones into thinking they would take the place of spinach or bran in giving bulk to the diet.

It is written by many nutritionists and physiologists that Eskimos get the necessary calcium by chewing bones. Their skeletons, as studied in our museums, indicate a plentiful calcium supply, and when I first heard that their calcium was derived from bone chewing it struck me as reasonable. There had certainly been in me no sign of calcium deficiency after ten Arctic years, about half of which were exclusively on meat and the other half on a preponderance of meat. And I could remember, thinking back, that I had chewed a great many bones. Now I worry somewhat, fearing I may have given written adherence to the calcium-from-chewed-bones theory, but take some comfort in the fact that I have not yet been able to discover this in my printed writings. For I realize now a flaw in the argument, serious if not fatal to it.

On the basis of the preceding discussion of the differences in flavor and anatomical structure between seal and caribou.

bones, it can be stated simply and flatly that the man who
chews a lot of bones in a caribou-hunting year will chew no
bones at all in a sealing year. I have myself never gone more
than, say, half a year at a time exclusively on seal, then eating
no bone, except cartilage; and perhaps in my case that span
could have been tided over by the calcium I got from herbivorous animals during the other six months; but there are
Eskimos who live practically exclusively on seal their whole
lives, and yet there is no indication while they live that they
are less healthy than the caribou eaters, nor do their skeletons show a lack of calcium. Thus calcium deficiency is as
absent from those meat-eaters who practically never eat
bones as from those who eat them nearly every day of their
lives.

In the Arctic and in New York we were fond of eating
skin. I always eat bacon rind. I am fond of pickled pig's
feet, mainly, I think, because I like the skin and the tendons,
for there is not much else to pig's feet, except fat. If there is
any part of a fried chicken that tastes better to a meat devotee
than the chewable bones, then it is the skin. The like applies
to all birds unless one has been on the verge of fat-overeat-
ing, in which case the fat attached to the skin may repel him.

Toward the end of the covenanted year Andersen and I returned to Bellevue for final intensive studies of some weeks
on the meat diet, studies which would then be caried through
our first three weeks on a mixed diet. At this end of the
experiment all went smoothly with me, but not so with
Andersen.

My trouble, it will be remembered, had been that at the
outset they stuffed me with lean. Andersen's difficulty, or at
least annoyance, began on the second day after he completed
a year on meat (January 25, 1929), when they asked him to
eat all the fat he could, permitting along with it only a tiny
bit of lean, about 45 grams per day. There they kept him, on
the verge of nausea, for a week. The second week they added

his first taste of vegetables in a year, thrice-cooked cabbage netting about 35 grams of carbohydrate per day. The third week they omitted the cabbage and retained the high proportion of fat to lean.

These three weeks, Andersen says, were the only difficult part of the experiment. Looking back at it now, he thinks if it were possible to separate the nausea from the other unpleasantness there would still have been a good deal left over—that at the end of the third week he wasn't, properly speaking, well. However, that is speculation, if not imagination.

Returning to facts, we have the ominous one that a pneumonia epidemic was sweeping New York. The hospital was crowded with patients; some of the staff got the disease, and with them Andersen. It was Type II pneumonia in his case and the physicians were gravely worried, for this type was proving deadly in that epidemic, carrying off fifty per cent of its Bellevue victims. Andersen, however, reacted quickly to treatment, the disease ran an unusually short course, and he convalesced rapidly.

The broad results of the experiment were, so far as Andersen and I could tell, and so far as the supervising physicians could tell, that we were in at least as good average health during the twelve months on exclusive meat as during the three mixed-diet weeks at the start. We thought our health had been a little better than average. We enjoyed ourselves and prospered as well on the meat in midsummer as in midwinter, and we seemed to feel no more discomfort from the heat than our fellow New Yorkers did.

It is ordinary experience that when one shifts from a mixed diet to exclusive meat, or from meat to mixed, the appetite falls off during the first week, most pronouncedly perhaps between the second and fourth days. It appeared reasonable to suppose that when going from exclusive meat to foods that have a high proportion of starches and sugars, like the ordinary American meals of today, any difficulty would be connected with sugar tolerance. For this and other reasons, our ability to handle sugar had been tested while we were still on the mixed diet, before we began the year of meat; now that the meat year was over a corresponding test was made. We drank glucose syrup in measured, large quantities—I think a pint and a half at a time—and were then subjected to the usual tests. The first glucose "meal," when we were immediately off the meat, showed a poor sugar tolerance; but in a week or so we were back to where we had been before the meat year began.

In view of beliefs that remain strangely current, it is worth emphasizing that we liked our meat as fat in July as in January. This ought not to surprise Americans (though it usually does), for they know or have heard that fat pork is a staple and relished food of the Negro in the Deep South. Our Negro literature is rich with the praise of opossum fat. Nor did Negroes develop the taste for fats in our southern states; for Carl Akeley brought from tropical Africa such yarns of fat-gorging as have not yet been surpassed from the Arctic. A frequent complaint of travelers in Spain is against foods that swim in oil, and there are similar complaints when we visit rural Latin America. In Puerto Rico, cracklings are sold like candy. So we really know, when we stop to think, that many if not most tropical people like greasy food. (I return to this topic in the chapter "Living on the Fat of the Land.")

Parallel to and as strange as the current view that one does not like fat foods in hot weather is the other belief that the largest meat consumption is in cold countries. True, the hundred-percenters are way up North, the Dogribs, Eskimos, Nenets, Chukchis. But almost the heaviest meat eaters who speak English are the Australians,* tropical and sub-tropical,

---

* It used to be stated with seeming authority, that Australia led all English-speaking countries in meat consumption; more recently it has been

while the nearest approach to an exclusive meat died among people of European stock is perhaps in tropical Argentina, where the cowboys live on beef and maté. They like their meat fat and (so an Argentinian New Yorker tells me) will threaten to quit work, or at least did forty years ago, if you attempt to feed them in any considerable part on cereals, greens, and fruits.

There are doubtless few men elsewhere, perhaps none, who will go to the extreme of the Eskimos, as I found them on the middle north coast of North America, and as others have reported them from a few of the more northerly districts, where they consider that roots and berries are not foods but substitutes for food—things that are eaten in foolery or in time of starvation. But it appears common, and has been found all over the world in all ages, that meat is considered the superior food, vegetables inferior or secondary. Carl Lumholtz reported, after living with the natives of tropical northern Australia, that they ate nothing vegetable if meat was on hand.

In searching for material on the history of navigation, a research associate of mine was going through *Hero Tales of Ireland,* collected by Jeremiah Curtin, Boston, 1894, and came upon a bit that seems to indicate the traditional Irish view on the comparative suitability of diets high in meats and others high in vegetables:

In the story "The Amadan Mor and the Grungach," the King of Leinster defeated and slew the King of Munster. The victor decided to live in Munster. The widow of the former king fled to the forest, where she gave birth to a child. They had no clothes, and hair grew out all over them. Eventually the queen went to the castle for dole. The attendants did not think she was human. She countered: "I have

reported· that the New Zealanders outdo them. New Zealand, of course, is not cold—the north island is somewhat warmer than England.

the look of a beast because I eat fruits and leaves of trees and grass of the earth."

This was, of course, long before the introduction of the potato. Curtin fails to give a date but says that the stories "relate to heroes and adventures of an ancient time, and contain elements peculiar to early ages of story telling."

A preference for meat foods, if not a prejudice against the others, can be traced through the history and literature of mankind in every age, clime and country. Except for wine which is from the kingdom of vegetables, the highest praise of Greek poetry, particularly the Homeric, is for meats. The same indication of preference runs through the Bible. What is said in Genesis, IV, 2-5, is considered more fully in a later chapter: that the Lord was not pleased with Cain when he brought an offering of garden produce but was pleased with Abel when he brought some fat mutton. This led to the tragedy in which Cain the gardener killed Abel the shepherd, foreshadowing that bitterness which the vegetarians still feel against those who persist in the eating of sirloins and chops.

A conclusion of our experiment which the medical profession seemingly finds difficult to assimilate, but which at the same time is one of our clearest results, is that a normal meat diet, where one eats at each meal as much lean and fat as he likes, is not a high protein diet.

A casual look at the meals we ate in Bellevue might lead to the conclusion that we were living chiefly on lean; but then you would be forgetting that in a medium or rare sirloin steak the red meat on your plate is mostly water, while the white suet has very little water in it.

Speaking in terms of calories Dr. Lieb, the clinician of the Russell Sage tests, put it this way:

"Stefansson averaged about 2,650 calories a day, 2,100 calories consisting of fat and 550 of protein. Andersen averaged about 2,620 calories a day, 2,110 calories consisting of fat and 510 of protein."

In another part of the same paper Dr. Lieb says that the ratio of protein to fat in Andersen's food and mine does not make this a high protein diet. He said elsewhere that while the protein percentage of our diet was perhaps a little above average, it was not as high as the protein ratio of a great many New York businessmen who are fond of meat and who can afford to eat as much of it as they like at their various meals. This is remembering, of course, that the said businessmen would be getting protein from a number of sources other than meat; as, for instance, from oatmeal, chocolate, baked beans, milk and eggs.

That meat, as some have contended, is a particularly stimulating food I verified subjectively during our New York experiment—it seemed to me that I was more optimistic and energetic than ordinarily. To the best of my memory and judgment, I looked forward with more anticipation to the next day or the next job, and was more likely to expect pleasure or success. This may have a bearing on the common report that the uncivilized Eskimos are the happiest people in the world. There have been many explanations— that an Arctic climate is invigorating, that a hunter's life is pleasant, and that the poor wretches just don't know how badly off they are. The suggestion is now added that the optimism may be in part directly caused by what they eat.

Some additional fairly precise things can be said of the way we fared during the year on meat. For instance, with Dr. DuBois as pacemaker, we used every few weeks to run around the reservoir in Central Park and thence to his house, going up the stairs two or three at a time, plumping down on cots and having scientific attendants register our breathing, pulse rate, and other crude reactions. These observations, when compared with others made just before the exercise, appear to show that our stamina increased with the lengthening of the meat period.

Andersen, who had suffered one head cold after another

when working nearly stripped outdoors in his Florida orange grove, contracted only two or three colds during the meat year in New York, and those were light. In Florida his hair had been thinning rapidly. It seemed to him there was a marked decrease in the shedding after he went on the meat diet; but he did not regain what had been lost.

As has been said, according to the reports of the doctors Andersen was troubled when he came from Florida with certain toxin-producing intestinal microorganisms in relation to which physicians at that time ordinarily prescribed elimination of meat from the diet. This condition did not trouble him while he was living on meat.

A phase of our experiment has a relation to slimming, slenderizing, reducing; the various treatments of obesity. I was "about ten pounds overweight" at the beginning of the meat diet, by life insurance standards, and lost all of it. This reminds me to say that Eskimos, when still on their home meats, are never corpulent—at least I have seen none who were. They may be well fleshed. Some, especially women, are notably heavier in midlle age than when young. But they are not corpulent in our sense.

Eskimos in their native garments do give the impression of fat round faces on fat round bodies, but the roundness of face is a racial peculiarity and the rest of the effect is produced by loose and puffy garments. See them stripped, and one does not find the abdominal protuberances and folds which are so in evidence at Coney Island beaches and so persuasive against nudism.

There is, however, among Eskimos no racial immunity to corpulence. That is proved by the rapidity with which and the extent to which they fatten on European diets.

One serious fear of the group of scientists conducting our Russell Sage trials at first seemed to be realized—the measured part of our diet for the year turned out low in calcium. This was not demonstrated by any tests upon Andersen or me, and certainly no one could have proved it by asking us or looking at us, for we felt better and looked healthier than our average for the year immediately previous. The calcium deficiency appeared solely through the analyses of the chemists.

Part of the routine at Bellevue was to give the chemists for analysis pieces of meat as nearly as possible identical with those we ate. For instance, a lamb would be split down through the middle of the spine. We got a chop from the right side to eat while the chemists got a chop from the left side to analyze; next they got a right chop, we a left—and so on, alternating. When the diet was sirloin, they received steaks matching ours. From these studies it was clear, on paper, that we were not getting enough calcium for health. But we were healthy. The first avenue of escape from that dilemma was to assume that a calcium deficiency which did not hurt us in one year might destroy us in ten or twenty.

When a doctor looks for a calcium deficiency, he studies bones. The thing to do, then, was to examine the skeletons of people who had died at a reasonably high age after living from infancy upon an exclusive meat diet. Such skeletons are those of Eskimos who died before European influences came in. The American Meat Institute was induced to make a subsidiary appropriation to the Peabody Museum of Harvard University, where Dr. Earnest A. Hooton, Professor of Physical Anthropology, undertook a thoroughgoing research on the calcium problem in relation to the Museum's collection of skeletons of meat eaters. Dr. Hooton reported no sign of calcium deficiency. On the contrary, there was every indication that the meat eaters had been liberally, or at least adequately, supplied. They had suffered from calcium deficiency no more in a lifetime than we had in our short year.

As the reader of this statement knows from what was said some pages back, there was here a possible source of error—bones in a diet would be a patent source of calcium, and some Eskimos eat many while others use few or none. We had not eaten them appreciably at Bellevue, when our diet was being measured, for it just did not occur to us to eat bones—we had no craving for them and, at that stage, no concern about them. But when we began to do our own cooking and to eat in restaurants, the lamb ribs we boiled at home and the young broiler chickens we ate at restaurants led us naturally back into our Eskimo habit of former years, the eating of those bones that were chewable.

Our technical supervisors in Bellevue did not realize this access of bone devouring after we left the hospital, and we did not realize the importance of telling them. When toward the end of the experiment the talk grew more insistent that calcium was lacking (in the measured diet) it seemed best to me not to try to talk them out of their worries but rather to encourage them to favor an independent skeletal study—the one above mentioned which was carried out by Professor Hooton.

There was, in fact, a special need for caution and precautions in the conduct of our test and in the announcement of the results; for even men of high standing in physiology, dietetics and medicine, who would not consciously misrepresent what had been done or the conclusions arrived at, were subconsciously so biased, so powerfully swayed by a tendency to harmonize our results with their previous beliefs, that what we had done was in fact repeatedly misstated, our conclusions misinterpreted, in textbooks, professional books and learned journals.

Of the incorrect things said about my writings concerning how we had lived in the North, and about the Russell Sage tests, probably the most serious were those which first praised us and then went on something like this: "Stefansson has proved, by his experience and observations while living with Eskimos and by his and Andersen's year on an exclusively carnivorous diet at Bellevue Hospital, that you can be healthy indefinitely on an exclusive meat diet, *provided you eat a large part of your food raw or underdone, and provided, further, that you eat the whole animal.*" In fact, my observation and experience in the North, and the results of the Russell Sage tests, run contrary to both of these provisos.

As to the degree of cooking: It has been explained in this and previous chapters that Eskimos cook their food on the average more than we do, and it has been stated in this chapter that during the Bellevue year Andersen and I ate little food that was raw or underdone but, instead, that Andersen tended to eat his food medium done and I well done. However, my "well done" is not to be interpreted to mean cooked to pieces, like a New England boiled dinner. With us it meant that the heart of each piece was slightly pink, about what restaurants speak of as "medium well" in relation to a sirloin.

Then it is significant that the northerly forest Indians, as late as when I lived with the Dogribs, Loucheux, and other northern groups in the period 1906-1914, still had that horror of underdone or raw meat which had given the Crees reason to apply the contemptuous term Eskimos, Eaters-of-Raw-Meat, to their more northerly neighbors. Since 1914, I am told, the white man's idea of how to cook steaks and roasts has made headway. When I was with them they spoke with abhorrence of rare meats, and cooked theirs usually to what we could call medium or medium-well.

Except for a few weeks in summer, when they were around the trading posts, these Indians were as exclusive meat eaters as the Eskimos; they did, however, sometimes eat intestines that had a little vegetable matter in them, whereas the Eskimos usually, and in my experience always, gave these to the dogs. Yet these forest Indians, eating at an average meats that we would call medium done, were as free from scurvy as the Eskimos—completely free, except a few who worked for white men, ate their food, and then developed scurvy like the whites.

The second proviso, that you must eat the whole beast, has, in my experience and observation, still less foundation than the first proviso, if that be possible. Both Eskimos and northern forest Indians, and whites who live with them, have a clear mental picture of each animal they butcher, dividing the carcass then or later so that certain parts go uniformly to the dog team, the rest to the family. These divisions of the carcass vary from one species of animal to another but do not vary within the species, unless slightly by season.

The way in which Eskimos divide, for instance, a caribou between men and dogs has been described with some detail; here the fact is emphasized that the organ commonly spoken of as richest in vitamins, the liver, is nearly always given to the dogs—as are the sweetbreads and, indeed, all things from the body cavity except the heart and kidneys. The kidneys are usually given to children, somewhat as if they were candy.

So far as I know the Eskimos of northern Alaska and north-western Canada, and the forest Indians just to the south of them, the only condition under which they ate nearly or quite the whole caribou was in time of famine. Ceasing to give the dogs the parts which normally are theirs was that stage of a famine which immediately preceded the killing and eating of the dogs themselves.

So far as present knowledge goes, there is in ordinary red meat, or in ordinary fresh fish, without the eating of anything from the body cavity, enough Vitamin C, or whatever it is that prevents scurvy, to maintain optimum health indefinitely, with a cooking to the degree which we call medium. Certainly this is true if the meat is cooked in large chunks, as with both Eskimos and northern forest Indians, rather than in thin slices, which latter style of cooking may, for all

I know, decrease the potency of the scurvy-preventing factor.

There is no intention to deny, of course, that cooking to medium will somewhat lessen the meat's antiscorbutic value. What is to be said is only that even with medium cooking there appears to be left over, in fresh red meat or fresh fish, an abundance if not a superabundance of all the vitamins and of all the other factors necessary for keeping a man in top form indefinitely. If results contrary to this are obtained from experiments on guinea pigs, rats or chimpanzees, then it may be advisable to restrict the conclusions in each case to the animal from which these results were drawn.

5

And Visit Your Dentist Twice a Year

A CLEAN tooth never decays. Brush your teeth after every meal, and visit your dentist twice a year.

These slogans carry the faith of our people. It is said and believed that we have the best dentists in the world, that we have more tooth brushes, and use them more, than any other people. Many agencies, from kindergarten to university, from town council to and through the governments of city, state, and nation, strive for the spread of dental knowledge and the enforcement of its discipline. For instance, the New York subways co-operated some time ago with the Commissioner of Health by displaying the notice:

FOR SOUND TEETH
BALANCED DIET WITH
VEGETABLES: FRUIT: MILK
BRUSH TEETH
VISIT YOUR DENTIST REGULARLY

—SHIRLEY W. WYNNE, M. D.,
Commissioner of Health.

During the same time the ether was filled and the magazine pages were crowded with advertising which told that mouth chemistry is altered by a paste, a powder, or a gargle so as to prevent decay; that a special kind of toothbrush reaches all the crevices; that a particular brand of fruit, milk, or bread is rich in elements for tooth health. There were toothbrush drills in the schools. Mothers throughout the land were scolding, coaxing, and bribing to get children to use the preparations, eat the foods, and follow the rules that were said to guarantee perfect oral hygiene. There was

endless repetition of the slogan: *A clean tooth never decays.*
Meantime there appeared a statement from Dr. Adelbert
Fernald, Curator of the Museum of the Dental School, Harvard University, that he had been collecting mouth casts of
living North Americans of all racial derivations from blond
to black, from the most northerly Eskimos through Canada
and the States south to Yucatan. The best teeth and the
healthiest mouths were found among people who never
drank milk since they ceased to be suckling babes and who
never in their lives tasted or tested any of the other things
which we usually recommend for sound teeth. These people,
Eskimos not as yet influenced by white men, never used tooth
paste, tooth powder, toothbrushes, mouth wash, or gargle.
They never took any pains to cleanse their teeth or mouths.
They did not visit their dentists twice a year or even once
in a lifetime. Their food was exclusively meat. Meat, be it
noted, is not mentioned as good for the teeth in the adver-
tisement sponsored by the Commissioner of Health of the
City of New York.*

Teeth superior on the average to those of the presidents
of our largest tooth paste companies are found in the world
today, and have existed during past ages, among people who
violate every precept of current dentifrice advertising. Not
all of them have lived exclusively on meat; but, so far as an
extensive correspondence with authorities has yet been able
to show, a complete absence of tooth decay from entire populations has never existed in the past, and does not exist
now, except where meat is either exclusive or heavily pre-
dominant in the diet.

* The poster to which this refers, and similar dental propaganda by the
City of New York, disappeared from the subways in the thirties, but similar
views have remained current. For instance, Dr. James W. Barton says in
the "That Body of Yours" column of the New York *Post* for November 30,
1944: "Research dental workers—dentists and physicians, state that proper
foods, particularly milk and milk products, and raw vegetables and fruits,
prevent decay from the inside of the tooth." In his presentation there is no
reference to meat.

Our Bellevue experiments threw a light on tooth decay, but the key to the situation lies more in the broad science of anthropology. I now give, by sample and by summary, things personally known to me from anthropological field work:

I received my first anthropological commission from the Peabody Museum of Harvard University when they sent John W. Hastings and me to Iceland, in 1905. We found there in one place a medieval graveyard that was being cut away by the sea. Skulls were rolling about in the water at high tide; at low tide we gathered them and picked up scattered teeth here and there. As wind and water shifted the sands we found more and more teeth until there was a handful. We got permission to excavate the cemetery, and eventually brought with us to Harvard a miscellaneous lot of bones which included more than eighty skulls and a great many loose teeth.

The collection has been studied by dentists and physical anthropologists without the discovery of a single cavity in even one tooth. So the Icelanders of the Middle Ages had no toothache, and none of that sloughing away of the teeth which is known as dental caries.

The skulls in the Hastings-Stefansson collection at Harvard University represent persons of ordinary Icelandic blood. There were no aborigines in that island when the Irish discovered it some time before 800 A.D. When the Norsemen got there, after 850, they found no people except the Irish. It is now variously estimated that in origin the Icelanders are from 10 per cent to 30 per cent Irish, 60 per cent to 80 per cent Norwegian, the remainder chiefly from Scotland, England, Sweden and Denmark.

None of the peoples whose blood went into the Icelandic stock are racially immune to tooth decay, nor are the modern Icelanders. Then why were the Icelanders of the Middle Ages immune?

An analysis of the various factors makes it pretty clear that it was their food which protected the teeth of the medieval Icelanders. The chief elements were fish, mutton, milk, and milk products. There was a certain amount of beef and there may have been a little horse flesh, particularly in the earliest period of the graveyard. Cereals were little imported and might be used for beer rather than porridge. Bread was negligible and so were all other elements from the vegetable kingdom, native or imported.

When Hastings and I were in Iceland, many people remembered, from the middle of the nineteenth century, a period when bread still was more rare than caviar is in New York today. As children they had tasted bread only a few times a year, usually when they went visiting with their parents. Thus the diet was still substantially that of the Middle Ages, though the use of porridge was increasing. The older people with whom we talked did not remember hearing of toothache in their early youth, but did remember accounts of it as a painful rarity about the time when the large emigration to North America started, following 1872.

Soon after arrival in the States (Utah, Wisconsin, Minnesota, Dakota) and in Canada (Nova Scotia, Manitoba), the Icelandic colonists became thoroughly familiar with the ravages of caries. In the United States and Canada they had, before 1900 at the latest, teeth as bad as those of the average native-born American.

There is, then, at least one known case of a North European people whose immunity from caries (to judge from the Peabody Museum collection and from common report) approached 100 per cent for a thousand years, down to about 100 years ago. The diet was mainly from the animal kingdom. Now that Iceland's diet has become approximately the same as average for the United States or Europe, Icelandic teeth show as high a percentage of decay.

I began to learn about another formerly toothacheless

people when I joined the Mackenzie River Eskimos in 1906. Some of them had been eating European foods in considerable amount since 1889; toothache and tooth decay were appearing, but only in the mouths of those who affected the new foods secured from the Yankee whalers. The Mackenzie people agreed that toothache and tooth cavities had been unknown in the childhood of those then approaching middle age, while there were many of all ages still untouched, the ones who kept mainly or wholly to the Eskimo foods. Here, and in many other places, this diet is somewhere between 95 per cent and 99 per cent from animal sources, if measured in calories—the vegetable food is chiefly fresh berries, picked in the open during summer and eaten the same day.

There are Eskimo districts, like parts of Labrador and of western and southwestern Alaska, where even before the coming of Europeans considerable use was made of native vegetables. Probably, however, the vegetable element nowhere furnished as much as 5 per cent of the average yearly caloric intake of the primitive Eskimo, even in southwestern Alaska. Some northerly groups ate no vegetables.

Dr. Ales Hrdlicka, the distinguished Curator of Anthropology in the National Museum, Washington, whose death was one of the chief losses to American science in 1943, wrote me shortly before that he had been able to verify no case of tooth decay among Eskimos of the present or past who were uninfluenced by European habits. Dr. S. G. Ritchie, of Dalhousie University, wrote after studying the skeleton collection gathered by Dr. Diamond Jenness on my third expedition: "In all the teeth examined there is not the slightest trace of caries."

I brought about 100 skulls of Eskimos, who had died before Europeans came in, to the American Museum of Natural History, New York. These have been examined by many students, but no sign of tooth decay has yet been discovered.

It seemed at one time that the record of the Museum's collection would have to be degraded from its hundred per cent rating; for Dr. M. A. Pleasure examined there 283 skulls said to be Eskimo of pre-European date and found a small cavity in one tooth. But when the records were checked it turned out that the collector, the Rev. J. W. Chapman of the Episcopal Board of Missions, New York City, had sent that skull to the Museum as one of an Athapasca Indian, not of an Eskimo.

The Eskimo record is, therefore, clean to date. Not a sign of tooth decay has yet been discovered among that one of all peoples which most completely avoids the foods, the precepts, and the practices favored for dental health by the New York Commissioner of Health, the average dentist, the toothbrush drillmaster of the schools, and the dentifrice publicists.

Through correspondence and printed information I have been able to discover in various museums throughout the world more than 800 skulls of men who are considered to have been during life exclusive meat eaters. Not one tooth in these skulls has yet been found that shows evidence of caries. Most of these are Eskimo skulls. There are included in this count of 800 some crania of Europeans who lived in Greenland during the Middle Ages, and the mentioned skulls from Iceland, as representative of people who supplemented their meat diet with milk and its products without losing their immunity to caries.

The incidence of caries among civilized Eskimos, who now eat a mixed diet, is heavy. As has been said, they have no racial immunity to this disease.

When addressing conventions and societies of medical men, I usually state the oral hygiene case somewhat as above, though in more detail. If there is rebuttal from the floor, it frequently takes the form of contending that the tooth health of primitive people is due to their chewing a lot, and to their eating coarse foods. The advantage of that argument to the dentist, whose best efforts have failed to save a patient's teeth, is obvious. It gives him an out—that not all your care, even when supported by his skill and science, can preserve teeth in an age of soft foods that give no exercise to the teeth and no friction to the gums.

But it is deplorably hard to square anthropology with this comfortable excuse of the dentist. Among the best teeth of the mixed-diet world are those of a few South Sea Islanders who as yet largely keep to their native diets. Similar or better tooth condition was described, for instance, from the Hawaiian Islands by the earliest visitors. But can you think of a case less fortunate for the chewing-and-coarse-diet advocates? The animal food of these people was mainly fish, and fish `is soft to the teeth, whether boiled or raw. Among the chief vegetable elements was poi, a kind of soup or paste. Then they used sweet potatoes, and yams are not so very hard to chew either.

It would be difficult to find a New Yorker or Parisian who does not chew more, and use coarser food, than the South Sea Islanders did on the native diets which are said to have given them, in at least some cases, better than 90 per cent freedom from caries, a record no block on Park Avenue can approach.

There are several obvious reasons why those who never lived with pre-white Eskimos have commonly imagined and frequently stated that Eskimos chew a great deal, and that what they chew is coarse food that gives more massage to their gums than our food does to ours. The contention is that from such chewing and massage results the complete absence of dental caries reported by all observers from pre-white Eskimo communities. The facts, however, lead to an opposite conclusion, as we see when we face them.

People whose diet is in considerable part cereals, and other things of vegetable nature, almost necessarily chew much; herbivorous animals chew a lot. Also we are educated to chew. At least since 1897 we have been taught that painstaking mastication is good for us. We learn from physiology texts in the grade school that chewing should mix the saliva thoroughly with the food in the mouth, for digestion begins there. (It is only the meticulous who differentiate here between the various foods.) These texts repeat the saw that valiant chewing is good for teeth and gums.

Between the dentists and the Fletcherizers, we of today chew in part from a sense of duty.

Analogizing carelessly to the primitive Eskimos, the usual textbook writer ignores that they have had no mastication coaching, and begins by assuming as a minimum that they chew at least as much as we. Then he imputes to them further chewing, on the basis of an assumed hardness and toughness of their food. For instance, dentifrice advertising shows us pictures of charming girls gnawing ham bones or legs of lamb; underneath we read: "Terrible, say the social leaders! Splendid, say the dentists!" The argument proceeds that in an (assumed) previous age people ate meat in the way illustrated by the charming girl, and that they developed and retained excellent teeth through much biting and chewing of tough and coarse victuals.

These advertisers find it convenient to ignore the fact that man has been a tool-using animal from the first, and that carnivorous primitives have knives. The method of handling meat is about the same whether you are at the beef feasts of the royalty and warriors of Ethiopia, as reported in the press and in books of travel, or at the caribou meals of the stone-age Eskimos as I saw them at Coronation Gulf in 1910. In either place you take a good-sized piece of meat in your left hand and a knife in the right. The knife may be anything from Sheffield steel through native copper to flaked stone. With your front teeth you nip lightly into the edge of the piece of meat, just so you get a good hold, and then you cut in front of your lips. The piece is not likely to be larger than we might cut with knife and fork at a restaurant when dining politely on a sirloin.

But, no matter how tender the steak, a European chews the piece a good deal—as said, because he is in the chewing habit through being partly herbivorous, and because he has been admonished to chew. The uncivilized Eskimo has never had practice in herbivorous mastication and his mother has never told him to chew for the good of his health. So he gives the piece a bite or two, rolls it around in his mouth once or twice, and swallows. He will, of course, chew efficiently should the piece feel as though it might be too large or too hard to be gulped down.

This description, true of cooked meat, is true for a greater reason with unfrozen raw flesh, which has in the mouth the feel of a raw oyster and slides down like an oyster—more readily, in fact, for the oyster is likely to be a great deal larger and no more slithery than the piece of raw beef you cut off for yourself. Raw fish is, if anything, still more like a raw oyster. Boiled fish is soft, though not so soft as if it were raw; so the Eskimo chews it just enough to get it covered with saliva.

When you eat raw flesh in the Arctic during winter, whether it is mammal or fish, you nearly always eat it frozen. Animal tissue at anything like —50° is like glass, so that if you drop a fish on a hard floor it splinters. Red meat or fish at these temperatures resembles cast iron in that when you touch it you freeze fast to it. If you were to give even the daintiest lick to a caribou ham at —50° you would lose a piece of tongue covering approximately the size of the area which came in contact with the ham.

Obviously that is not the kind of frozen food on which we breakfast. We let it lie around indoors until it gets about as soft as hard ice cream or frozen pudding. Then we cut it, first into thickish slices and thereafter into smaller pieces, chewing each about as much as you would lumps of hard ice cream.

Excepting tendons and connective tissue, no meat is tough unless cooked. When it is cooked, two main causes determine toughness: the age of the animal and the manner and extent of cooking. The chief food animal of the inland Eskimos is the caribou. With them, as with cattle, the older the beast the tougher the meat. A young caribou is as fleet of foot as a heifer; an old one is as slow as a cow. The wolves get the clumsy old ones that drop behind when the band flees, and the Eskimos seldom have a chance to secure an animal that is more than four or five years old. Such young caribou are not tough, no matter how cooked. It is the wolves and not the Eskimos who get the tooth-and-gum benefit (if any) of chewing old caribou.

I do not know a corresponding logical demonstration for seals, but I can testify from helping to eat thousands of them that their meat is never tough—at least not in comparison with the beefsteaks you sometimes get in city chophouses.

Then there are Eskimos who live almost exclusively on fish. As has been said, raw fish are so raw-oysterish that you can't chew them; there is not much more chewing when they are eaten boiled. The only condition under which fish become tough, or rather hard, is when they are dried. Some Eskimos use dried fish sometimes; others never do.

There is for separated districts a wide difference in the amount of Eskimo chewing, but no one has reported that the health of the teeth is better among the heavier chewers. How could it be when as yet no caries has been found either among the lightest or heaviest masticators?

As has been said, there is one kind of Eskimo food which gets a deal of chewing, dried fish—or dried red meat. Some districts never have such dried foods at all. Certain districts may have them one year and not another year. There is no district where desiccated food is likely to represent more than 10 per cent or 15 per cent of the annual diet.

It happens that the districts almost or quite the most given to drying their flesh foods are the ones which also have an appreciable quantity of vegetables. In Kotzebue Sound, Alaska, for instance, in the early days dried fish and *masu* (knotweed) roots preserved in oil were likely to be served at the same meal. The fish would take a good deal of chewing, and the roots a great deal. This heavy use of the teeth on food which at times had much sand in it wore them down to the gums when people grew middle aged, but no alveolar abscesses were produced, for reasons dealt with below. Nor was there tooth decay due to the introduction of carbohydrates from the roots; seemingly not enough starch was contributed by them for that result. These dry fish and masu root eaters, worn of tooth and perhaps a bit unsightly for that, were just as free from caries as the hundred percent flesh eaters.

Many Eskimos now eat a good deal of food similar to ours, and therefore chew more than they used to. The communities nearest us in diet have the worst teeth, some as bad as ours.

It is a second line of defense for the heavy-mastication advocates that, even if Eskimos perhaps do not chew their food so very much, they do chew skins a great deal. The chewing of leather is, however, far less than one might believe from what has been said by a particular kind of writer and pictured in certain movies. In any case, skin chewing is done mainly by the women, and it is not easy to see how the wife's chewing would preserve her husband's teeth.

Once, at a talk to a medical group, I encountered a further argument: Was it not true that Eskimo men use their teeth a great deal in their crafts? Do they not bite wood, ivory, or metal to hold, pull out, twist, and so on? The best reply I could think of was to agree that Eskimos pull nails with their teeth, and to follow by suggesting that it is more likely they bite nails because they have good teeth than that they have good teeth because they bite nails.

There are several reasons why the teeth of many Eskimos wear down rapidly. By some anatomical cause their front teeth usually meet edge to edge, where ours frequently overlap, and direct opposition tends to cause wear. Some Eskimos wind-dry fish or red meat, sand gets in, and, to an extent, acts like sandpaper. Both sexes, but especially men, use their teeth for biting on hard materials. Both sexes, but especially the women, use their teeth for softening skins. A wearing toward the pulp may, therefore, take place in early middle life. What then happens is stated by Dr. Ritchie (previously quoted) with relation to the Coronation Gulf Eskimos as they were before 1918:

"Coincident with this extreme wear of the teeth the dental pulps have taken on their original function with conspicuous success. Sufficient new dentine of fine quality has been formed to obliterate the pulp chambers and in some cases even the root canals of the teeth. This new growth of tissue is found in every case where access to the pulp chambers has been threatened. There has therefore been no destructions of the pulps through infection and consequently alveolar abscesses are apparently unknown."

So total absence of caries from those who live wholly on meat is definite. Cessation of decay when you transfer from a mixed to a meat diet happens usually, perhaps always. The rest of the picture is not so clear.

Caries has been found in the teeth of mummies in Egypt, Peru, and in our own Southwest. These semi-ancient peoples were mixed-diet eaters, depending in considerable part on cereals. Their teeth were better than ours, though not so good as those of the Eskimos.

It appears that if you want a dental law you can approximate it by saying that the most primitive people usually have the best teeth, but that no people of the past or present are known who had complete freedom from tooth decay unless they were hunting, fishing, pastoral in their way of life, and got little or none of their food direct from the vegetable kingdom. You might add that in some cases a highly vegetarian people, while not attaining the 100 per cent perfection of meat eaters, do, nevertheless, have very good teeth as compared with ours.

However, these partly immune vegetarians would not be those who go in heavily for agriculturist foods, like rice, wheat, oats, corn and sugar. Rather would they be heavy eaters of what, seriously as well as humorously, we call "monkey food"—the things to eat which are discoverable in tropical forests by ape or primitive man, such as fruits, shoots, tubers and succulent plants.

Incidentally, the definite correlation of tooth decay with the eating of starches and sugars makes any cavities discovered in the teeth of skeletons exhumed by archaeologists a clew to a former way of life. Men, it is universally assumed, were in the earliest stages hunters and gatherers; later they became herdsmen and farmers. The change from hunter to herdsman did not bring with it decay of the teeth; the change to farming did. A skeleton with decayed teeth is therefore presumably that of a farmer or at least the victim of an agricultural civilization. For, in most parts of the world, gatherers would have a time finding enough carbohydrates with which to ruin their teeth.

It is contended by the Hawaiian Sugar Planters Association Health Research Project that the shift from good to execrable teeth among the mixed-diet Polynesians has been due to a change from the native taro and yam to cereals. I have seen no comment of theirs upon the doubtless great increase of sugar consumption which has been at least as synchronic with the deterioration of Hawaiian teeth as the shift from yams to cereals.

On the strength of the view that diet is the greatest factor in saving teeth, the anthropologists have been getting support from experiments conducted by institutions and by scattered students. Some dentists are here contributing nobly to a research, and to a campaign of education, that seem bound to deplete their income. My probing has not revealed thus far corresponding unselfishness among the dentifrice manufacturers.

To sum up: Any people who eat vegetables, even the softest, anyone who eats bread or leafy vegetables, is bound to chew a good deal more than the average for a carnivorous people. Yet the Eskimos, or meat eaters comparable to the Eskimos, and pastoral people like the medieval Icelanders, all of them mastication slackers, are the only ones ever found in present or former times who can show 100 per cent freedom from caries. There is, accordingly, in the study of such diets and habits of life no aid or comfort for those who believe that the decadent teeth of our civilization are a result of decreased chewing.

Those who seek explanations for the relative soundness of the teeth of hunting and pastoral man, as compared with those of the eaters of mixed diets, have suggested that the temperature at which the food is eaten may have something to do with it. Certainly there are few differences more striking than those between the usual temperatures at which the Eskimos and we eat and drink.

In the drinking of water the primitive Eskimo was about even with those of us who usually chill our drinks. In summer he would dip fresh water off the surface of sea ice; or he would drink from rivers which, although by no means ice cold, were on the average colder than ours. In winter, when he melted snow or ice, he would usually put snow or ice back in his water, before drinking, if it was appreciably warm.

In warm drinks the difference was striking. He had nothing to be compared with the tea and coffee that many of us gulp almost scalding hot. He did have broths to correspond to our soups; we like them almost as hot as our tea, but he would set his aside to cool down to what we think of as lukewarm.

There was the same difference in cooked food. We like our meats almost as hot as our drinks, and so with baked and boiled potatoes and many other things. But the Eskimo housewife was not supposed to offer a piece of meat to a guest, or to a member of her family, until by repeated touching she had ascertained that it was nearly the temperature of her hand. True, this rule was not always observed, particularly when appetites were keen, where children or others of small patience were concerned.

It was not true, as implied by the usual northern movie and by some writers, that Eskimos preferred to eat their food raw. A few things were preferred raw, among them seal liver; but most were preferred boiled or roasted, and if they were eaten raw it was usually for convenience. Still it is true that the Eskimos ate wholly uncooked meats more frequently than we do.

On the north coast of Alaska, and of western Arctic Canada, on our first expedition, 1906-07, and again on the second expedition, 1908-12, we saw among the local Eskimos the transition from their methods of cooking and eating to ours. Even in 1906 there were a few who drank very hot tea, and these were proud of the accomplishment; the rest were something like people learning to eat green olives, proud of each slight advance in ability to tolerate the new experience. It was striking that, in the early years, the eating of very hot foods and the drinking of very hot drinks was strictly confined to the ones introduced by the whites. The same man who drank his tea nearly scalding, with seeming enjoyment, would be as careful as he ever had been that his broth should be lukewarm. Those who ate doughnuts piping hot from the grease would see to it that a chunk of boiled caribou was cooled nearly down to body temperature.

Boiled meat was eaten perhaps usually at temperatures between 110° and 130° F.; it was explained, some pages back, that frozen meat was usually thawed to about the consistency of rather hard ice cream, thus to somewhere between 32° and 20° F. I was so used to thinking of these meats as resembling ice cream in temperature and texture that it never occurred to me, so far as I can now remember, that one would feel materially colder than the other against teeth, tongue or palate. Seemingly there is a difference, and a logical one when you come to think of it.

Inspector A. T. Belcher, of the Royal Canadian Mounted Police, tells me that Eskimo prisoners in his charge, who liked the taste of ice cream, complained that it felt too cold in the mouth. This interested him and he inquired carefully of several Eskimos, making informal experiments—getting them to eat both ice cream and frozen meat at the same meal or under similar circumstances. They stuck to it that the ice cream felt colder than the frozen meat. Upon trial, the Inspector's own observation agreed with theirs.

Given the fact of the Belcher experiment, a theory to explain it comes to mind at once. Ice cream is a better conductor than frozen meat—it is a somewhat better conductor than lean muscle tissue and a much better conductor than suet.

The Belcher trials within the mouth cavity can be checked with experiments on one's own skin. Put one of your bare feet into ice water at the same time as you put the other into a bucket of snow. The shock of the ice water will be more severe—because water is a better conductor than snow.

The Icelanders (as previously shown, a sedentary pastoral group, of ancestry derived from Scandinavia and Ireland) were until the early part of the nineteenth century as free from caries as the nomadic hunting Eskimos who are of Mongolian stock, one kind of North American Indian. It happens that in the matter of hot foods and drinks there was in Iceland about the same kind of change as among the northern Canadian Eskimos at the time when caries began to appear.

The drinks of the Icelanders had been milk, whey, and to a small extent beer. They resembled the average European, and differed from the Eskimo and modern American, in that they drank relatively little cold water. Their milk was sometimes heated, but there was nothing to correspond with the large volumes of hot liquid which began to be taken when the coffee habit developed, in the first half of the nineteenth century. There was probably also at least a slight increase during the same period in the eating of cooked foods, and probably the very custom of drinking hot coffee tended to increase the taste for higher temperatures in food generally. Still it is clear that before the introduction of coffee the Icelanders consumed far more hot food than did the Eskimos prior to the introduction of tea.

We do not have, then, as to the change in food and drink temperatures, either with the Eskimos or with the Icelanders, the clarity of a test under laboratory conditions. Among the Eskimos sugar and starch were being introduced, as well as new forms of protein, during the period when tea and hot foods were being introduced, so that the shift from an approximately 100 per cent meat diet to a mixed diet, and the shift from colder to warmer foods and drinks, both coincided with the beginning and then the rapid increase of dental caries. The same double and overlapping correspondence held true, though to a less degree, when the Icelanders were shifting from a diet which had been chiefly mutton, fish and milk to one high in sugar, starch and proteins of vegetable origin.

Although there is probably no racial difference, there certainly is a considerable individual difference with regard to tooth decay. While it seems that Eskimos, Scots and Zulus have caries about in relation to the chemistry of the food they eat, if large numbers are averaged, it is equally true that members of a single household, though blood relatives, who appear to eat nearly the same food, may differ greatly in the soundness of their teeth.

Thus the only thing which matters greatly with regard to the health of the teeth is the chemical composition of the diet—the higher the percentage of carbohydrates, the lower the percentage of animal proteins and fats, the greater the tooth decay.

However, pending further study, it is better to be a little cautious here and say that, while we do know that diets of which the calories are derived 95 per cent or more from animal fats and animal proteins will guarantee against caries, we do not know for sure that a 75 per cent meat diet, with 25 per cent of carbohydrates, is much better for the teeth than one that is 50 per cent meat, the other 50 per cent carbohydrates. It may be that one would have to confine himself to meats, supplemented if desired by dairy foods and eggs, if he wanted to be sure to avoid the dentist.

There are scientists (among others, Professor L. M. Waugh of the School of Dental and Oral Surgery of Columbia University) who are of opinion that while carbohydrates produce tooth decay, the starches among them are relatively innocent, the practically exclusive villains being the sugars. This is a little hard to reconcile with the common view that, upon digestion, starch turns into sugar. Still there is at least a ground for suspending a blanket judgment against all of the carbohydrates, lest some be found in deeper sin than others.

It has been pointed out, for instance by Dr. Collins, who is quoted below, that the incidence of caries seems to be heavier among those primitive peoples who get their starches from cereals than among those who get them from sweet and

Irish potatoes. There appears little reason to doubt what has already been said, that there were people in the South Sea Islands who had a considerable starch percentage in their diet, obtained from things like yams and poi, and who nevertheless had better teeth than the corn eaters of the North American pueblo region or the small-grain eaters of Babylonia and ancient Egypt.

It may be said, perhaps, that the possibility of protecting the teeth by selecting the diet is not an established fact but merely a theory held by a few. Now there is a profession which devotes itself to the study of mankind, with special reference to such things as human skeletons, of which the teeth are an important part. This profession of anthropology seems nearly unanimous in agreement with the main contentions of this chapter. They have a sort of official clearing house for the United States, an organization of high standing by worldwide comparison, in the Smithsonian Institution of Washington. We have already quoted its Curator of Physical Anthropology, Dr. Ales Hrdlicka, to the effect that he did not know of a single decayed tooth in any skeleton of a man who had lived chiefly or exclusively by hunting and who had died before European foods were introduced. We quote now Henry B. Collins, Senior Ethnologist of the Bureau of American Ethnology of the Smithsonian, from a letter dated August 10, 1939.

In this letter Collins refers to the idea that chewing hard, tough or coarse foods will keep the teeth sound and terms it "an old wives' tale." He says that, by his own observation, Eskimos who have the soundest of teeth are more likely to gulp than to chew their food, which is chiefly boiled or raw meats. He goes on: ". . . the 'hard chewing' hypothesis [to explain sound teeth] seems at best an impediment and a distraction from the main issue, which is the extremely important role of diet in the formation and condition of the teeth.

"It would not be difficult to point to other examples of an inverse relationship between vigorous chewing and good teeth: Consider the prehistoric Indians of coastal Florida who, to judge from the skulls in the National Museum, had fully as robust jaws and almost as perfect teeth as the Eskimo, and yet their principal food was oysters and other shellfish which surely required little chewing. Their immunity from dental caries and the splendid development of their teeth and bones in general is to my mind a condition directly correlated with their diet; for consider on the other hand that without exception every prehistoric or modern Indian population that depended to any extent on grain agriculture shows susceptibility to dental caries.

"I base this generalization also on the extensive skull collections in the National Museum. From examination of these collections I have the definite impression that there is a rather close correlation between dental ills and grain consumption—the more intensive the agriculture the higher the incidence of caries. At one end of the scale are the Pueblos, prehistoric and modern, whose worship of the Corn deity has not prevented them from having the most wretched teeth of any American aborigines. Dental decay is also much in evidence among the Eastern and Southern Indians, mostly inland, who also were agriculturists (the California Indians, mostly acorn-eaters, also have quite bad teeth).

"Ascending the scale somewhat, we find that the prehistoric Plains tribes, e.g., the Arikara, who practiced agriculture to some extent, show some caries; while later Plains Indians, of whatever group, who have given up agriculture for a nomadic [hunting] life, have splendid teeth."

There has been as yet no excitement in the newspapers over the discovery, or the alleged discovery, that no one has caries who lives on meat, whether or not supplemented by milk and milk products; but every now and then there is a furor because a community has been located where no one has caries, allegedly because of a special chemical composition of the water. This seems to mean that people are not interested in protecting their teeth by changing their food but that they are interested in protecting them by changing their drinking water.

This may be one more case of a fundamental, subconscious wisdom in mankind. For if we face the issue whether to protect our teeth by an all-meat diet, serious questions arise, among them:

Teeth are only teeth. A good set comes handy, but there are not many who fear the dentist so that they would care to make avoiding him the chief concern in life. False teeth, individually or by the set, are getting better. And the advertisers claim they are so cheap now that practically anyone should be able to afford a complete outfit of uppers and lowers.

Meat is costly. Ask the butcher the price of six pounds of lean sirloin steak and a pound of suet, for that is about what you will need if you work hard through a long day on an exclusive meat diet. You could do with cheaper cuts, but many of these are bony and you would require more pounds of them.

Finally, if we all started living on meat, to protect our teeth or for some other reason, we would soon come to the end of the world's resources. The most fundamental of all the reasons why it is better to live on pork and corn pone than on pork by itself is that if we first feed the corn to a pig and then eat the pig we waste something like six-sevenths or seven-eighths of the food value of the corn—not thinking, for the moment, of vitamins, minerals and things of that sort but merely of caloric value.

There are, of course, many other good reasons why the world is not about to become one federation of carnivora—among them religious prohibitions (as in India), mixed diet beliefs, established food habits. The main thing is that it could not be done anyway; for we should not be able to produce enough meat in the world, at least not by old-fashioned methods, such as ranching cattle or hunting moose.

This does not, however, lessen the academic interest of considering how things are and what follows when one omits from his diet sugars, starches and all that comes direct from the vegetable kingdom, living on meat, either exclusively or in combination with things like eggs and milk. A part of what follows is that this meat-eater will then have teeth which remain sound throughout the longest life and that he will visit the dentist, if at all, only for cosmetic purposes— and, of course, for troubles like pyorrhea; for it is only caries, and perhaps malformed jaws and impacted teeth, that one avoids by avoiding carbohydrates.

6

Living on the Fat of the Land

Klára vín, feiti og mergur med
Mun thar til rjetta veitt.

THESE ARE lines from an old Icelandic religious poem
and mean: "There (in paradise) the feast will be set
with clear wine, fat and marrow." It is a sentiment proper
to Iceland; for, by usual belief, the people of northern
countries love fat meats better than sweetmeats. Actually the
quotation rests upon Mediterranean sources; for it is a translation from the Hebrew, covering the Biblical passage that
is rendered in English by Isaiah xxv, 6, of the King James
version: "And in this mountain shall the Lord of hosts make
unto all people a feast of fat things, a feast of wines on the
lees, of fat things full of marrow."

Though it is from Palestine, this passage might well have
had its origin in Iceland; for the concept that fat is the best
of foods has been universal with mankind in all lands and
climates. When Christianity spread northward beyond the
Mediterranean, the Biblical phrase "to live on the fat of the
land" was readily understood in Greece, Italy, and France;
in Britain, Sweden, and up among the Lapps. In English
speech fat food was called rich food, which was the highest
praise.

The fattest was best, among men and gods, in most religions and in all countries.

To the Jews, the Bible, foundation of the Christian and
some other religions, is at once history and holy book; it
can testify for them, a southern people, both on what they
liked to eat and on what they believed concerning Jehovah.

The usual family Bible of fifty years ago, the huge kind with silver clasps that was sold by the book agents, contains a "Dictionary of the Bible," by William Smith. Under the heading "Fat," we are told:

"The Hebrews distinguished between the suet or pure fat of an animal, and the fat which was intermixed with the lean (Neh. vii, 10). Some parts of the suet, viz., about the stomach, the entrails, the kidneys and the tail of a sheep, which grows to an excessive size in many eastern countries, and produces a large quantity of rich fat, were forbidden to be eaten in the case of animals offered to Jehovah in sacrifice (Lev. iii, 3, 9, 17; vii, 3, 23). The ground of the prohibition was that the fat was the richest part of the animal, and therefore belonged to him (iii, 16)."

Most anthropologists, and other students of the relation of man to his religion, seem to agree that the foods considered best for sacrifice, or generally thought to be agreeable to gods and powerful spirits, are the same as those which the people themselves preferred when the religion was in its formative stage. Genesis, then, would represent, in what it says of the preferences of Jehovah, the preferences of the Hebrew people themselves when they were living in the region of Babylonia and Egypt 3,000 or 4,000 years ago.

However that be, the first reference to fat in the Bible shows both the preference of Jehovah for meat over garden truck and for fat meat over lean. It is in the fourth chapter of Genesis, from the second to the fifth verse:

"And Abel was a keeper of sheep, but Cain was a tiller of the ground.

"And in process of time it came to pass, that Cain brought of the fruit of the ground an offering unto the Lord.

"And Abel, he also brought of the firstlings of his flock and of the fat thereof. And the Lord had respect unto Abel and to his offering.

"But unto Cain and to his offering he had not respect."

In Genesis xlix, 20, we have: "Out of Asher his bread shall be fat, and he shall yield royal dainties"; in Nehemiah viii, 9: "Then he said unto them, Go your way, eat the fat, and drink the sweet."

The passage which has made "to live on the fat of the land" a part of our common speech, with a clear and familiar meaning to the least erudite, is found in Genesis xlv, 17-18:

"And Pharaoh said unto Joseph . . . Take your father and your households, and come unto me; and I will give you the good of the land of Egypt, and ye shall eat the fat of the land."

As I was mulling this over, two things occurred to me, that I was not sure what kind of fat the Biblical writer had in mind (perhaps olive oil) and that I had recently met a man whom I had long admired, the famous Biblical scholar Edgar Johnson Goodspeed, author of many learned works and known to a wide public as editor and translator of *The Complete Bible: An American Translation*, published by the University of Chicago Press. So I wrote Dr. Goodspeed. He replied December 12, 1936:

"I have a frightful feeling that your letter of some time ago has been neglected, and if so I am exceedingly sorry. The fact is I handed it at once to some of our Old Testament experts for their concurrent judgment on the point and did not get it back for a good while.

"Anyway, if it's not too late let me say that I have talked to four or five of them (yesterday) and we agree that the *fundamental* figure, the figure at the bottom of the expression, the 'fat of the land,' is an animal one, the idea that the fat is the best part of the beast, the part to be offered in sacrifice, and all that. Animal tissue—meat—was of course a rarity with the Biblical people; they did not have it every day; it was a delicacy; and the fat was the greatest delicacy of all, it seems.

"Of course the *figure* was meant to suggest more than animal fat—the wheat and oil and so on—but the fundamental idea was the animal."

As with the subtropical Jews, so it was with the Greeks just northwest of them, beyond the Mediterranean; they, too, liked their meat fat and believed that their demigods and heroes preferred it so. Like most ancient peoples, they seldom praised foods and drinks other than fat meat and sweet wine. I have gone over *The Iliad Done into English Prose,* by Andrew Lang, Walter Leaf and Ernest Myers, and have found a number of things that bear on this study.

There was, for instance, the case of "Agamemnon, king of men," who "slew a fat bull of five years to most mighty Kronion." That was in the second book of the Iliad. In Book IX, "Patroklos hearkened to his dear comrade [Achilles]. He cast down a great fleshing-block in the firelight, and laid thereon a sheep's back and a fat goat's and a great hog's chine rich with fat." In Book XIII is the speech of Serpedon: "Verily our kings that rule Lykia be no inglorious men, they that eat fat sheep, and drink the choice wine honey-sweet."

And so with the literature of the rest of Europe as one goes north in the time before the coming of sugar, when few except the queens were able to sit in the kitchen eating honey with their bread. These ancient and medieval writings show no marked northward increase or decrease in the praise of rich foods until the investigator comes to Iceland that lies in the sea hard by the Arctic Circle and meets with a proverb: *Fleira er matur enn feitt kjöt,* meaning that fat meat is not the only decent food, a saying which mothers no doubt used for encouraging children to eat lean meat, porridge, and bread that did not have quite enough butter on it.

Incidentally, the taste of the British of the present time does not vary, it seems, from that of the Old Testament Hebrews. They like mutton, lean or fat; or so we are told in a dispatch from Joseph Barnes, Foreign Editor of the New York *Herald Tribune,* which was published by that newspaper May 30, 1944, with a London dateline and under the heading: "Britain Looks to the Future." The opening sentence reads: "Saddles of mutton with mint sauce and boiled silversides with dumplings are reported to play a large part in the dreams of Britishers these nights as the promised liberation of the Continent hangs heavy over their sleep."

That the Britsh prefer their mutton fat is certified by their prose writers, among them Dickens, and by their poets, among them Thomas Love Peacock, who was beyond doubt in harmony with the national taste when he wrote:

> The mountain sheep are sweeter,
> But the valley sheep are fatter;
> We therefore deemed it meeter
> To carry off the latter.

As shall be shown in subsequent pages, one longs for fat intensely if there is too little of it, and is promptly satiated when he has had enough. However, really intense fat-hunger occurs only when one is unable to secure fat's approximate dietetic equivalents, the starches and sugars. Accordingly, little is heard of fat-hunger except from people who are unable to substitute these equivalents for the olive oil, seal oil, cream, bacon or butter to which they are accustomed. So there are few signs of fat-hunger in the records of grain-fed Egypt, although they are not absent. Neither is there much of this in the records of ancient China. Still, the learned Dr. Hu Shi, recent Ambassador from China to the United States, tells me that in the fragments of knowledge which still exist about the most remote Chinese religions, there are indications that the people were extremely fond of meats and particularly of fat meats; in that religion, as in others, there is the implication or assertion that the gods, demigods and ancient heroes had an abundance of fat on their tables.

It is easy to see in the literature and history of western

Europe during the last few centuries how the dominance of fat as a luxury and a delicacy has gradually waned, in step with the increased use of sugar. Shakespeare has many references to good food as rich; and of course with the intent that "rich" means "fat." It would have been a compliment for him to say that the cooking in a boarding house was greasy. Indeed, this does not appear to have been a derogatory remark until within the last hundred years, which are the years during which sugar has risen from a negligible to an actually commanding position.

It is difficult, at least for me, to discover figures that seem reliable for sugar's creeping into the economy and dietary of European nations. But it is clear that two hundred years ago sugar was as yet negligible. It remained until long after that a compliment to say that food was rich; and the history of the language makes it clear that "sweetness" is a more recent connotation of that word than "fatness." Indeed we seldom, even now, call a thing rich just because it is sweet; it has to be fat as well.

This is not a study of the increase of sugar consumption, except incidentally; concern is with the decrease in the popularity of fat. It is barely possible that there is no causal relation; but it seems clear that as one of these foods increased in popularity the other declined.

Soldiers, at least those of the United States, are great hands at complaining about food, although it is said that there was less of this formerly—that the real epoch of bellyaching about the grub started with the Spanish-American War and was at its highest point in World War I. However that be, there was complaining about food even in the Revolutionary War; a good deal of it, for instance, at Valley Forge. But a friend who lives in the Valley Forge neighborhood, and has studied the history and local tradition, tells me that the distressing winter spent there by the Continental Army brought forth no complaint on the score of sugar. Yet they had little or none. It seems that Washington's contemporaries looked upon sugar not as a food but as a condiment, and one of which they were not sufficiently fond to deplore its absence.

In connection with a historical study made for the Office of the Quartermaster General, trying to determine why there has sprung up in the Army a prejudice against pemmican, a rich food highly favored by previous generations, I appealed for help to the Department of Commerce, trying to determine how likely it appeared that the declining popularity of fat was due to the growing ascendency of sugar in the national diet. From them, from the American Meat Institute of Chicago and from the Sugar Research Foundation of New York I received figures of per capita annual sugar consumption from 1791 to 1941:

SUGAR CONSUMPTION IN THE UNITED STATES

Year	Pounds per capita	Year	Pounds per capita
1791	7.5	1880	42.7
1800	8.0	1900	65.2
1820	8.3	1920	86.5
1840	14.1	1940	97.2
1860	30.5		

That is how the table goes, by twenty-year periods. There was in 1941 a rise to 114.1 pounds per capita, after which there are no "normal" figures; thereafter they are affected by rationing.

It seems that the entire sugar consumption of the United States is not represented in the table and that the actual is somewhat greater. At least, that is what may be gathered from a study, *Summary of Estimated Per Capita Consumption of Foodstuffs in the United States Since 1889,* by C. Roy Mundee, Chief of the Bureau of Foreign and Domestic Commerce; these figures are given for the period 1927-31:

Sugar 102.24
Candy 12.15
Corn sugar 7.11
Corn syrup unmixed 6.30
Mixtures of corn and other syrups.... 1.82
Total 129.62

Now, the average sugar consumption of the years 1927-31 is given in the separate sugar table furnished by the Department of Commerce as 102.26 pounds per capita, essentially the same as the 102.24 found in the Mundee study for sugar alone, which shows that the Department does not tabulate candy, corn sugar and corn syrups as sugar, although they would be so recognized by the digestive functions. Nor does honey appear to be a sugar in the statistics; and they do not, of course, reckon with the sugar content of fruits that are eaten.

Following up the same inquiry, I wrote the Librarian of the Army War College, Colonel A. Gibson, saying that I had heard that there was neither sugar nor complaint of its lack at Valley Forge, and wanting to know about this food in the dietetic history of the Army. Colonel Gibson replied on June 8, 1944:

"The following is copied from an article prepared in the office of the Quartermaster General, and published in the *Quartermaster Review* for September-October, 1931, pp. 9-21:

"Sugar, once a luxury in the army, now occupies a most important place among the components of the ration. In the Revolutionary War, before its value as an article of food was recognized, and when it was considered a luxury by both soldier and civilian alike, sugar formed no part of the ration of the Continental soldier. In fact, it was not until 1838 that sugar made its first appearance on the authorized rations of the soldiers, and we find in tables issued at that time a daily allowance of 1.62 ounces of sugar per man. This allowance was maintained without change until the outbreak of the Civil War in 1860, at which time it was increased to 2.4 ounces per day.

"The next increase came with the Spanish-American war in 1898, at which time the daily allowance for a soldier was increased to 3.2 ounces. This allowance was maintained at practically the same level until the outbreak of the World War in 1917, when it was increased, for troops serving in the war zone, to 4 ounces a day per man, and in addition each soldier was allowed one-half pound of candy every ten days. Troops at home during this period, however, were allowed no increase in sugar, but received the 3.2 ounces per day authorized in 1898, and no allowance of candy. Shortly after the World War the sugar ration was increased for all troops, regardless of the place they were serving, to four ounces a day, at the level where it now stands.

"In addition, many other components containing sugar have been added to the ration."

The sugar ration of World War II remained as in World War I.

It is a usual assumption that the increase of sugar in the diet has been paralleled by a decrease in the use of fats, and this is probably true. Still, it is possible that what has actually taken place is not so much a decrease in the popularity of fats as a decrease in the attractiveness of certain words used for fats, among them the terms "fat," "grease," "tallow." The same person who tells you he dislikes fat may add that he is very fond of butter, cream, bacon. The man who tells you he dislikes beef fat may be fond of beef gravy and of suet pudding. In fact, many find that the expression "rendered beef suet" does not have a disagreeable connotation but that "beef tallow" does; yet the two expressions are synonymous. The word "blubber," though you have never tasted blubber or spoken with anyone who has, will likely give you a feeling of revulsion.

In these reflections there is one more answer to the Shakespearean "What's in a name?"

My own description of the taste of the fresh blubber of the bowhead whale, and of the other whales with which I am familiar, is that it reminds of fresh cow's cream, with a barely perceptible suggestion of walnut flavor. When Dr. Elisha Kent Kane, famous polar explorer and aristocrat of the Pennsylvania Kanes, discovered that seal and whale blubber tasted delicious, he was probably right when he protested: "Oh, call it not blubber!" He felt that the trouble was not with the thing itself but with the name, which somehow had acquired a bad connotation.

It has been suggested that the repulsive connotation of "blubber" is not from the sound or other intrinsic quality of this element of speech but must be derived from the experience of people who found blubber disagreeable. The argument runs that blubber turns rancid easily, and that in the great days of the whale "fishery," when animal oil was used in the lamps of Europe and America, people in London and New York occasionally tasted the blubber that was landed from the whaling ships and found it disagreeable—hence the present connotation of the word.

Except that there is proverbially no use arguing about taste, it might be called illogical to have a revulsion against fresh blubber just because it gets rancid easily and then does not taste or smell good; for people do not feel disgust at the names of cream and butter just because cream goes sour easily when it is not pasteurized and butter becomes rancid when it is not salted.

Then, as to the disagreeable smell of rancid blubber, it is common experience that things do not necessarily taste bad though they smell bad, as with cheeses. Or perhaps it is rather that things which smell bad to those not used to them do not necessarily smell bad to those who like them.

Perfectly fresh cheeses taste good, except perhaps a little

flat; cheeses that stink, in the opinion of the novice, may be the delight of the connoisseur. So it is with cream. There are large sections of America, and smaller ones of Europe, where cream is preferred fresh, and both the smell and taste of sour cream are disliked; but there are also large sections of Europe, and smaller ones in America, where people relish the smell and taste of sour cream and prefer it to the fresh.

The like is true of the fresh blubber of the seal and whale. Those used to it, and most novices who try it, think it tastes good and find it nearly or quite odorless. To the habitué, fresh blubber corresponds in taste to cottage cheese, good enough but rather insipid; to him the fermented blubber, or oil, is what Camembert and Limburger are to our gourmets. The man who makes the same effort to get to like strong blubber that we make in getting to like strong cheese, will both acquire the taste and come to the conclusion that the correct descriptive word is "fermented," not "rancid." For involved in the process is an acid reaction; so that, if one likes oil that has been in a skin bag through a long and hot summer, he will describe it as tasting and smelling something like French dressing. Perhaps a description of the smell might be that it suggests a blend of soft Camembert and vinegar.

But what is the use of arguing, unless perhaps with the gourmet? If I were trying to introduce fermented blubber to the dinner tables of New York, I would begin with the connoisseurs of Chinese eggs, English game and Norwegian gammelost. Even then I would change the name. With Kane I would say: "Oh, call it not blubber!"

That it may be the name, but not fat itself, which has lost popularity is suggested by a special memorandum of June 14, 1944, made up for me by Charles E. Lund, Acting Chief of the Foodstuffs Unit of the Department of Commerce:

"There is no decreased consumption of edible fats—both

total and per capita, it has been rising throughout the years
here and in England. It is not believed that there is any
correlation in the use of the fat and protein group, with the
carbohydrate products like sugar, except that as incomes
diminish, people 'fill up' on the cheaper carbohydrates, such
as grain products.

"The per capita use of edible fats has shown an upward
trend from the first definite record in 1912 * of United
States consumption. By 1931 the per capita disappearance
was 47.2 pounds and in the last full pre-war year, 1940,
it had risen to 50 pounds. These figures are for commercially known edible fats—lard, butter, shortening, margarine, and cooking and salad oils. They consider butter on
a 100 per cent basis, although the fat content is actually 81
per cent.

"There has also been an increasing use of so-called invisible fats in this country. It is estimated that in 1939 the
per capita consumption of edible fats in the United States
was 95 pounds, of which 46 pounds came from prepared products (butter on an 81 per cent basis) and 49 pounds from
'invisible' fats, including bacon, meat, fish, cheese, milk, ice
cream, eggs, cereals, nuts, cocoa and mayonnaise. In 1943,
although some of our fats and oils supplies had been ra-
tioned, total per capita consumption had risen to 102 pounds,
with 45 pounds from visible fats.

"A study seeking to establish a correlation between sugar
and fat consumption for any sizeable portion of the human
race over a period of years would constitute a research project of considerable dimensions. We have no reference to
any such study."

The point made by Dr. Lund in his first paragraph is, of

* The statement is, then, that fat consumption has increased in the last
three decades, during which period the use of sugar rose from around 80
pounds per year to around 100 pounds. This would not say that no decrease occurred during the previous century while sugar was rising from
8 pounds to 80 pounds per year.

course, of paramount importance—that people with small incomes (and those who are trying to save money irrespective of income) will buy the cheaper foods. Starches and sugars are cheaper than the fats. As this is written the prices in a certain neighborhood store are by the pound: butter, 50 cents; bacon, 38 cents; lard, 20 cents; sugar, 7 cents; flour, 6 cents. Even with fat a little more than twice as nourishing as sugar or starch (which many people do not know), there is a strong pocketbook motive for working off on boarders, or even the family, dishes in which cereals and sugar play the leading roles.

Dr. Lund suggests that the hidden fats are being consumed in growing quantities. That has a pocketbook motive, too, for they average cheaper than the other fats.

In this study, the significant thing is that people like what they are used to. It may have been poverty, or a desire to set money aside for a rainy day, that induced one's parents to feed him so largely on bread, potatoes, porridge, cake, jam, syrup and sugar; but that is what he has grown up on and he is the victim—or the beneficiary—of established food habits according to which he likes these cheap things because he is used to them. Not only that, he has a strong emotional bias in their favor as, in his opinion, proper food, good food, American food.

Lest any reader think that I believe I am presenting here something new in dietetics, I mention that I have myself argued at some length, in at least three books,* that one likes eating what he is used to eating; nor did I, as the presentation shows, think this a new doctrine in 1913 when the first of these books was published. Most writers, including me, present the view not as special to dietetics but as a general principle, a law of taste, applicable to climate, landscape, music, deportment, pretty well everything.

* These books are: *Anthropological Papers*, 1913; *My Life with the Eskimo*, 1914; *The Friendly Arctic*, 1921.

As this is being written the Associated Press carries under a Washington dateline a news story summarizing the findings of the Committee on Food Habits of the National Research Council. They have come to the usual conclusion—which, however, they state in an unusual phrase. Instead of repeating the hackneyed "You like to eat what you are used to eating," they say: "People like what they eat rather than eat what they like." I quote from the *Christian Science Monitor* of September 25, 1944:

"The Committee . . . sent investigators into selected areas to ask the folks what they ate and why they relish those particular victuals. Interviews with selected housewives representing varied income brackets in a Midwestern city disclosed that meat tends to be less frequently mentioned as a favorite dish with decreasing income level. Vegetable dishes showed an opposite trend and were mentioned significantly more often by the low-income groups.

" 'This may be interpreted as supporting the hypothesis that people like what they eat rather than eat what they like,' a Committee bulletin concluded."

The reporter adds that "The discovery . . . is considered of vast importance in long-range plans for upgrading American diet."

While cheapness may create a liking for an article of food, through the establishment of a habit that derives from economy, there is also another and reverse tendency to favor a thing because it is costly, presenting the full application of Thorstein Veblen's "Doctrine of Conspicuous Waste." We all know people who serve strawberries in January more frequently than in May and June, even though it is a common experience that berries imported from afar, as out-of-season luxuries, are seldom of as good flavor as the neighborhood product is when in season. Here the desire to show off triumphs over the combined motives of economy and flavor.

People who do things of this kind will rationalize, if put on the defensive. They will tell you they belong to the "I want what I want when I want it" school, that they can afford it, and that tradesmen would not get along so very well if men of means like themselves did not put money into circulation. Such defense arguments may or may not be sound; but at any rate there are those who eat caviar and truffles partly because they cost a lot. Still and all, this factor that tends to produce taste for costly things is of small power compared with the strength of food habits that are established in childhood and adolescence through the force of economy motives in home, boarding house and boarding school.

Fat—the word is now under nearly as strong a taboo complex of feelings as "blubber"—our average citizen does not eat if he can help it. This means he does not eat the things which he calls fat. He does not eat tallow under that name, almost as reprehensible as "fat"; but he loves beef gravy, which may contain a large amount of tallow. He trims the fat off his steak and leaves it behind on the plate, not wholly or mainly, as Veblen might have diagnosed it, in order to distinguish himself by conspicuous wastefulness; rather he does it because this part of the steak comes under the taboo name of "fat," for which reason he has avoided it from childhood, has scarcely ever tasted it, and is sure he does not like it. Meantime he eats a lot of fat under its agreeable names of cream, butter, bacon, gravy, shortening, salad dressing. He eats tallow not merely as beef gravy but in several other ways, for instance as suet in suet pudding.*

Still, in spite of all the taboos, there is a widespread understanding that fat-hunger is not only possible but normal.

* The Royal Canadian Mounted Police, who make journeys where lightness, compactness and convenience are important, formerly used canned lard. As this is written (December, 1944) comes word that on the north coast of Canada lard, and also butter to some extent, have been replaced on police sledge journeys by beef tallow in rectangular bricks.

At one stage of World War II we were trying to talk our-selves into various beliefs about the weakness of Germany; then it was frequently alleged that the Nazis were suffering from fat-hunger, which condition would help in bringing them to their knees. Later we heard about fat-hunger in occupied countries, from Norway south, and not least in the Balkans and Greece. To this degree, at least, and in spite of the common belief that fat is more necessary in cold than in warm weather, we realize generally that fat is desirable whatever the climate.

Some chapters back, in the account of the year on exclu-sive meat in New York, I mentioned that, although Andersen and I ate more of both fat and lean during cold than warm weather, still the proportion of fat to lean remained con-stant, if we were able to choose our food at each meal ac-cording to taste, with nothing to choose between but lean and fat.

Except as tastes are controlled by propaganda and fashion, the longing for fat, summer or winter, depends on what else one eats. If his is an exclusive meat diet, then he simply must have fat with his lean; otherwise he would sicken and die. On a mixed diet, since fats, sugars, and starches are in most practical respects dietetically equivalent, he eats more of any one of them if the combined amount of the other two is decreased.

It has been considered strange by some, but really is not strange if one knows the local conditions, that extravagant praise of fat occurs neither in the usual conversation nor in the folk tales of Eskimos. The animals they hunt are usually so fat that when they have secured all the lean meat they need they have on hand more fat than they can use; so when they have eaten all they want there is enough fat left over for fuel and light. And, as I keep saying in this book, it makes no difference how fond one is of fat, he is bound to turn against it as soon as he has had all that is good for him.

Of all foods, fat is preeminently the one where enough is enough.

Among hunting people, the chances of fat-hunger increase toward the Equator; for the animals on which they depend are more and more skinny the farther south they go, until in places like tropical Africa there are only a few species that accumulate fat, chiefly the hippo and the eland. Quite naturally, therefore, we get from central Africa and northern Australia the most extreme stories of fat-hunger.

Two of the most reliable and competent authorities on the tropics whom I have known personally are Akeley on Africa and Wilkins on Australia.

In the fourth chapter of this book I have referred to what Akeley used to tell of African fat-hunger when we were housemates in New York.

Sir Hubert Wilkins, when he and I were in the Arctic together, both living at times exclusively on meat, gave me what remains my best single instance of how fats are crowded out.

Sir Hubert's father, the first white child born in South Australia, told that when he was young (around 1840) the herdsmen, who were the majority of the population, lived almost exclusively on mutton (sometimes on beef) and tea. At all times of year they killed the fattest sheep for their own use, and when in the open, which was frequently, they roasted the fattest parts against a fire with a dripping pan underneath, later dipping the meat into the drippings as they ate.

Then gradually commerce developed, breads and pastries began to be used, jams and jellies were imported or manufactured and, with the advance of starches and sugars, the use of fat mutton and fat beef decreased. Now, except that the Australians eat rather more meat per year than people do in the British Isles, the proportion of fat to the rest of the diet is probably about the same in Australia as elsewhere within the British Commonwealth of Nations.

Sir Hubert is usually thought of as an Antarctic and Arctic explorer, which is right. But he is also distinguished for his tropical research through the two-year expedition he conducted for the British Museum in northern Australia, as told in his book *Undiscovered Australia,* London, 1928.

The Swedish explorer Carl Lumholtz was in tropical Australia long before Wilkins and reported that the natives ate their meals on the principle children apply when they raid a cupboard—they used up the best things first and did not eat anything but meat whenever they had enough meat; and the fatter the meat the better. This Wilkins confirmed, and added certain observations along the same line.

Wilkins found that the missionaries were having some trouble in breaking the natives of cannibalism, and that the difficulty was serious in proportion to the fatness of the deceased. When an emaciated man died, little was needed beyond a stern admonition; but when a corpulent man was buried, they had to stand watch over the grave, and corpses sometimes disappeared weeks and months after burial. Seemingly the natives liked their cadavers high, as the English like their game and the Norwegians their cheese, or at least did not mind them getting that way if they were fat enough.

Background for the tropical fat-hunger that drove the Wilkins cannibals of northern Australia to the exhumation of their corpulent dead comes from a particularly tropical section of western Africa through a letter written by a medical missionary, Dr. G. W. Harley, who has been in Liberia most of the time since 1926, when he founded there the Ganta Mission of the Methodist church, of which he is still (in 1945) superintendent. For his qualifications as a witness, in addition to a residence of eighteen years, I looked him up in *American Men of Science.* From that and other sources it appears that he was born in North Carolina, graduated from Duke University, received his medical degree at Yale, has studied in the Harvard Graduate School, is Phi Beta Kappa, and has the degrees A.B., M.D., Ph.D. His experience is not wholly tropical, for in 1924 he served at the Harrington Hospital of the Grenfell Mission in Labrador. He has been research associate of the Peabody Museum of Harvard since 1932. He has published numerous medical and geographical articles, is at work on a book about the Negro culture of Liberia for the Peabody Museum, and is author of *Native African Medicine,* published by the Harvard University Press, 1934.

A good deal less than such a record would have created a presumption of competence as a witness for Dr. Harley, who writes from the Peabody Museum, August 31, 1944, in part:

"Meat-hunger is striking and constant among the tribes I have contacted. While meat of any kind is in great demand, it is interesting to note that the following are the favorite cuts:

"1. Brisket of beef with the fat and cartilages.

"2. The skin and subcutaneous fat of a wart hog. Pig skin is never saved for rawhide and leather. It is too valuable as food, and is eaten after singeing off the hair, and prolonged boiling. Plump cow skin is similarly eaten. A lean cow skin will be saved for rawhide and leather.

"3. The hog's head; brains and fat are both delicacies.

"4. The liver of any animal.

"5. The hands and feet of monkey, because of the fat content.

"Wild meat in Liberia is seldom fat. Even the fat of wart hogs is mostly subcutaneous. Antelope are lean all the way through. Even domestic cattle are lean. Consequently, it is interesting to note that certain animals which normally store more fat than others are preferred for that reason.

"1. The giant rat, *Cricetomys gambianos liberiae,* called 'possum.'

"2. The domestic dog, fattened by the Kpelle people especially for eating.

"3. The cow that has turned out to be sterile and so has never suckled a calf, but grown fat instead.

"4. Porcupines.

"5. Wart Hogs.

"6. Snakes, e.g., *python, bitis gabonica* and *mamba.*

"7. A leopard in its prime—plump and fat.

"8. A snakefish—very fat.

"My own experience for twenty years has been that of a person very active physically, consuming meat whenever available in amounts comparable to that eaten in temperate climates. It was not unusual for us to put up a whole hog in tin cans for our personal use.

"Moreover, when meat was not available for making gravy, we had a gravy made of palm oil, flavored with meat stock or bouillon cubes. We had gravy three times a day and three hundred and sixty-five days in the year. We also used all the milk, eggs and butter we could get, and the four of us consumed between one and two pounds of peanut butter a week.

"We had fresh vegetables every day from our own garden, whatever the season; but it was for meat and butter that we often felt hungry.

"On returning to the United States, I arrived during a heat wave, and hungrily devoured fat pork and country sausages in Washington, D. C.—was disappointed when I could not get sausages with pancakes in Boston because it was 'too hot for sausages.'

"In the tropics, the men who last longest and are happiest are the ones who either get some exercise (golf, tennis, hunting and fishing) or actually do a reasonable amount of physical work. If they work, they must eat. Calorie requirements are relatively high because the millions of sweat glands are

working overtime and the skin could be termed the largest
single organ of the body.

"Men who work in hot places (stokers) do not avoid meat
and fats, rather the opposite."

Such are the views of a doctor of medicine with long
experience of the humid tropics. From him, turn to George
H. Seybold, distinguished for success in the tropics as business man rather than scientist. He spent six years in the
Philippines as a school teacher, more than a decade in Su-
matra representing the United States Rubber Company,
and then six years in Liberia for the Firestone interests. He
came to believe, and to act on the belief, that much of the
so-called enervating effect of a tropical climate is due to
faulty nutrition; in the case of white men he believes the
"enervation" traceable to faulty theories of diet that physicians and others bring with them from the temperate zone,
particularly the theory that you should go light on meat in
hot weather and that if you do eat meat it should be lean.

Mrs. Seybold believes in varying meals a good deal, but
allows her husband considerable fat meat. When she is away
from home he has only two meals a day, noon and evening.
At both he eats pork chops two inches thick, with at least
three quarters of an inch of fat all the way around the outer
edge of each. During one absence of his wife, every meal he
ate for six weeks consisted of these chops.

In the United States Mr. Seybold has trouble getting food
he likes at restaurants—the pork chops they serve are not
thick enough, and they trim the fat from them before
cooking.*

During the New York year of exclusive meat described in
a previous chapter, my impression was that we endured the

* In a more technical book, which is in preparation, will be cited a variety
of testimonial and theory on the relation of dietetic practice to success and
failure in tropical and Arctic living. Here we let the testimonies of Dr.
Harley and Mr. Seybold stand as typical for that large class of persons who
believe in eating what they feel like eating when in the tropics.

heat of the city and neighborhood, which in summer can be uncomfortable to most New Yorkers, somewhat better than did the average of our fellows.

We were frequent victims of the commiseration of friends who "knew" that meat is bad for people in hot weather, that fat is a good food in winter and bad in summer, things of that sort. We rather took pleasure in undeceiving our friends, doubtless parading more than was called for our relative comfort in the heat.

Another situation was embarrassing. One of the most famous members of the Who's Who medical committee that supervised our test was Dr. Graham Lusk, a distinguished physiologist, part of whose distinction rested on work he had done to show that body temperatures might be controlled to advantage in summer by the food one ate. According to him, a person could be relatively comfortable if he ate things like fruits, green vegetables; what had to be avoided, particularly, was meat. Here we were, with the summer heat coming on, forced to live wholly on meat. At first Dr. Lusk showed, as we understood it, kindness and commiseration. He was worried about us and was trying to hearten us—the summer might not be so hot, we were going to have a cottage up near Croton and could lie around in the shade of the trees, avoiding exertion. On the whole he felt that we would get through all right.

But when a spell of hot weather came early in the season, while we were still in the city, and when we assured Dr. Lusk we were not feeling it particularly, we had the impression that he was at first puzzled and later wistful in his questions, hoping he could elicit from us some confirmation of his theory that meat was a food which made people feel specially uncomfortable on a hot day.

We had also the feeling that, in spite of being sponsor of the theory, Dr. Lusk was more open-minded about it than our lay friends. I think he considered we were giving him evidence which was difficult to reconcile with his theory; I am afraid that many of our other friends thought we were just putting it on—that we were so wedded to our eccentric food notions that we simply would not own up to how wretched we felt in the heat. Some of these friends, especially those who did not see us frequently, are still telling about the awful time we had that summer, what with the extreme warm spells and our heat-producing diet.

Shortly after the close of our New York year on meat, an old friend, Earl Parker Hanson, who had already spent four years in subtropical Chile, left for a two-year survey of the Orinoco and Amazon basins for the Carnegie Institution. As he tells it now, he still had then the usual North American beliefs about South American food habits, to the effect that the local people were pretty well all wrong and that North American knowledge of dietetics enabled us to devise regimens better suited to the humid tropics than what the people of those tropics were eating, and liking to eat. When he was gradually converted away from this view he also began to learn, through what eventually became a wide reading of Amazon literature, that others before him had arrived there at the same conclusions by similar steps—but, of course, without influencing the prevailing dietetic theories of North America and Europe, which, in the main, are deduced from animal experimentation and from chemical facts, the matter of their applicability to humans being rather easily taken for granted.

There was, for instance, Henry Wallace Bates, contemporary and friend of Darwin, who spent about eleven years living in and traveling all over the Amazon basin. His book, *A Naturalist on the River Amazon,* is one of the great classics of tropical exploration. It is now available in Everyman's Library, in which edition he says on page 106:

"I had found out by this time that animal food was as much a necessary of life in this exhausting climate as it is in the north of Europe. An attempt which I made to live on vegetable food was quite a failure."

As is told more fully in the chapter "Second Pemmican War," there was in Washington in the spring of 1943, a controversy within the Army as to whether pemmican should be used as a military ration, or as an element in one. The chief argument against its use, except for the allegation that soldiers would not like it, was that, because of a high fat content, it was not an all-climate ration but one useful only in cold weather, thus good only half the year in the temperate zone and no good at all in the tropics.

At this stage Hanson was one of the tropical advisers of the Quartermaster General, though later he went to Africa in charge of a mission to study Liberia for the Foreign Economic Administration. From his own experience of the humid tropics, from the verbal reports of fellow explorers whom he met in the Explorers Club of New York and elsewhere, and from his reading of tropical literature, he was convinced that the high fat content of pemmican was no argument against its use in hot weather; he felt that if it was a good food in the Arctic it would be equally good in the tropics. So he decided to try it out through a part of the Washington summer, where the maximum temperatures of June, July and August are demonstrably higher and, in Hanson's opinion, more discomforting than, for instance, at Manaos on the Amazon.* He has been so kind as to give me a statement, dated February 29, 1944. It deals with pemmican and was intended by him for use in one of this book's pemmican chapters; but his facts and views seem even more pertinent to the question of fat as an element in hot-weather diet, so I am using his letter here:

"My experiences with pemmican grew out of the personal conviction that meat—including the proper amount of fat

* For Hanson's account of the Amazon and Orinoco country, climate and people see his *Journey to Manaos*, New York, 1938.

—is every bit as necessary for health and energy in the tropics as in the North. I have long wondered about the glaring discrepancies in the nutritionists' arguments to the contrary. On the one hand they say that fat is the most efficient energy food known; on the other they talk in doleful tones about the 'debilitating' effects of the tropical climate. Why you should be careful to avoid energy-giving foods in a climate that supposedly saps your energy has always been beyond me.

"The pygmies of the tropical Ituri forest will run miles to gorge themselves on the fat of a recently killed hippopotamus. That sort of evidence from natives in various parts of the tropics, both humid and dry, you have in plenty. So I confine myself to giving my own experiences and stating my own conclusions.

"My first personal experience with fat shortage came on my Orinoco-Amazon expedition of 1931-33, when my canoe Indians practically went on strike because I hadn't included sufficient lard or other fat in my supplies. Almost every newcomer to the Orinoco runs into that situation; his Indians make sure, before starting a journey, that he has with him plenty of fats.

"I bought enough fat to please my Indians, and then proceeded to eat on the journey from a separate pot, because I 'couldn't stand their greasy food.' It wasn't many weeks, however, before I avidly grabbed at every turtle egg I could get hold of—for its rich oil as I now realize—and at every Brazil nut, avocado pear, and every other source of vegetable fat, when I couldn't get animal fats. In those days I did not correlate that craving with my food tastes and habits; now I do. If today I were to go on another extended journey through the Amazon basin I would either take pemmican with me from the United States or spend some time, first of all, making it down in Brazil.

"Recently a lady ethnologist told me that I was all wrong

in my claim that any healthy white man can stay in perfect health (as far as food alone is concerned) on any diet that keeps native populations and 'primitive' peoples in health. She said she had tried it for a number of weeks in Mexico, with almost disastrous results. But when I asked her if she hadn't had trouble adjusting her taste to the 'greasy' food of the Mexicans, she stipulated that 'of course' she and her companions, while eating 'exactly what the Mexicans ate,' had taken pains to prepare the food in an appetizing way, by leaving out the grease! Then she went on to describe her own subsequent troubles in the typical terms of fat-shortage: constant hunger, a vague discomfort, lack of energy, distended stomach, etc.

"With such convictions to start with, growing out of years of personal experience in the tropics, I went on a pemmican regimen in the summer of 1943, staying on it for nine weeks. I was leading a sedentary life of office work, and it was one of the hottest summers on record in New York and Washington, where my activities were mainly centered, with temperatures that went higher on a number of occasions than I have ever experienced them in the Amazon basin.

"In the beginning I took sugarless tea with my pemmican, but later I saw no sense in brewing tea, and simply drank water. There were six occasions on which I didn't have pemmican with me, and ate something else; on all of those, I simply ate fresh fat meat, which is dietetically the same as pemmican. Some of the results of the 'test' are listed below.

"*Vitamins.* When I first started, you warned me that the kind of pemmican I was using had been overcooked * and was therefore probably deficient in Vitamin C, with the danger that it might—for reasons of faulty preparation and not because it was all-meat—result in scurvy. So you advised

---

* In the pemmican used by Mr. Hanson the lean meat had been cooked before drying, as against the Indian method of drying it uncooked. Then, as Mr. Hanson tells us, he used to cook his pemmican again before eating it, so that it was by then twice cooked.

me to add vitamin pills to my diet. Foolishly I replied that I wasn't afraid of scurvy, knowing how to cure it, and that it would be interesting to find out whether this type of pemmican would bring it on, how long that would take, what the disease would be like in its early stages, and how quickly it could be cured. I still think my reasoning was right, except that I hadn't counted on the nutritionists. When I did develop the preclinical symptoms of scurvy, after a little more than four weeks, the nutritionists took it to mean that pemmican is no good.

"For a week, at this stage, I did have a rather difficult time with the diet. But I added vitamin pills as well as a number of lemons—which have practically no food value outside of their antiscorbutic properties—got back on an even keel, and stayed on pemmican for something like five weeks longer, using pharmaceutical vitamin preparations as the only supplement to the exclusive pemmican.

"In any event, that experience with vitamin shortage has nothing to do with the suitability of fat meat in the tropics, where plenty of antiscorbutic animal and vegetable foods are available.

"*Fat content.* The dietitians warned me when I started that I was endangering my health, because they 'knew,' from years of research, that a fat content of more calories than about 35 per cent in the diet is dangerous. (I believe this may be correct for a mixed diet, but know it to be absolutely incorrect for an all-meat diet.)

"My pemmican was one of three types: Type A was so designed that 80 per cent of the calories came from the fat and 20 per cent from the lean, meaning a ratio of about 50-50 by weight; type B had 70 per cent of the calories in the fat and 30 per cent in the lean; type C had 60 per cent of the calories in the fat and 40 per cent in the lean.

"At first I preferred the lean 'Type C' pemmican, because I wasn't used to eating much fat. It wasn't long, however, before I began to realize it was unsuitable. I tried the other kinds and found that where ¾ pound per day of the fat pemmican (Type A) was absolutely satisfying, I would eat well over one pound per day of the lean pemmican (Type C), and still feel hungry, *with a craving for fat.* In one period of a few days, when I had nothing on hand but Type C, I added bacon grease and roast beef drippings to this pemmican, and so got along very well.

"After sixteen days some of the nutritionists got hold of me, showed me figures provided by the National Research Council to the effect that man can't assimilate more than 35 per cent of fat in his diet, and so 'proved' to me that I was either dead or coasting along on my last reserves of energy. It was a gorgeous battle, especially in view of the fact that I had more 'pep' for such purposes as arguing with nutritionists than I remembered ever having had before. I was in the very pink of condition, with all the minor difficulties of the first, mainly psychological, adjustment to an all-meat diet behind me. I finally gave up such fruitless argument, however, when the nutritionists asked me in despair whether I didn't even believe the National Research Council!

"The important thing is that during the entire nine weeks, in very hot weather, my appetites and 'cravings' constantly demanded a high fat content, of around 75 to 80 per cent by calories. That was to me one of the most striking results of my experiences.

"Being highly concentrated, pemmican is tricky stuff, resulting in almost immediate cravings to warn of shortcomings, where less concentrated foods seem to take much longer to give warning signals. In the beginning it took only an hour or so, after eating the lean pemmican, before I knew from the way I felt that I had had too little fat. Later, after I had learned to trust to my own appetites and reactions, that adjustment was automatic.

"*Quantities taken.* I had learned from you that when a man considerably overeats of fat, in hot weather or cold, he becomes nauseated and vomits, and is then all right again; but that if he overeats of starches and sugars, he may feel bloated, get a stomach-ache, etc., but will not be nauseated, or at least not easily. I also reasoned that in the beginning of the pemmican regimen I would not have the juices inside of me to take care of an all-meat diet, and that what would amount to overeating during the first days might actually be undereating later on. I therefore made it a rule to trust my own appetites rather than the nutritionists' rules, and to eat only when hungry and as long as hungry.

"The first three or four days I ate almost every hour, nibbling just a little. I became nauseated only once, and that was when I forced myself to eat more than my appetite called for—just as a test. During that period I several times started eating with gusto, only to find, after a few bites, that the pemmican was extremely distasteful. By merely interpreting that distastefulness as nature's warning that I'd had enough for the time being, I ate with gusto again the next hour.

"During the first five days I ate about half a pound or less per day. By then I was on an even keel, where I ate about three-quarters of a pound per day, and ate at regular mealtimes only. In other words, the nutritionists had been perfectly right when they had explained to me that the Eskimos can assimilate an all-meat diet perfectly because they have been conditioned to it; they were wrong in claiming that such conditioning takes centuries. It actually takes about five days.

"Three-quarters of a pound per day was my normal consumption, almost without variation, while I was doing office work. But when I went to the country week-ends, and indulged in rather heavy physical exercise, my consumption immediately went up to about nine-tenths of a pound per day. It never did exceed one pound of the fat pemmican, as against the unsatisfactory lean.

"*Water.* In the beginning I drank rather large quantities of water, not necessarily because I was thirsty, but primarily because I was not used to the lack of bulk, and felt rather empty. As I approached the point where the lack of bulk no longer bothered me, I drank less and less water, and surprised myself at the small quantities consumed.

"That I drank less during the second half of the period than during the first was no doubt in part because of my initial prejudice against fat, and because of the other circumstances which made me use the lean pemmican, Type C, in the early part of the test. For I have no reason to doubt those who say that a high protein intake requires a large water consumption.

"It was when I was getting the highest percentage of my calories from fat that I drank least. It is this which makes me suggest that a high-fat pemmican, Type A or fatter, would likely prove an excellent life-raft or desert survival ration.

"Those are, I think, the main points about my experiences to be brought out in a letter of this kind. I might add that, except during the one week of repairing the damage done by vitamin deficiency, I never once had a craving for anything but pemmican. In fact I attended several dinner parties during the nine weeks and was perfectly content to eat my pemmican while the rest ate their roasts and vegetables.

"It is now about six months since I returned to a mixed diet. I am in perfect health, as attested by two medical examinations, but have changed my food habits to the extent that I now eat all the fat I can get hold of, where previously I had usually cut the fats from my meat and left them on the plate. In fact, there are times now when I have a real craving for fat, and a longing to return to the pemmican regimen.

"I know this: As soon as wartime restrictions are lifted on meats, and such animal products as cheeses, my diet is undoubtedly going to consist very largely of such foods. And if I return to the Amazon basin, I will never again differentiate between my meals and those of my Indians on the ground that the latter are too fat."

In a discussion of pemmican, hereafter, I quote Admiral Sir Leopold McClintock to the effect that he paid no attention to the prohibitions of a dietetic theory, which happened to be in vogue among the doctors in a given year, if he knew that the food condemned by the theory had been found wholesome and in other ways desirable by large numbers of people through long periods; he said he always preferred experience to theory if the two were in conflict.

Perhaps, in giving adherence to McClintock's rule, I may suggest a corollary. It is that when a precept of the nutritionists, like the one against fat in warm weather, is in conflict with the tastes and practices of many people in many countries through many centuries, then it is likely the nutritionists themselves will eventually learn, probably through animal experimentation or by deduction from some recently announced or recently noticed chemical fact, that the opposite of the previously held theory is true.

So one may reasonably expect, within not too many years, that the dietitians will announce they have discovered Jehovah was right for Palestine, Achilles for Greece, the Australian Black and the Amazonian Red Man for the humid tropics, in liking meat in those climates, and in liking it fat.

7

The Blackleg in Shakespeare's Time

EUROPE'S dread of the frozen North, "with its still-
ness of white death, its gloom of the six-month night,"
was apparently stronger during the seventeenth century
than at any time before or since. It is difficult for us now
to understand how real such imagined terrors can be. And
they were not wholly imaginary; for a miasma of death
spread through the encampments of those who wintered in
the North, the more terrifying because the doctors of the
time imagined they knew how to prevent the scourge. Somehow it is more unnerving to a man to discover himself
powerless before a condition which he had thought he understood, and was able to cope with, than before another
which he had from the beginning looked upon as a force of
nature against which no strength might prevail.

Apart from the numerous superstitions about the so-called
Frozen North, and apart from man's fear of the unknown,
the dread of the northern winter has rested upon facts that
are horrifyingly real. The most serious are those of the
disease scurvy, known also by several other names, the commonest of which is blackleg. Doctors who wrote in Latin
called it *scorbutus;* the preventives and cures, supposed or
real (chiefly supposed), were *antiscorbutics.*

The doctors of the late Middle Ages and early modern
times were more familiar than we now are with the symptoms of scurvy, and their descriptions might be used except
that it is now considered they included a number of other
diseases, most of them less serious, an inclusion which confuses their descriptions, since it introduces symptoms that
do not belong to the proper scurvy. Accordingly, I make up

a new description, based upon my own experience and upon consultation with a number of doctors who have specialized in the disease, chief of them the late Dr. Alfred Hess of New York City, who, during the last third of his professional career, was usually recognized as about the foremost authority.

If an observer were watching for the onset of scurvy and had in mind, among other things, the psychiatric aspect, the first symptom noticed would probably be an emotional or temperamental change—the victim becomes more argumentative, more irritable, likelier to take affront, more inclined to pessimistic interpretations. At this stage it would seem that no physical examination could reveal any gross sign of the coming trouble nor would the patient be likely to admit that there was a mental change.*

As full development of scurvy draws nearer, the mental condition changes from aggressive and argumentative irritability to pessimism. Then appears a slight and thereafter steadily growing disinclination to physical effort; and similarly with mental effort, particularly in that the patient more and more often finds himself in a "what's the use" mood.

Now comes the first symptom that a patient will notice, but only if watchful. It is that when he jumps up from a sitting or lying position he will stagger momentarily, though not enough to feel it as a dizzy spell. It will not be many days, however, until this is recognized as dizziness, and likely the patient will fall back into the seat from which he has just risen.

After this come symptoms that are more readily discernible. There will be a tendency to bleed from the gums, as

---

* It has been suggested by child specialists, for instance Professor W. C. Davison, of the Medical School of Duke University, that these symptoms are represented among babies by an increased tendency to cry. The former interpretation was that the child cried because he was in pain, or at least in noticeable discomfort; Dr. Davison's view is that the crying is likely a mere sign of such irritability as has been described above for an adult.

when the teeth are brushed. The patient begins to feel a stiffness and perhaps a slight pain in one or another of his joints. He may identify the bleeding from the gums as pyorrhea, and so may his doctor or dentist; the soreness of joints will be labeled a touch of rheumatism.

The pain in a joint will appear first where there is most use. A blacksmith would feel it in his arms, a mail-carrier in his legs; irrespective of use, the trouble spreads from joint to joint until finally there is pain in every one of them.*

As the pain is spreading among the joints the other symptoms develop, and presently the one that gave the disease its sailors' name, blackleg. Tiny blood vessels rupture beneath the skin, usually first and most conspicuously on the calf of the leg, no doubt because of the strain, since all of us do more or less walking. The dead blood is visible through the translucent skin as black spots; the spots increase in size, spread and coalesce, until there are patches; the legs are getting black and the patient is a blackleg.

The mental symptoms are now rapidly aggravated. The victim is no longer quarrelsome; he is too gloomy for that, too lacking in energy. Perhaps three weeks or a month before death the gloom is as deep as seems humanly possible, except that there is no tendency toward suicide. It appears to the patient, as he thinks back after the cure, that he was not so much powerless to move as powerless to decide that he wanted to move.

In two cases which I have observed, and which never got quite to the full depths of gloom, one man was unable to walk while the other was able to stagger along, holding on

---

* Dr. Norman Jolliffe, New York City specialist on scurvy, who has read this discussion of symptoms, comments in a letter of March 20, 1944: "I have observed two patients who developed 'scurvy sclerosis.' This is due to fibrosis-tissue replacement in the hemorrhagic areas so that eventually the knees were immobile. This occurs in people who have had repeated attacks of acute scurvy superimposed on chronic."

behind a sledge. At this stage the gums were as soft as "American" cheese, you could cut them about as readily as Edam cheese if you pressed on them with a sliver of wood, like a tooth pick. One of the men, when he thought he was pulling on something between his teeth, was actually pulling on a tooth and it came out, so that he found himself looking at it between his fingers. This was nearly or quite without pain. The gums had then receded from the teeth. When the cure had been worked, so that these two men were "perfectly" well, the qualification had to be that the gums never did regain their former position.

It was noted in late medieval and early modern times, though it is not found in all the commentaries, that the appetite remains normal or that it increases; those writers who speak of it as ravenous are no doubt exaggerating. According to the cases I have seen, or heard of intimately and in my opinion reliably, there is not likely to be a serious digestive disturbance until a few weeks before death, perhaps three or four weeks.

The progress of the disease seems very rapid toward the end, increasing with something like a geometric ratio. This may perhaps be explained on the assumption that from a previously adequate diet the patient has stored in his body antiscorbutic elements which are gradually used up. In that view, when the stored antiscorbutics are gone the worsening of the patient is likely to be rapid.

Death is from hemorrhage, usually of the digestive tract or lungs. No doubt sudden deaths from scurvy are from ruptured blood vessels in the brain.

With this description, or one at all similar, it is difficult to see how the epithets "a scurvy fellow" and "blackleg" got their meanings. This is somewhat clarified if the reader remembers, first, what has been said about a number of other diseases having been included formerly under the scurvy classification, and, then, that the disease was supposed to depend in part on a man's character and his disposition.

From our point of view this last is putting the cart before the horse. To us the quarrelsomeness of the patient, the fault-finding, suspicion, lack of energy amounting to what some nowadays call "a breakdown in will power," are symptoms or results of the disease; to the seventeenth and eighteenth centuries these were causes of the disease. We think that a man is cranky, suspicious, lazy, because he already has scurvy; they thought that men who were lazy, cranky, and suspicious were thereby predisposed to contraction of the disease. On that reasoning the doctors classified as preventives such things as exercise, cultivation of a cheerful disposition, music, parlor games, any suitable entertainment.

These moral considerations explain somewhat the meaning of "blackleg"; the differing connotation of "scurvy fellow" is perhaps due to a verbal confusion. The Oxford Dictionary first defines scurvy along the lines of what has here been said; then it gives another scurvy which differs in meaning and derivation, though it has the same spelling. For this second scurvy the Oxford has the first meaning: "Covered with scurf; suffering from, or of the nature of, skin disease; scurfy, scabby."

In the cases of true scurvy which I have seen, and in those about which I have seemingly reliable information, the disease does not have, as a symptom or result, any scabby appearance of the skin. This was especially impressed upon me in New York City hospitals when I was occasionally called in as a consultant for the diagnosis of scurvy during the period immediately following the publication of my first paper in the *Journal* of the American Medical Association ("Observations on Three Cases of Scurvy," November 23, 1918). One woman I remember in particular, who was a delicate Nordic blonde in appearance, looked especially dainty and ethereal at the beginning of her treatment, more so than she did later when she had partly recovered. Looking at such a patient, it was difficult to understand how scurvy could have received its Shakespearean connotation; but that connotation would be easy for one who confuses the disease we are here describing with some other which is characterized by a scurfy or scabby appearance of the skin.

Under the present view, the causes of scurvy are wholly dietetic. We find it interesting, therefore, when we go as far back at we can in the literature, say, to the thirteenth century, that we have a constant recurrence of views similar to those of the present. There is the further striking similarity that only now and then are we told by the older writers that fresh meat will cure scurvy, but we are constantly told that fresh vegetables are a cure. However, the idea *fresh* never got a very strong hold. For instance, in the nineteenth century the usual view of lime juice or lemon juice as an antiscorbutic was that the efficacy depended on acidity. Accordingly, in the reports of polar expeditions there is frequent reference to the acid content of the antiscorbutics carried, but mention of the age or comparative freshness of the juice occurs rarely, if ever.

In seventeenth- and eighteenth-century theory of scurvy causation, a canvass of the literature reveals great variety and ingenuity. The precepts which most frequently crop up are that the leader of an expedition must see to it that his men are cleanly, that they exercise in the fresh air, that they have plenty of sunlight, that they are kept in good spirits by suitable entertainment—views still held as to the general preservation of health, though discarded as particularly applicable to scurvy.

This is an Arctic study, and develops only those views on scurvy which had a bearing on Europe's dread of the northern winter. They are in chief:

1. Vegetables are necessary for health. They are difficult

to secure in the North, which makes wintering there dangerous.

2. Lack of sunlight and of solar warmth tends to cause scurvy, which poses the difficulty that for a long period the sun is absent from the sky, if one is wintering far north, and that the winters are long and cold.

There would seem to be no reason for disagreeing with the opinion, common down through the centuries, and held today, that vegetables (nowadays *fresh* vegetables are usually specified) are an excellent preventive and cure of scurvy. Accordingly, I confine myself here to a few remarks on the views that were generally held by the medical profession concerning the relation of meat to scurvy.

Not merely was it usual during the seventeenth and eighteenth centuries for the medical books to charge that salted meats were among the leading causes of scurvy; there were also those in high places who considered fresh meat an active cause. Fresh vegetables were nearly always praised as curative agents; dried vegetable foods, such as bread and porridge, were rarely blamed and at least occasionally praised. Preserved meats were seldom if ever praised, and fresh meats rarely. I present first the average view on meat, and then the extreme, before passing on to sunshine and tropical warmth as preventives and cures.

In Britain a leader of eighteenth-century medical science, a great teacher though perhaps not one of the great innovators, was William Cullen, whose *First Lines of the Practice of Physic* appeared in four successive volumes during the years 1776-1784. I quote and paraphrase from volume three of the "New Edition" as published in Boston, 1790.

Animal food, says Cullen, is difficult to digest. Contrariwise, foods like bread and porridge "which are in a great proportion the food of infants, of women, and of the greater part of mankind, can hardly be supposed to be food of difficult digestion. And with respect to the production of scurvy there are facts which show that unfermented farinacea, employed in large proportion, have had a considerable effect in preventing the disease." According to this, bread, porridge, and other such standard foods of seamen, were preventives of scurvy; they would have a curative tendency.

Of meat, Cullen says: "It must however be allowed that the principal circumstance in causing scurvy is the living very much and very long upon animal food, especially when in a putrescent state."

So meat in any form is bad; especially bad if not fresh. By implication, foods of the vegetable kingdom are in any state better than meats in a corresponding state. The only class of foods properly curative is fresh vegetables.

As has been said, the charge that fresh meat is a chief villain was leveled occasionally. I quote from page 15 of *Free Observations on the Scurvy, Gout, Diet and Remedy* . . . by Francis Spilsbury, Chymist, London, 1780:

"It is well known, that could the mariners have a constant supply of fresh meat only to feed on, they would expose themselves more to the hasty inroads of the Scurvy, and much sooner sink under its baneful influence."

It seems strange, when the literature of the seventeenth and eighteenth centuries is scanned, that anybody could think fresh meat a direct cause of scurvy, in view of the sporadic references to it as a cure. It is even more strange that warmth and sunlight could have been thought of as preventives and cures. For not many stories can have been better known to Europeans, in the broad aspects, than those of tropical voyages, whether of discovery or of commerce. Magellan, the first known circumnavigator, lost a third of his men from scurvy in the tropics, and there were times when everyone aboard was so affected that the men barely had strength for handling the sails and rudder. From the time of Columbus there was an unbroken chain of these tropical narratives, with scurvy as villain. I have choice of many, and select for quotation only because it is the best known the story of Anson's circumnavigation, which started from Britain in 1740 and which ended there in 1744. Quoting from the edition of G. Laird Clowes, Boston and London, 1928, I reproduce the description at the end of the Southern Hemisphere summer, in the latitudes of the subtropics:

"Soon after passing Streights Le Maire, the scurvy began to make its appearance amongst us; and our long continuance at sea, the fatigue we underwent, and the various disappointments we met with, had occasioned its spreading to such a degree, that at the latter end of April there were but few on board who were not in some degree afflicted with it, and in that month no less than forty-three died of it on board the *Centurion*. But though we thought that the distemper had then risen to an extraordinary height, and were willing to hope, that as we advanced to the northward [i.e., toward the equator] its malignity would abate, yet we found, on the contrary, that in the month of May we lost near double that number: And as we did not get to land till the middle of June, the mortality went on increasing, and the disease extended itself so prodigiously that after the loss of about two hundred men, we could not at last muster more than six fore-mast men in a watch capable of duty."

The *Centurion*, separated from the rest, cruised in a vain search for relief. On May 22 ". . . it was resolved to take advantage of the present favorable season . . . and to make the best of our way for the Island of Juan Fernandez. . . . we were by this time reduced to so low a condition that instead of attempting to attack the places of the enemy, our utmost hopes could only suggest to us the possibility of saving the ship and some part of the remaining enfeebled crew, by our speedy arrival at Juan Fernandez."

By May 28th the crew were dying four, five, six in a day. They missed the island, and on the 30th saw the coast of Chile. "In this desponding condition, with a crazy ship, a great scarcity of water, and a crew so universally diseased that there were not above ten fore-mast men in a watch capable of doing duty, and even some of these lame and unable to go aloft . . . we stood to the westward."

On June 9th they reached Juan Fernandez: ". . . we were by this time reduced to so helpless a condition, that out of two hundred and odd men which remained alive we could not, taking all our watches together, muster hands enough to work the ship on an emergency, though we included the officers, their servants, and the boys." They were hardly able to reach the island after sighting it. "To so wretched a condition was a sixty-gun ship reduced, which had passed Streights Le Maire but three months before, with between four and five hundred men, almost all of them in health and vigour.

"At four in the morning the Cutter was dispatched . . . to find out the bay (anchorage) we were in search of, who returned at noon with the boat laden with seals and grass; for though the Islands abounded with better vegetables, yet the boats-crew, in their short stay, had not met with them; and they well knew that even grass would prove a dainty. . . . The seals too were considered as fresh provision; but as yet were not much admired, tho' they grew afterwards into more repute: For what rendered them less valuable at this juncture was the prodigious quantity of excellent fish, which the people on board had taken, during the absence of the boat."

Soon after the *Centurion* berthed, they saw a sail which proved to be the *Tryal Sloop*. Her commander, Captain Saunders, informed them that out of his small complement he had buried thirty-four men and that the others were so afflicted that only himself, his lieutenant and three of his men were able to stand by the sails.

The ships got their sick ashore. During the first ten or twelve days the fatalities continued and they buried about six a day. It was nearly twenty days after landing that the "mortality tolerably ceased."

The island abounded in vegetables which were recognized as antiscorbutic. "These vegetables, with the fish and flesh we found here . . . were not only extremely grateful to our palates, after the long course of salt diet which we had been confined to, but were likewise of the most salutary consequence to our sick in recovering and invigorating them, and of no mean service to us who were well, in destroying the lurking seeds of the scurvy, from which perhaps none of us were totally exempt, and in refreshing and restoring us to our wonted strength and activity."

On the 21st of June the *Gloucester* was sighted and Anson, believing she might be in the same distress from illness, sent out a boat loaded with fresh water, fish and vegetables, "which was a very seasonable relief to them; for our apprehensions of their calamities appeared to be but too well grounded. . . . They had already thrown overboard two-thirds of their complement, and of those that remained alive, scarcely any were capable of doing duty except the officers and their servants."

On August 16th, they were joined by the *Victualler Anna Pink,* the last of their squadron to make the rendezvous. (The *Severn* and the *Pearl* turned back to Brazil; the *Wager* was lost, though some of the crew were saved.)

The *Centurion,* the *Gloucester* and the *Tryal Sloop* had left England in 1740 with 961 men on board; of these 626 were dead by August of 1741, nearly all of them from scurvy.

In early modern times, from Magellan on, the books of narrative and of medicine were filled with tales like these that came from the tropics; and yet the belief persisted, among those who sailed northerly from Britain, Holland and Scandinavia, that chilly weather and the long winter absence of the sun were among the prime causes of scurvy.

It was generally believed, and may have been true, that

scurvy in this period was more prevalent on shore in northern Europe than in central Europe or on the Mediterranean;
but, if that was so, conditions have changed a good deal, for
nowadays scurvy is quite as likely in southern countries. Of
lands under the flag of the United States, for instance, scurvy
has been most frequent, during the last few decades, in
Puerto Rico.

Three hundred years ago the sailors to the Davis Strait
fishery off the west coast of Greenland, and to the "Greenland" fishery around Spitsbergen, did not know as we do
now that in those very regions, particularly on the west coast
of Greenland, it has been demonstrated that of itself there
is nothing unwholesome to Europeans about northerly living. For the medieval European colony, as we know from
archaeological and historical studies, moved northward along
the west coast of Greenland through the eleventh, twelfth
and thirteenth centuries, until some of them were living
around and beyond Smith Sound, more than a thousand
miles north of the Arctic Circle.

The northern stories which the mariner of Shakespeare's
and Milton's time knew, who cultivated the Spitsbergen
fishery, were such as those of the Englishman Willoughby,
the Hollander Barents, the Dane Munk.

Of Sir Hugh Willoughby the seventeenth century had no
connected narrative, nor have we today; but what they knew
filled them with dread. They knew that he, and the entire
company of his ships the *Bona Esperanza* and *Bona Confi-
dentia,* had gone into winter quarters during September,
1553, on the north coast of Lapland, with considerable if not
ample stores, that most of them had been still alive in January, 1554, but that none lived through the winter. It was believed, and is still believed, that most of them died of scurvy.

In contrast, the seventeenth century's knowledge of the
Barents expedition was explicitly terrifying. The crew had
built themselves a house of driftwood, which was abundant

on the shore of Novaya Zemlya; they had plenty of fuel to keep them warm and plenty of food of the sort that was then standard—meal for porridge, flour for bread, preserved meats, with herbs and other things which were considered preventives and cures of scurvy. Yet the scurvy came, and five out of seventeen men died while the survivors kept diaries.

A story typical of the belief, and indeed of the happenings, of the sixteenth and seventeenth centuries was that of the Danish expedition under Jens Munk which spent the winter of 1619-20 in what is now the harbor of Churchill, Manitoba, the Hudson Bay terminus of the Canadian National Railway, and which was from the seventeenth to the middle of the nineteenth century an important seaport of Canada.

With two ships, the *Unicorn (Enhiörningen)* and the *Lamprey (Lamprenen)*, Munk sailed from Copenhagen May 9, 1619. The *Unicorn* had forty-eight people and the *Lamprey* sixteen.

For winter quarters, September 7, we are told: "I caused . . . the sick people to be brought from the ship on shore; and we gathered some cloudberries, gooseberries, and other berries. . . . I also had a good fire made on shore every day for the sick whereby they were comforted, and in time nicely regained their health." So the scurvy that had developed on the the long voyage was cured by fruits and such other things as were then standard antiscorbutics.

A fateful recurrence in the history of military operations, of seafaring, and of exploration, reference to which is here repeated for its pertinence to the Munk expedition, is the frequent conversion of laymen to the view that scurvy is preventable and curable through the use of fresh meat, and the medical profession's refusal to let these conclusions sink in deeply enough to become integral in the doctrine of medicine.

Cures with meat were referred to sporadically in seventeenth- and eighteenth-century medical literature, and I plan to study this in detail in the longer and more technical work to which this book is a sort of preface. It will then appear that those who realized that meats had been curative on expeditions were comparatively so few, commanded so little respect, and were indeed usually so unemphatic in their statements, that members of the medical profession were unimpressed. If impressed at all, it was but for the moment, and they relapsed into the doctrine that, among foods, only those from the vegetable kingdom would cure scurvy.

There were of course a great many other "specifics," such as mercury, and a great many other preventives, such as baths, exercise, sunlight and fresh air; but the single issue of present concern is between animal and vegetable food preventives of scurvy.

In field practice, the situation was that commanders of ships and of armies desired meats as good sound food; they rarely considered them as antiscorbutics, thinking in that connection only of vegetables.

The members of Munk's Danish expedition did their best to secure meat as food. The entry for September 12 says: "In the morning early, a large white bear came down to the water near the ship, which stood and ate some Beluga flesh, off a fish [whale] . . . which I had caught the day before. I shot the bear, and the men all desired the flesh for food, which I also allowed. I ordered the cook just to boil it slightly and then to keep it in vinegar for a night, and I myself had two or three pieces of this bear-flesh roasted for the cabin. It was of good taste and did not disagree with me."

On October 22nd: "After this day, the crew commenced to go on shore in the day time in pursuit of game." Some trapped, others lay in ambush, some went shooting "because there was plenty of ptarmigan [a small northern type of grouse] and hares, as well as all kinds of birds, as long as the snow was not too deep. . . . At that time, all the men liked to go into the forest or open country for shooting because they never went on shore when the weather was fine but that they carried home something good."

November 10th: ". . . which was St. Martin's Eve, the men shot some ptarmigan, with which we had to content ourselves instead of St. Martin's goose." On November 15th they caught three foxes, but the record does not tell whether they were eaten.

On November 21st some of the men "shot ptarmigan which were of great assistance to us; whilst others visited and put in order their traps, in which they caught animals." That day they buried their first dead, a man who had long been ill. It is not clear whether he died of scurvy, but there is no doubt about most of those who followed."

"On the 12th of December, one of my two surgeons . . . died."

"On the 20th of December the weather was fine and mild so that the whole crew was on shore. A part of them went shooting so that we might have some fresh meat for the approaching Christmas Holy Days. . . . In the evening [they] returned and brought a number of ptarmigan and a hare."

The early part of January the men were catching foxes and sables, but there is no mention of their being eaten; so probably the usual taboo of North Europeans was observed.

On January 10th the chief cook died; the priest and the remaining surgeon took to their beds. Munk asked the surgeon if he had any idea of a remedy for the scurvy; he replied that he had already tried them all.

January 18: ". . . the men who were still in health were in the forest, each about his business, but principally shooting in order to get some ptarmigan for the sick."

January 23rd the priest sat up in his berth and preached his last sermon. That day one of the mates died; on January 27th a lieutenant and a seaman died.

Tracks of reindeer (caribou) were seen, but there was no

success with the hunt. On February 2nd two ptarmigan "were very welcome for the use of the sick."

Two ptarmigan are about equal to a single grouse and, with full antiscorbutic value as we recognize it today, would not have been much to divide among four dozen men, even if everything had been eaten raw or slightly cooked, thus with its full virtue. But one of the unfortunate beliefs of Munk's day was that, while the healthy might eat foods that were medium or undercooked, the sick must use only meat that was thoroughly boiled. By preference it was cooked to pieces, the invalid drinking the broth. It appears from various references in the Munk narrative that this was the idea of the Danes, so that the pathetic two small birds were of less curative value than otherwise, perhaps of no value.

On February 10th there were two deaths; on February 12th two ptarmigan were again divided among the ship's company.

On February 16th: "During all these days, there was nothing but sickness and weakness; and every day the number of the sick was continually increased, so that, on this day, there were only seven persons in health that could fetch wood and water and do whatever work there was to be done on board. On the same day died a seaman who had been ill the whole voyage."

February 17th one man died. Of the crew "there had already died twenty persons. On that day we got a hare, which was very welcome."

The priest died on February 20th, a servant to one of the officers on February 25th, two sailors on March 1st. The strongest were now so weak that they had difficulty in burying the dead.

On March 4th they secured five ptarmigan. The sick men drank the broth but were unable to eat the flesh because their teeth were loose with the scurvy and dropping out.

Two men died on the two days March 8th and 9th. March

21st the surgeon and another man died. "Now and afterwards, the sickness raged more violently every day, so that we who were still left suffered great trouble before we could get the dead buried."

On March 25th the skipper of one of the ships died. Munk gathered some frozen berries that he picked from their stalks up on the land; the next day he gathered a few more. They were given to the sick, which now meant everybody.

March 29th two seamen died, on the 30th the carpenter. Munk says: "I was now obliged myself to run about in the ship, to give drink to the sick, to boil drink for them, and get for them what I thought might be good for them, to which I was not accustomed, and of which I had but little knowledge."

The last of March the second mate died, during the first five days of April five more, "and the number of men in health was now so small that we were scarcely able to bury the dead."

Between the 5th and 10th of April three men died, one of them William Gordon, the English pilot, another Munk's lieutenant. On April 14th "only four, besides myself, had strength enough left to sit up in the berth and listen to the homily for Good Friday." The next week four more died.

April 20th they got three ptarmigan. The same day they secured two Canadian grouse "which was due to God's special providence because the sick could not eat any of the salted meat, but only broth of such fresh meat as we obtained."

Four men died the week following April 22nd. Between May 3rd and May 6th three died, among them John Watson, the second English pilot. No one now had strength to leave his berth except Munk and the second cook.

On May 10th great numbers of geese arrived, and they secured one. 'We were eleven persons alive, counting the sick."

During the week from the 12th to the 19th of May, four men died. On May 20th, the weather was fine and mild. "It was a great grief to us that, whilst God gave such an abundance of various kinds of birds, none of us was strong enough to go into the country and shoot some of them."

Between May 20th and May 28th three men died. During that week they caught one goose that was "lame"—it had suffered an injury, so they were able to catch it. On June 4th four men were living, of the original sixty-four.

Munk could no longer stand the smell of unburied bodies, and on June 8th he decided to die in the open. Two of his men were on shore and helped him move. The fourth man, in the ship, died.

"Later on, we crawled about everywhere near, wherever we saw the least green growing out of the ground, which we dug up and sucked the main root thereof."

The turn of the tide came for Munk on June 18th, when they began to cultivate the sea. They had not understood that in the North fish live beneath ice, and so they had set no nets and had not captured fish with hooks during the winter. Now the spring thaw was producing open water, fishing conditions which they understood. They set a net that yielded six large trout the first day. Every day thereafter they got enough fish, and by degrees they recovered. With the renewed health they began to hunt and secured a few birds.

On June 26th they had the strength to board their ships. They could manage at best only one, and more easily the smaller, so they transferred the essentials from the *Unicorn* to the *Lamprey*, "for our use in crossing the sea, as far as we three persons could manage." On September 21st they reached harbor in Norway.

Such were the stories of Willoughby, Barents and Munk, and of many another northern wintering party, that were the common lore. The dread that came from such knowledge is strikingly brought out by the fact that four criminals in

England were given the choice of being executed or wintering in Spitsbergen. They were so terrified by the hangman's noose that they agreed to spend a northern winter, if suitably outfitted as to housing, clothes and food. But when Spitsbergen lay before them and their ship was about to put them ashore, they pleaded with the captain that he take them back to be hanged in England, for this quick death would be preferable to the slow terror and the eventual death of the Arctic winter.

Apparently the chief reason why these criminals were not executed when they got back to England was the feeling that they had been greatly punished already through the anguish they must have endured while facing the prospect of wintering in Spitsbergen.

8

The Blackleg in Our Time

THUS from the beginning of modern exploration had scurvy been the great enemy of the explorer. During the circumnavigation by Magellan's expedition, 1519-22, many died from it. When Scott's party went by sledge to the South Pole four centuries later, in 1912, their strength was sapped by scurvy; they were unable to maintain their travel schedule, and died.

Nor has scurvy been the nemesis of explorers only. In the First World War the British army in the Near East was seriously handicapped by it; in October, 1935, an American doctor reported that a hundred Ethiopian soldiers per day were dying of scurvy among the troops which struggled against the Italians; there was scurvy among United States troops in the Second World War. The disease wrought havoc during the Alaska and Yukon gold rushes following 1896, when scores of miners died from it.

It was a medical delusion for several hundred years that doctors knew exactly how to prevent and how to cure scurvy.

The premise from which the doctors started was that vegetables, particularly fruits, prevent blackleg. Since diet consists of animals and plants, the statement came to take the form that scurvy is caused by meat and cured by vegetables. Finally the doctors standardized on lime juice as the best of preventives and cures. They named it a sure cure, a specific. Lawmakers followed the doctors. It is on statute books that during long voyages the crew is to be supplied with lime juice and induced or compelled to take it.

From officers of the Royal Canadian Mounted Police, and from sourdoughs, I have in my notebooks many a case of suffering and death caused by scurvy in the Alaska and Yukon gold rushes. The miner generally began to sicken toward the end of winter. He had been living on beans and bacon, on fresh bread, rice, oatmeal, sugar, dried fruits and dried vegetables. When he recognized his trouble as scurvy, he made such efforts as were possible to get the things which he believed would cure him.

Apparently the miner's faith was strongest in raw potatoes. These had to be brought from afar, and there are heroic tales of men who struggled through the wilderness to succor a comrade with a few pounds of what Alaska called spuds. There were similar beliefs in the virtue of onions and some other vegetables. Curiously, there was either no faith in those vegetables which were locally obtainable, or else a belief that they should be treated in a way which, we now understand, destroys their value. For instance, a man might have been cured with a salad of the leaves or the green bark of trees. What the miners did with the pine needles and willow bark was to cook them for hours and drink the tea. If they had fresh meat, which would have been curative as an underdone steak or roast, they boiled it to shreds and drank the broth. Death frequently occurred in two to four months.

Ignoring the decimation of armies which has been taking place in our time, and the burden of scurvy in many walks of civil life through past ages, we turn to the explorers, the class most widely publicized as suffering from and dying of scurvy.

It is usual to rank Captain James Cook of the late eighteenth century with the foremost explorers of all time, part of which fame rests on the assertion that he discovered how to prevent and cure scurvy. Medical books name him as pioneer in the field, saying that we owe to him the conquest of a dread disease. For he demonstrated that with vegetables (again, particularly fruits) scurvy could be prevented on the longest voyages. By statement or inference the books assert that from this developed the knowledge according to which we extract and bottle the juice of the lime, stock ships with it, prevent and cure scurvy.

The good physicians retained their faith in lime juice as a specific by overlooking its constant failure upon severe test.

How stoutly the medical profession kept the faith is shown in connection with many a British polar expedition; for instance, that of Sir George Nares. When he returned home in 1876, after a year and a half in the field, he reported much illness from scurvy, some deaths, and a partial failure of his exploration program as a result. In his own view fresh meat could have saved his men. But the doctors, as will be seen when we consider how they later advised Scott, soon forgot whatever impression was made by the opinion of Nares and the facts he adduced to support it. They seem to have squared themselves with the old doctrines by a series of assumptions: that the lime juice used by the Nares expedition failed because it was deficient in acid content; that some of the victims did not take as much of it as was needed; and that perhaps it was too much to expect even the marvelous juice to cope with all the northern conditions which tended (in the view of that time) to bring on scurvy—absence of sunlight, bad ventilation, lack of amusement and exercise, insufficient cleanliness.

Particularly because the Nares medical court of inquiry had closed on a note of cleanliness and "modern sanitation," one would think the medical men might have felt a severe jolt when they read some twenty years later how Nansen and Johansen had wintered in the Franz Josef Islands in 1895-96. They had lived in a hut of stones and walrus leather. The ventilation was slight, to conserve fuel; the blubber fire smoked, so that the air was additionally bad; within the house there was not a ray of daylight for months, and the two men practically hibernated, seldom going outdoors at all and taking as little exercise as appears humanly possible; they never bathed and seldom washed face or hands. Yet their health was perfect all winter and they came out of their confinement in as good physical condition as any men ever did out of any kind of Arctic wintering.

Their food had been exclusively meat, the lean and the fat of walrus, eaten fresh and usually boiled.

Tens if not hundreds of thousands of scientists in medicine and the related branches must have seen this account, for Nansen's books were best-sellers in practically every language, and newspapers were full of the story. Yet the effect upon medical practice was negligible. The doctors and dietitians still continued to pontificate on how meat produced scurvy and on the contributory bad effects, on polar expeditions and in sailing ships, of what they called insufficience of ventilation, cleanliness, sunlight, and exercise. They still prescribed lime juice and put their whole dependence on it and other vegetable products.

Excuses for lime juice, and explanations to show why it must not be charged with seeming failures, have persisted to our day. It was, for instance, demonstrated with triumph a few years ago that the meaning of "lime" had changed during the last hundred years, this to justify the claim that it worked better in the eighteenth century—then the juice was made from lemons called limes; now it is made from limes called limes; and "lime juice" from lemons is more potent than lime juice from limes.

The antiscorbutic value of lemons may be far greater than that of limes, per ounce, but that does not go to the root of the matter. For proof of this consider how Nansen's experience was re-enforced and interpreted by four expeditions during the following twenty years, two of them commanded by Robert Falcon Scott, one by Ernest Henry Shackleton, one by me.

Scott, in 1900 and 1901, sought the most orthodox scientific counsel when outfitting his first Antarctic expedition. He followed advice by carrying lime juice and by picking up quantities of fruits and other vegetable things as he passed New Zealand. He saw to it that the diet was "wholesome," that the men took exercise, that they bathed and had plenty of fresh air. Yet scurvy broke out and the subsequently famous Shackleton, among others, was crippled by it on a journey. They were pulling their own sledges at the time, so they must have had enough exercise. There was plenty of light with the unsetting sun beating upon them, and there was plenty of fresh air, for they were out of doors. To believers in the catchwords and slogans of their day, and to believers in the virtues of lime juice, the onset of the scurvy was a baffling mystery.

That it was Shackleton's scurvy which most interfered with the success of the first Scott expedition was particularly unfortunate, in the light of the jealousies it aroused, the enmities it caused. Scurvy, as diseases go, is really one of the cleanest and least obnoxious; but in English the name of it is a term of opprobrium—"a scurvy fellow," "a scurvy trick." Shackleton may have smarted as much under that word-association as he did under the direct charge that his weakness had been Scott's main handicap. The passion to clear his name drove him to the organization of an expedition which many in Britain considered unethical—a subordinate, with indecent haste and insistence, crowding forward to eclipse his commander.

The crucial element in the first Shackleton expedition, to the student of scurvy, is the fact that Shackleton was an Elizabethan throwback in the time of Edward VII. He was a Hawkins or a Drake, a buccaneer in spirit and method. He talked louder and more than is good form in modern England. He approached near to brag and swagger. He caused frictions, aroused and fanned jealousies, and won the breathless admiration of youngsters who would have followed Dampier and Frobisher with equal enthusiasm in their piracies and in their explorations.

The organization, and the rest of the first Shackleton expedition, went with a hurrah. They were as careless as Scott had been careful; they did not have Scott's type of backing, scientific or financial. They arrived helter-skelter on the shores of the Antarctic Continent, pitched camp, and discovered that they did not have nearly enough food for the winter, nor had they used such painstaking care as Scott to provide themselves with fruits and other antiscorbutics in New Zealand. Compared with Scott's, their routine was slipshod as to cleanliness, exercise, and several of the ordinary hygienic prescriptions.

What is important is that Scott's men, with unlimited quantities of jams and marmalades, vegetables and fruits, grains, curries, and potted meats, had been little inclined to add seals and penguins to their dietary. With Shackleton it was neither wisdom nor the acceptance of good advice but dire necessity which drove to such use of penguin and seal that Dr. Alister Forbes Mackay, physician from Edinburgh, who was a member of that Shackleton expedition and later physician of my ship the *Karluk,* told me he estimated half the food during their stay in the Antarctic was fresh meat.

In spite of the lack of care (indeed, as it now appears, because of that lack), Shackleton's expedition had better average health than Scott's. There was never a sign of scurvy; every man retained his full strength; and they accomplished that spring what most authorities still consider the greatest physical achievement of southern exploration. With men dragging the sledges a considerable part of the way, they got to latitude 88° 23′ S., practically within sight of the Pole.

Just short of a decade after the first expedition, Scott began his second venture as he had begun the first, by asking the medical men of Britain for protection from scurvy and by receiving from them once more the good old advice about lime juice, fruits, cleanliness, ventilation, and the rest. In winter quarters he again placed reliance on that advice and on constant medical supervision, on a planned and carefully varied diet, on numerous scientific tests to determine the condition of the men, on exercise, fresh air, sanitation in all its standard forms. The men lived on the foods of the United Kingdom, supplemented by the fruit and garden produce of New Zealand. Now, as on their previous expedition, they had with them so much which they were used to that they ate comparatively little of what they had never learned to like, the lean and fat of penguins and seals. They apparently ate a good deal more on the second than on the first Scott expedition of fresh animal food, but clearly not as much as the Shackleton party had used, as can be seen from the sequel.

In 1911, as in 1902, they started their sledge travel after a winter of sanitation. On the first expedition the results had been disappointing; now they were tragic. Scurvy did not prevent them from reaching the South Pole, but it commenced to sap their strength in the early part of the return journey and progressed so rapidly that the growing weakness prevented them, if only by a few miles, from being able to get back to the final provision depot.

Those who have ignored the scurvy have sometimes claimed that if Scott had reached the depot he would have been able to make his way eventually to the base camp 150 miles away. This becomes more than doubtful when you realize that the progressive decrease of vigor, both mental and physical, was not going to be averted by even the largest meals, if those meals were of food lacking antiscorbutic value.

The story of Scott and his companions, especially through the last few weeks, is among the noblest in any language; through it they became national heroes and world heroes.

But in the speech of their countrymen (though not in many another European tongue), scurvy sounds unclean. It appeared necessary to Scott's surviving comrades, and to those in Britain who knew the truth, to take care that the tabooed word should not sully a glorious deed.

To suppress the association of an abhorred disease by playing up the beauty and heroism of Scott's death may have been worth while at the time; but it can scarcely be deplored by anyone, and must be praised by scientists, that Commander Edward R. G. R. Evans, later Admiral, Scott's second-in-command, after a time gave out the information about scurvy, including the statement that he himself had been afflicted.

It is irrational, at least now that emotions have calmed, to blame Scott. No one was to blame, for they all acted according to the light of their day. If anybody was to blame it was primarily those who gave medical advice to the expedition before it sailed; secondarily, it was the chief medical officer of the party, rather than the commanding officer.

It seems strange, now, that a comparison of the Scott and Shackleton experiences did not fully enlighten the doctors on the true inwardness of scurvy; but of course part of the explanation is that some of the Scott medical information was suppressed. Therefore, it remained for my own expeditions to demonstrate, so far as polar explorers are concerned, and for the Russell Sage studies to call to the attention of the medical profession, the most practical and only simple way of preventing and curing scurvy. For no matter how good the juice of limes (or lemons), it is difficult to carry in bulk; it deteriorates, whether in bulk or pill; and it may be lost as by a shipwreck. The thing to do is to find the antiscorbutics where you are, pick them up as you go.*

* This can be done in the Arctic, on sea and land, everywhere except on the Inland Ice of Greenland. In the Antarctic it can be done on the coasts, where penguins and seals abound, and are easier to secure than any beasts of the Far North; but it cannot be done there inland, for land game is wanting from the interior of the southern continent.

On my third expedition it happened, as circumstantially related in my book called *The Friendly Arctic*, that three men came down with scurvy through disobeying the instructions of the commander and living without his knowledge for two or three months chiefly on stored foods when they were supposed to be living chiefly on fresh meat.

It seems to take from one to three months for even a bad diet to produce easily recognizable scurvy. In the case of my men it was about three weeks (as they later thought) after they first noticed the trouble, and about ten days after they complained of it to me, when one of them had become so weak we had to carry him on a sledge, while the other was barely able to stagger along, holding on behind. By then every joint hurt, their gums were as soft as cheese, their teeth so loose that they came out with almost the gentlest of pulls.

We were sixty or eighty miles from land on drifting sea ice when the trouble started, and we hastened ashore to get a stable camp for the invalids, and made it in a week or so of sledging. It would have been no fun, with sick men on our hands, if an ice floe that was the site of our camp had started disintegrating under pressure, the fragments tumbling about, and drifting in various directions.

We reached an island, about 900 miles north of the Arctic Circle, the coast of which was known although the interior had never been explored. We traveled a few miles inland, established a camp, hunted caribou (there were two of us well, out of four), and began the all-meat cure. Fuel was pretty scarce, so we cooked only one meal a day; besides, I thought raw food might work better. We cooked the breakfast in a lot of water. The patients finished the boiled meat while it was hot, drank some of the broth warm and kept the remainder to drink cold during the rest of the day. For their other meals they ate slightly frozen raw meat, with normal digestion and good appetite. We divided up the caribou in ordinary Eskimo style, so the dogs got organs and entrails, hams, shoulders, and tenderloin, while the invalids and we hunters got heads, briskets, ribs, pelvis, and the marrow from the bones.

On this diet all pain and gloom disappeared within four days. Inside of a week both men said that they had no realization of being ill as long as they lay still abed. In two weeks they were able to begin traveling, at first riding on the sledges and walking alternately. At the end of a month they felt as if they had never been ill. No signs of the scurvy remained except that the gums, which had receded from the teeth, never quite regained their position.

By comparing notes later with Dr. Alfred Hess, mentioned previously as a leading New York authority on scurvy, I found that when I was getting these results with a diet from which all vegetable elements were absent, he was getting similar results in a similar length of time through a diet where the main reliance was upon grated raw vegetables and fruits and upon fresh fruit juices.

There is no doubt, as the quantitative studies have shown, that the percentage of Vitamin C, commonly looked upon as the scurvy-preventing factor, is higher in certain vegetable elements than in any meats. But it is equally true, for some reason or other, that if one has considerable fresh meat in his diet every day, and does not overcook it, there will be enough of whatever prevents scurvy to do the preventing.

It is clear, then, that if one lives exclusively on *fresh* meat he gets from it enough vitamins not only to prevent scurvy but, as I have said, to prevent all other deficiency diseases as well. We proceed to a consideration of whether it is essential that meat be fresh in order to have antiscorbutic values.

The article "Observations on Three Cases of Scurvy," mentioned already as published by me in the *Journal* of the American Medical Association in 1918, created a bit of a sensation within that limited circle which took it seriously. For I was in effect announcing that scurvy could be cured about as quickly and effectively by an all-meat diet, then supposed to have no curative value, as by a diet containing any or all of the recognized antiscorbutics, such as the juices of limes and lemons.

It was assumed by me at the time, and was no doubt taken for granted by most readers, that this cure was effected by the meat *because it was fresh*—that it could not have been effected had the meat been preserved by salting or drying. It is beginning to seem now that perhaps the cure might have been accomplished by using dehydrated meats—almost certainly not by salted meats, for nothing seems better established than the absence from them of qualities preventive in this disease.

The suggestion that dehydrated meat is a preventive of scurvy, or at least not provocative, is bound to seem reasonable to students of the frontier, particularly to those who specialize on the fur trade. For, in reading the source documents and the histories, one continually runs into such striking contrasts as those between coastal Hudson's Bay Company posts, where scurvy was troublesome, and inland posts where the disease was rare or absent.

Thus, preoccupied as most people have been the last twenty years with the idea that the near-worthlessness of lime juice in the sailing-ship days was due to its usually being too old, and that an antiscorbutic should be fresh in order to be effective, it has usually been assumed that the explanation of scurvy on the coast, against freedom from it inland, lay in the fact that cereals and salted meats brought from Europe were the chief foods at seaports, their place being taken by fresh meats in the interior.

But analysis of the historical records will tend to show, though it may not demonstrate fully, that if dehydrated meats were as conducive to scurvy as are porridge, bread and salted meats, then there should have been a good deal of scurvy in the interior of North America. For there were every now and then such periods of misfortune in the hunt or fishery that both Europeans and natives lived for months at a time with as little fresh meat to supplement their inland diet of pemmican and jerky as the coast dwellers had to supplement their imported salt meats and cereals.

On European preserved meats, bread and porridge, scurvy seems always to have developed if the period of deprivation from fresh meats lasted several months; in a corresponding spell of jerky and pemmican the scurvy appears never to have shown itself, or at any rate so seldom that the belief grew within the fur trade that salted meat was a cause and dried meat a cure. But this is a question to be developed hereafter, in the chapters on pemmican.

So far as I have been able to canvass the record for North and South America, scurvy appears to have been far less serious here, at the time of first exploration, than in Europe, the difference corresponding approximately to the lower agricultural status of the New World.

In Europe, scurvy may not have been unknown two thousand years ago. It seems to have increased steadily with that relative decrease in the importance of hunting, fishing and pastoral life which accompanied progress in the cultivation of cereals. About the worst scurvy centuries of northern Europe were, seemingly, the late Middle Ages and early modern times, when flesh foods became less and less common among the peasantry, with greater and greater dependence on porridge and bread, with doubtless also a parallel increase in the use of salt for the preservation of meats, as against an earlier custom of slaughtering animals when food was needed or of preserving meat by drying it.

Not By Bread Alone

The tendency in Britain and the rest of northern Europe toward increased scurvy was finally arrested and reversed by a growing dependence upon gardens as against grain fields. For there was a certain force in the medical doctrine that vegetables and fruits would prevent and cure scurvy; it was a salutary doctrine when applied at home, through the eating of one's own or a neighbor's garden produce, though of little worth when applied by the medical profession to the preserved juices of the lime and lemon that were often nearly or quite as well aged as the wines that were carried on long seafaring and exploring journeys.

In the extreme south of South America, on whichever side of Magellan Strait, there seems from the record to be no indication of scurvy, active or subclinical, as long as the people lived in native style. These groups were non-agricultural hunters, fishers and gatherers. There is no sign, indeed, of pre-white scurvy a long way northward, toward Brazil, at least so far as was discovered by research at Columbia University carried forward during two years, 1939-41, by Gitel Poznanski as a fellow in anthropology studying the lives of the hunting peoples of South America.

For northernmost North America the evidence that scurvy was formerly absent is equally clear from parallel Columbia University anthropological studies done in the same years by Dr. Natalie Joffe. No one appears ever to have reported true scurvy,* in the time of early exploration, from among

---

* As the Oxford Dictionary says, scurvy was sometimes used to mean scurfy, having scurfs or scabs, and was applied to diseases like the itch. Descriptions of this sort of scurvy do appear in some of the early northern records. For instance, in Samuel Hearne, *A Journey from Prince of Wales's Fort in Hudson's Bay to the Northern Ocean*, London, 1795, we find on pages 336-337: "A scorbutic disorder, resembling the worst stage of the itch . . . is never known to prove fatal. . . . In the younger sort it always attacks the hands and feet, not even sparing the palms and soles. Those of riper years generally have it about the wrists, insteps, and posteriors; and in the latter particularly, the blotches, or boils as they may justly be called, are often as large as the top of a man's thumb. This disorder most frequently

the Eskimos or the northern forest Indians. Its absence from native communities is frequently remarked upon by the explorers, particularly by those who were having trouble with it among their own crews.

When natives ate European food it became evident promptly that no racial immunity was involved; for Eskimos who went along as guides on polar expeditions, or took employment with miners in Alaska, came down with scurvy like the whites, Negroes, and South Sea Islanders who made up the rest of the parties. There was, in some cases, a specious appearance of racial immunity through instances where the rest had scurvy and the Eskimos did not; but analysis of the evidence shows that the difference was in the food used —the Eskimos, though eating to some extent with the miners, would now and then get a seal, or some other local animal, of which they would eat a larger share than the rest of the company.

At any rate it seems clear that scurvy was not as common among the Indians in any part of North America as it was among whites in most parts of Europe during the seventeenth and eighteenth centuries. During this period the Indians, although in some contact with the whites, still maintained largely their older food habits. Records which show scurvy among people living on native foods apparently go scarcely at all up into Canada, perhaps only through the Niagara peninsula and nearby parts of Ontario where diets were similar to those of the Iroquois of New York, who were to a considerable extent an agricultural people. From there southward scurvy records grow more and more common. They do not increase uniformly southward, by latitude, but are found in the more agricultural sections, depending thus on the state of culture of the natives and

makes its appearance in the Summer, while the Indians are out on the barren ground." Obviously this is not scurvy, in our sense of the word, but a disease so named by Hearne in the sense of scurfy, scabby.

upon geographic features other than mere distance north and south.

In primitive American agricultural communities scurvy was recognized as a disease connected with famine, which meant that it appeared when the hunting was bad and people were compelled to live in the main or wholly on stored-up cereals. There is, for instance, General de Trobriand's account of wintering in Dakota. I quote him first on scurvy among whites and then among Indians.

General Philippe Regis de Kerredern de Trobriand, son of one of Napoleon's generals, made his first trip to the United States in 1841. After several visits he came here to live. In 1861 he became colonel of a French regiment from New York and served through the War Between the States, about which he published *Four Years with the Army of the Potomac*, Boston, 1889, which is a translation of a work he wrote in the French language, published at Paris 1867-68. He was brigadier general and major general by brevet in the war but reverted to a colonelcy at its close. He served in Dakota from 1867 to 1869. His journal for this period was translated from the French by George Francis Will of Bismarck, North Dakota, and is published as one of the Lakeside Classics, Chicago, 1941.

It appears that General de Trobriand had the opinion, common among frontiersmen in this period, that scurvy could be prevented and cured by vegetables, whether they were fresh or not, and that it could be similarly prevented and cured by meat, but only if it were fresh. In illustration we quote from pages 263-264:

"Wednesday, April 8 [1868]: Yesterday in the afternoon died two of our men, one of heart trouble complicated by scurvy, the other of scurvy alone. This disease has noticeably weakened our little garrison during the winter and reached its maximum during the last month.

"At this time we have in the hospital thirty-two sick of

scurvy, and thirteen more are exempted from service with their companies, having only light attacks or being convalescent and on a diet. To this number must be added six employees of the quartermaster who are being treated at the hospital, which makes a total of fifty-one cases of scurvy, equal to a fourth of the garrison.

"This regrettable condition is the result of the long deprivation of fresh vegetables, and the infrequency of the rations of fresh meat which are distributed but twice a week.

"The principal food of the men consists of salt pork and salt fish; hence the sickness . . . Happily the trials are approaching a conclusion, thanks to the impending arrival of the steamboats and the fresh provisions which they carry."

The following year the scurvy was among the Indians. Quoting from page 355:

"Sunday, February 28 [1869]: Upon receiving news that an epidemic is declared to exist among my Berthold Indians, especially the Crees, I have sent Dr. Goddard to make sure of the fact and to identify the disease. He has returned this morning announcing that it was a matter of the scurvy which has made serious ravages during the past two weeks. Twenty or twenty-five of the Indians, mostly old people, have died of it and thirty-two are still sick with it. . . .

"The scurvy among them is a result of their privation and sufferings; they have suffered especially from cold and hunger, having nothing but a very little corn to sustain life."

In an earlier generation these Indians would likely have possessed stores of jerky and pemmican. But at de Trobriand's period meat was no longer to be had in quantity, for in 1869 the buffalo were gone and cattle had not as yet sufficiently replaced them. Cereals had replaced pemmican as the food stored against a time of scarcity.

9

The Nature and Early History
of Pemmican

PEMMICAN is controversial. An admiral of the United
States Navy has said it is the best concentrated food
known. He believes it to contain more nourishment per
ounce than any other complete food, and considers it to be
the only condensed ration upon which a man can maintain
his health and strength indefinitely, using it as the main dish
at every meal 365 days in the year. He adds that in twenty
years of use he and his men never tired of it. Yet nutritionists of the United States Navy are responsible for instructions that pemmican shall not be used in that service.

A general of the United States Army who used pemmican
and studied the history of its use through a century by fur
traders and pioneers, has said: "It formed a very palatable
as well as nutritious food"; but army dietitians reported
during World War II that they have tried it out, that it is
so unpalatable soldiers will not eat it, that men on this
food lose their strength in three days, that they become ill
from it, and that they will rather starve than eat it.

A number of scientists are on record that pemmican is
good in cold weather, unsuitable in hot climates. But Europeans first encountered this food invention of the Plains
Indians in the Texas-Missouri-Dakota-Manitoba sector,
where midsummer temperatures go above 120° in the shade
occasionally and above 100° frequently. Pemmican was there
chiefly a summer food—because it was a travel food, and
journeys were usually made in summer. Its most impressive
record as the exclusive diet, or nearly so, of large numbers

of men for long periods, is from transportation crews of the fur trade working twelve to eighteen hours a day and straight through the noon period with its scorching or steaming heat.

For British army use pemmican has been recommended as a standard ration by officers of long familiarity, with rank as high as major general; it has been recommended for United States Army use by officers of long pemmican experience, with rank up to brigadier general. But these recommendations have never been accepted by those in control of army commissariats in either Britain or the United States. So far as I know, the only army that formally approved this American invention for use in the Second World War was the German.

The extreme supporters of pemmican recommend it as the most concentrated food known to man, or possible within the modern concepts of physiological and chemical science. They say that it is a complete food in the sense that it will keep a hard-working man in top form for any length of time in any climate. They maintain, indeed, that it is the only concentrated food which ever has been tried out by large numbers of men for long periods and which has met these specifications. But those who oppose pemmican say that it is not a complete food, that it is not a wholesome food, that it is not capable of maintaining full health and strength indefinitely.

The advocates of pemmican say that it is as palatable as other standard foods, such as bread or roast beef. Those who oppose say that it is so unpalatable that this quality by itself would prevent its use.

There appears to be no disagreement among historians of the North American frontier that pemmican is among the most preservable of foods. Cases are on undisputed record where packages, shielded only by rawhide, were in good condition after ten, twenty and more years, without any preservative, such as salt, and without protection from

the rain of summer other than that given by the leather
covering—a premise being that the bags would be in such
position, as on a scaffolding, that they would have a chance
to dry out between showers. These preservability records are
chiefly from the Dakotas of the United States and from the
Prairie Provinces of Canada, thus from a climate suitable
for corn-wheat agriculture. Yet scientists, during World War
II, have stated that the control of enzyme action in pemmican is as yet an unsolved problem and that the food will
spoil rapidly unless canned.

Proponents say it is a great merit of pemmican that it
may be cooked but does not require cooking and that it is
good to eat under practically all conditions. Opponents say
that pemmican is never, properly speaking, fit to eat; consequently, its readiness for use is an irrelevant factor.

Pemmican seems to be the only food about which a war
has ever been fought in North America. At least it is the
only one to have a war named for it.

The Pemmican War of 1814-1821, although mainly in
Canada, spilled over into the United States, and reference
to it can be found in works such as the *Dictionary of American History*. The disputes between those who wanted to use
pemmican in the Second World War and those who were
determined it should not be used became so emotional, violent and broadly spread, at home and abroad, that it was
suggested we had a war within a war, the Second Pemmican
War within the Second World War.

All these are introductory statements, trying to forecast
what the shooting is all about in this row within the armed
forces and between the current dietitians. I shall document
the points as we go along.

It is considered that the first reference to pemmican by
a European is found in the account of the 1540-42 Coronado expedition into what is now the southwestern part
of the United States. We quote from the translation by the

historian and bibliographer George Parker Winship, in the 14th Annual Report of the Bureau of Ethnology of the Smithsonian Institution, Washington, 1896, pages 527-528: "They dry the flesh [of the buffalo] in the sun, cutting it thin like a leaf, and when dry they grind it like meal to keep it and make a sort of sea soup of it to eat. A handful thrown into a pot swells up so as to increase very much. They season it with fat, which they always try to secure when they kill a cow."

The published authorities (without any exception I have seen) speak of this as a reference to pemmican, and usually as the first reference to pemmican in the known literature. But on its surface the passage seems to fit more nearly pounded meat, an ingredient of pemmican which is described hereafter.

Nor can the first use of pemmican by its eventual chief patrons, the overland explorers and the fur traders, be determined to everyone's satisfaction. The favored man, place and date would seem to be Henry Kelsey, the present Saskatchewan district and the year 1691.

In his paper, *The Journal of Henry Kelsey,* presented to the Historical and Scientific Society of Manitoba, 24th May, 1928, Charles Napier Bell supposed that Kelsey was not merely the first white man to see the buffalo within the borders of what is now Canada but also the first to observe the making of pemmican from buffalo meat, perhaps the first to observe the making of any sort of pemmican.

The view that Kelsey was the first to use pemmican is seemingly adopted by Professor Arthur S. Morton, in his *History of the Canadian West to 1870-71,* who says: "Kelsey must have turned to spend the winter (1691-92) on the prairies north-east of Saskatoon, hunting buffalo to procure pemmican for the return journey, and trapping furs with the Assiniboins."

Thousands of Europeans used pemmican during the exploration and colonization stages of North America. Of these only a few kept diaries that have been preserved to us; a still smaller number wrote books. I cite testimony gathered from these published and unpublished documents, quoting chiefly men whose standing is widely recognized, men who are known as dependable witnesses in general and who should therefore be reliable in the particular case now before us, the debate concerning the advantages and drawbacks of this food. But first I must describe and define, to show what the witnesses are testifying about.

However, before quoting the definitions and descriptions of the standard authorities, let me emphasize what some of them merely imply, that in the way the Indians and early whites looked on pemmican it had only two ingredients, lean and fat; any others were considered accidental and extraneous, such as hairs and fragments of bone, or else as flavoring, which latter with the Indians was dried berries and with the early whites might be salt, raisins, sugar, etc. At the height of pemmican's use by whites, around 1820, from 1 per cent to 5 per cent of it will have been of the flavored or holiday sort, the cake variant of the "bread of the wilderness."

The Merriam Webster dictionary, 1939 edition, gives as the first definition: "Among the North American Indians, lean buffalo meat or venison cut in thin slices, dried in the sun, pounded fine, mixed with melted fat, and packed in sacks of hide." For a second definition Webster has: "Also, a similar preparation, as of dried beef, suet, raisins, and sugar, used by explorers, etc."

From these definitions Webster derives a third: "Hence, information or thought condensed into little compass."

Perhaps not wholly because the dictionary is more voluminous, but rather because the word made a stronger impression on the British, there is a longer and more detailed account of pemmican in the Oxford.

That the British were so impressed with pemmican was perhaps because among the leading families a favorite investment of the eighteenth and nineteenth centuries was in shares of the Hudson's Bay Company; and the success of the Company, as is explained hereafter, depended to a considerable extent on pemmican.

A saying of wide use in the United States was "The only good Indian is a dead Indian"; for the colonists wanted to farm, and both the Indian hunter and the animals he hunted were in the farmer's way. To the Hudson's Bay Company, which then controlled most of what is now Canada and part of what is now the United States, the only good Indian was a live Indian, for he hunted, trapped and sold furs to the Company. For business success, if for no other reason, they had to keep the Indian alive, which made it necessary to store up food in a good year against the scarcity of a bad one. So when game was plenty they encouraged the Indians to sell them as much pemmican as possible, which they accumulated in the post storerooms—to be sold back to the Indians, in due course, at a profit.

The stockholders of the Company were in the main the nobility and gentry of Britain. They were travelers, readers of books, students of what it was that made the Company's stock such a good investment; so they naturally became pemmican-conscious. The explorers of wild North America were much bigger heroes in remote England than practically at home in Virginia, New England or eastern Canada. Books on or by the great pioneers, like Samuel Hearne who discovered the Coppermine, Alexander Mackenzie who discovered the Mackenzie, John Franklin, the tragic hero, and many another, were printed in England and widely read. Even following the Louisiana Purchase, United States explorers, like Lewis and Clark, were more eagerly published and more widely read beyond the Atlantic than in their own country.

This, I imagine, or something like it, is back of the long
and interesting discussion of pemmican which appears in
the Oxford Dictionary:

"Pemmican, sb. Also pemican. (a. Cree *pimecan, pimekan,*
f. *pime* fat.)

"A preparation made by certain North American Indians,
consisting of lean meat, dried, pounded, and mixed with
melted fat, so as to form a paste, and pressed into cakes;
hence, beef similarly treated, and usually flavoured with
currants or the like, for the use of arctic explorers, travellers,
and soldiers, as containing much nutriment in little bulk,
and keeping for a long time.

"*1801* Sir A. Mackenzie *Voy. St. Lawrence* Pref. 121 The
provision called Pemican, on which the Chepewyans and
other savages in the N. of America chiefly subsist in their
journeys. *1827* Chronin *Ann. Reg.* 58/1 Pannican, a concentrated essence of meat dryed by a fire of oak and elm wood,
so as to reduce 6 lb. of the best beef to 1 lb. *1835* Longf.
Hiaw. xi. 31 Then on pemican they feasted, Pemican and
buffalo marrow. *1869* E. A. Parkes *Pract. Hygiene* (ed. 3) 245
The Pemmican of the arctic voyagers is a mixture of the best
beef and fat dried together.

"*b. Fig.* Extremely condensed thought, or literary matter
containing much information in a few words.

"*1870* Huxley *Lay Serm.* xii. (1874) 257 A sort of intel-
lectual pemmican. *1888 Spectator* 8 Sept. 1211/2 It (Sir F.
Bramswell's Address) is really a wonderful specimen of
thought and knowledge, reduced to pemmican.

"*c. attrib. 1831 Westm. Rev.* XIV 441 Who will . . . give
us a chance . . . of . . . getting rid of the soup and pemmican
diet we have so long been doomed to. *1895 Daily News* 1 Oct.
5/7 Their big pemmican cache, 124 miles distant. 1900
Athenaeum 8 Dec. 749/2 A certain tendency to what may be
described as the pemmican style.

"Hence *Pemmican v. Trans.,* to condense, compress,

'squeeze.' So *pemmicanize* v.; whence *pemmicanization. 1837* T. Hook *Jack Brag* vi. As if he had seen all the daemons of the Hartz Forest pemmican'd into one plump lady. *1839*— in *New Monthly Mag.* LV. 1 So elaborated a history . . . which . . . might be Pemmicaned into a comparatively few pages. *1892 Pall Mall G.* 1 Sept. 3/2 The modern man is rarely inclined to read his history in many volumes. He much prefers it pemmicanized. *1901 Westm. Gaz.* 16 Dec. 4/2 What one may call the era of the Pemmicanization of life is rapidly approaching."

The *Encyclopaedia Britannica,* 14th edition, says:

"PEMMICAN. A North American Indian (Cree) word for a meat prepared in such a way as to contain the greatest amount of nourishment in the most compact form. As made by the Indians it was composed of the lean parts of the meat, dried in the sun, and pounded or shredded and mixed into a paste with melted fat."

In spite of these definitions there occurs now and then as the literature is studied a confusion of terms. So we build up our own definitions and descriptions.

The first step in the making of pemmican, as correctly given by the dictionaries and the Britannica, is that the lean is sliced thin and dried. To make the drying effective, all fat should be removed. The lean is then about what is called "biltong" in South Africa and "jerky" throughout the Americas, except that these (especially jerky) may sometimes have more or less fat adhering.

With most of the pemmican the drying was by sun and wind, so the speed and effectiveness of the process depended on season and climate. In regions of cold winters, for instance the Mackenzie valley, one might perhaps speak of frost-drying. If at temperatures varying from 30° to 60° below zero a wet handkerchief is suspended from a tree, it dries in something between three and ten days, the lower the temperature the slower the drying. Thus, if thin slices of lean were hung up in winter, under such conditions, they would dry eventually; but the time required would be several weeks, even months if the pieces were at all thick. There would be the advantage in winter of no danger from maggots or decay.

In a rainy season, or if there was great hurry, the drying might be done over a slow fire. This was the method of the British when they came to make pemmican at home for the use of their soldiers, sailors and explorers.

Sometimes in a wet season meat was suspended within the teepee and became smoked incidentally. There were sections of North America where smoking was deliberate, as part of the drying, most likely in places where the climate was damp.

The next pemmican step was to pound the dried lean into shreds—with a wooden mallet on a wooden block, or on a stone, or with a stone hammer on wood or stone. To catch all the shreds and powder, a buffalo or other hide was spread out and upon it was laid the stone or wooden block that formed the anvil.

At this stage we have what the Hudson's Bay Company referred to as pounded meat. It was stored in bags of any sort, usually suspended within the teepee or warehouse. If kept outdoors it would be shielded from the rain by leather tarpaulins.

Next came the making of special rawhide bags for the pemmican. The hide was that of the animal which was being used, buffalo with buffalo meat, caribou with caribou meat. The buffalo bag was about the size of one of our pillow cases, with the hair out. When filled it was supposed to weigh ninety pounds; the actual weight usually ran from eighty to a hundred pounds, with the average not far from ninety.

The bag prepared, the Indian would fill it lightly and fluffily with shredded lean, somewhat as we fill a pillow with feathers. Suet was then tried out and, in some cases at

least, was brought to the temperature used in frying doughnuts. This very liquid fat was poured into the bag so that
it percolated everywhere, a film of it covering every shred
of lean.

According to some descriptions, it appears that the fat
was barely liquid. In that case a small amount of shredded
lean would be put in the bag, a small amount of fat poured
on it, and the whole stirred; then there would be a second
layer of pounded meat and a second of fat, and so on till the
bag was full.

In still other cases the fat, also barely liquid, was kneaded
with the pounded meat in a bowl somewhat as bread dough
is handled in making loaves. Handfuls of the resulting mixture were then stuffed into the bags.

The sack filled, its mouth was sewed up and the seams
were rubbed with tallow to seal them. Then, before the fat
became hard, the bag was flattened out by trampling upon
it, or through some other form of pressure, to the ordinary
thickness of six or seven inches.

When the fat had set thoroughly the bags were piled up
like cordwood, the lowest layer being kept from the ground
by stones or pieces of wood.

Such a bag was known as a *piece* of pemmican, and was
looked upon as of convenient weight for back-packing. It
became the practice of the Hudson's Bay Company to divide
any goods that were to be carried by men on their backs
over mountains, river portages, etc., into parcels of ninety
pounds, so that eventually the word "piece" came to mean a
weight of ninety pounds, and might consist in goods of any
nature that were transported by canoe and portage in summer or by dog sled in winter. As has been said, most of the
journeys of the eighteenth- and early nineteenth-century fur
trade were made in summer.

It is the belief of some writers that pemmican was originally a military invention, used by Indian scouts and raid-

ing parties where each man had to carry his own food that would suffice for many days, and where it was necessary that provisions be light for easy and rapid travel. Pemmican had as well the other most necessary qualities of a military ration, that it would keep under practically any condition and that it could be eaten without building a fire, the smoke of which would be visible to the enemy by day, as the flame would by night.

However, pemmican was also to the Indian a food that could be preserved from a season of plenty to one of scarcity. This, as is dwelt upon hereafter, became an important though secondary feature of its use in the fur trade of the Plains.

The idea that pemmican would last five years, which is encountered frequently in the writings, would seem to derive from a usual practice of the fur traders to keep buying pemmican from the Indians through four or five successive years; then they were likely to quit buying on the score of having in their storehouses by then a large enough stock to take care of the next famine.

Although the expression "will keep good five years" is frequent in the books, there are also numerous references to pemmican which was ten or twenty years old and still in excellent condition.

The reason why pemmican kept good indefinitely was, first, because the water had been dried out of the lean so that, as long as it remained dry, it was preserved on the principle of mummification. Every lean particle had a coating of fat, which protected it from moisture and from the air. The rawhide of which the bag was made had the same preservability that is found in vellum manuscripts, some of which are a thousand or more years old and still of good appearance in libraries. Air could not penetrate this rawhide, partly because the inside of it at least was greased. Air would not come through the seams, for they were proofed by essentially the method that frontier housewives have used with preserve jars, which they sealed with tallow when they did not have wax.

Quite apart from all the theoretical explanations, we have the clear fact, attested by witnesses from every decade of 150 years, and from a number of different North American climates, that pemmican remains for ten, twenty, thirty years as good as the day it was made—if once properly made.

Because it was easy to keep and to carry, pemmican was an important commercial item before the time of the whites, and Indian tribes that did not make it came from afar to buy. This trade was barter, of course; sometimes dried salmon and other fish pemmicans, made on or near the Pacific coast, were exchanged for jerky and for pemmican made of buffalo, elk, moose or caribou farther east. The fish pemmican was a soft paste in bags, for the fat was an oil. It was not exclusively a West Coast product. We have records of fish pemmican from the Lake Winnipeg country, from Hudson Bay and elsewhere.

Four main grades or sorts are recognized in the literature, winter and summer pemmican, plain and berry pemmican. There was also "fine" pemmican.

Winter pemmican was made in the autumn, a difficult season for drying meat. Accordingly, winter pemmican might or might not be of lean that was dry enough to keep indefinitely. Since the Indians did not usually travel much in winter, weight did not greatly matter; nor did keeping qualities, for the chill of the weather would act as a preservative.

What the narratives of exploration and the fur trade speak of as bad pemmican, spoiled pemmican, etc., was usually winter pemmican that had been kept into the summer.

Summer pemmican was made in the spring or summer and was the kind described above, in which six pounds of fresh lean were dried down to about a pound of jerky. By the usual half-and-half relation of dehydrated lean to rendered fat, a pound of summer pemmican represented three pounds of fresh lean to which had been added half a pound of suet.

Plain pemmican, whether summer or winter, had no components but fat and lean. Berry pemmican differed in that it was flavored with dried fruit of some sort, in the early days usually with choke cherries or saskatoon berries. Most authors seem to think that this flavored kind was in use by the Indians before European contact; but some writers have suggested that the inclusion of berries may have been upon European initiative, an attempt by the whites to make it resemble more nearly foods to which they were used, such as plum duff.

Within historic time Europeans have never been exclusive meat eaters; but seemingly they would have liked to be. For it appears from the social history of Europe that meat was the admired food; the trouble was that it was usually hard to come by. In medieval times only a few of the nobility and gentry had as much meat as they would have liked. It is a commonplace of the literature in the late Middle Ages and early modern times that the best food was meat. Reference is made elsewhere to the diary entry of Pepys that he had a sumptuous fine dinner of seven courses, six of which were meat and the seventh meat and cheese. That was the kind of dinner those had who could manage it.

Only a few of the Europeans, however, were nobility and gentry. The rest lived on bread, porridge and garden produce. The child of the commoner grew to maturity liking these foods, for they were the ones to which he was used.

The Europeans who settled North America were chiefly commoners, and so had an inherited taste for bread and porridge. On the Atlantic seaboard, as in Europe, cereals and garden foods were abundant and therefore cheap; so the transplanted Europeans who came in touch with pemmican on the Western plains were men who liked bread and porridge, pie and cake, fruit and garden vegetables. In order to make pemmican seem a little more like what they were used to, they would blend it with fruits or cereals; alternatively, they would use it as they customarily used meat, along with bread, potatoes, things of that sort.

The balance of opinion seems to be that the Indians did have berry pemmican originally, and that they looked upon it not as a standard food but as a special dish for celebrations or to entertain a visitor.

Through the combined force of Europeans wanting foods more nearly like what they were used to and the slowly developing notion that diets ought to be varied, there began the practice of using berry pemmican as a standard ration. An early account of this is in the narratives of the search for Sir John Franklin, about the middle of the nineteenth century, when large quantities of pemmican were made in England, some of it sweetened with sugar, some flavored with raisins or currants, some with both sugar and dried fruit. This was for the use of British sailors and other members of the expeditions not previously familiar with pemmican.

There is no definite evidence as to when commercial makers first began to blend with cereals, but this practice was not favored prior to about 1900. Admiral Peary was, for instance, badly annoyed when he found that a dealer had pawned off on him an article that contained pea meal as an ingredient. Whether this was before or after the turn of the century is beyond determination, but in *Secrets of Polar Travel*, published in 1917, Peary refers to one of his expeditions * without dating it, and then says:

"On a still later expedition I was persuaded to purchase some so-called pemmican of a foreign make. This, after I had sailed and it was too late to remedy the error, I found to be largely composed of pea-flour."

The introduction of ingredients like pea meal was, then,

* Peary's expeditions began in 1886 and closed in 1909.

for three reasons: People like what they are used to, and most Europeans are used to a certain amount of cereals; there was a growing belief in the advantage of variety, and variety is increased if a cereal is added to meat; and, finally, there was coming in the theory, discussed elsewhere, that "fat burns only in the flame of the carbohydrates," meaning that the fat element of pemmican could not be utilized unless there was along with the fat enough carbohydrate to do the "burning."

There were plain pemmicans that varied according to the care in the making, and according to the sort of fat used. If it was to be the best kind, fine pemmican, one would be very careful to pick out and remove from the pounded meat any pieces of tendon or fragments of bone, and might even assort the lean, putting into one batch only the finely shredded portion and the fine powder. Thus fine pemmican was plain pemmican made with the greatest care, with the best lean ground fine and with the best fat, usually marrow fat.

It is not in the literature but can safely be inferred that fine pemmican must have had the disadvantage of not keeping so well; for fat grows rancid more quickly the softer it is.

The necessary detailed information as to the keeping qualities of the various buffalo fats, even as to what the Plains Indians believed, is not available. The Eskimos of northwestern Canada believe, for the caribou, that the fats which resist rancidity best are from the kidneys and from the "back slab," the layer on the back that extends from the horns to the tail and a little way down along the flanks. Kidney fat is the hardest. Less hard is the fat from the ribs and brisket. Softest of all, and most easily "spoiled," is the marrow fat.

If in commercial manufacture it is desired to make full use of a merit of pemmican considered important in the olden days, that it would keep for years under almost any conditions, it will be necessary to study what sort of fat to use. Butter and lard become rancid easily and they are messy to handle. Some form of tallow would be used, certainly. It is probable that from this angle the best of all would be mutton tallow, since the harder the fat the less subject it is to rancidity. Then many nowadays dislike greasy food, or think they do, and butter and lard are more greasy than tallow. The kidney tallow of sheep will be the driest, the least greasy, and is about the most nearly tasteless of domestic animal fats.

However, rendered beef kidney suet, which to many is the most agreeable of the beef fats, may be the practical ingredient for commercial pemmican. It also keeps well. Some pemmican made with it, and canned on the theory that it might otherwise grow rancid, was opened by Colonel E. W. Wentworth of Armour and Company in the summer of 1943 and kept open in a desk drawer of his Chicago office, subject to increase and decrease of steam heat as well as to seasonal and daily changes of weather. After nearly a year it was still perfect in July of 1944. In my own New York place a can of the same pemmican was open two years, from 1943 to 1945, without developing rancidity or suffering any other deterioration which could be detected.

Butter or lard, so processed that they would be as hard as the tallows and no more greasy, could be used. But there is at present dispute as to the digestibility of at least some of the chemically hardened fats.

That pemmican rightly made will keep indefinitely under almost any conditions, is testified by many. However, this meaning is usually taken solely by inference, from the trend of a narrative, as when it is said that so many pieces were left at a certain place under certain conditions and were picked up so many years later and used. One of the first of the explicit testimonies is that of the famous Alexander Henry, the younger, whose journals are published in the three-volume *New Light on the Early History of the Greater Northwest,* New York, 1897, as edited by Elliott Coues.

For the passage quoted below, it is necessary to keep in mind the climate of North Dakota, especially as to temperatures. According to *Climate and Man,* of the United States Department of Agriculture, one of the most interesting books that has been published by our government, the hottest day ever recorded in the State of North Dakota reached 122° in the shade; there are few years which do not see 105°, and probably no summers that do not reach 100° somewhere in the region. The most humid section of the State is the Red River valley, and Henry, writing in December, is speaking of pemmican that had been stored over the summer of 1803 near Pembina, right at the river:

"I had a few bags remaining from last spring, which had been lying all summer in a heap covered with a leathern tent, and never had been stirred or turned, in a damp storehouse. I was apprehensive it was spoiled, from the complaints made by my friends about the bad quality of the Lower Red River pemmican, but surprised to find every bag excellent. This was clear proof to me that the bad pemmican must have come from another quarter—I suspect Portage la Prairie, as I am confident my method of mixing and preparing it is good."

The explanation here given for "bad pemmican" runs through nearly or quite every fur trade account of spoiled pemmican—that it had been carelessly made, or that it had been made with deliberate intent to cheat through leaving water in, so that it would bring more when sold by the pound. Sometimes the explanation was that winter pemmican had been misrepresented to be summer pemmican.

Most inventions, even the ones considered epoch-making, like mechanical flight, are arrived at by a combination of previously known facts and principles, so that the patent office sometimes has difficulty in showing that the greatest inventions are inventions at all. This would have been the case with pemmican, had there been a patent office to which rival claimants from among the Plains Indians could have submitted their evidence.

The drying of lean meat is the initial step in the invention, and this stride was probably first taken by nature without the assistance of man. For meat that clings to bones of animals which have been devoured by wolves, and, indeed, small animal bodies (as a fish thrown up on the beach or a squirrel that dies among the branches of a tree) may be entirely or partly so dehydrated, whether by slow drying through the intense cold of a long northern winter or quick drying in a hot desertlike climate of summer, that the preservation will be indefinite, a natural mummification. When there is skin on the mummified meat another step in the pemmican invention has been taken—the protection which dry rawhide gives through shedding rain and at least partly excluding oxygen.

Accordingly, the basic invention—called "jerky" through the Americas, "biltong" in Africa, and by the equivalent of "dried meat" in the languages of many peoples—is ancient and of worldwide use.

A second long step toward pemmican would come about through the toughness and hardness of jerky. Lean meat dry enough to last even in a damp and warm climate is so hard that it is slow and difficult to chew with the best of teeth; it is particularly unsuitable for young children who do not as yet have their teeth, and for old people who have lost them. The natural answer was pounding the meat. At first this was, no doubt, usually done with individual pieces just before eating. Later it would be found practical to make quantities of pounded meat and to store it in bags or boxes.

But anyone who tries it will discover that pounded meat is dry and difficult to swallow, while if pinches of it are dipped into water the result is a rather tasteless food. The flavor and feel in the mouth are much better if wads of pounded meat are dipped into melted fat or into a fat that is liquid by nature, as a vegetable or animal oil. Accordingly, it is a universal practice that people dip the shredded lean into fat before placing in the mouth. The next best thing is to bite off small pieces of suet, tallow, butter, or whatever fat is available, to mix in the mouth with the shredded lean as it is chewed.

The dipping of pounded meat into fat at meals would naturally lead a housewife to prepare dishes where the fat and lean were already mixed. If not finished at a given meal, this would harden into a cake, and that would be pemmican. At the next meal it might be warmed up to its original softness, or it might be used cold, somewhat like our hunks of bread or slabs of eating chocolate.

The final step in the invention would be to make the pemmican in quantity and to save it not against the next meal but against the next journey or a future year of bad hunting. So the Plains Indians made it in quantity, placed it in rawhide bags, and stored it by protecting it from dogs and damp. It was not always considered necessary to shield the pile of bags from a rain storm, for the rawhide covers were waterproof and their wet outsides would dry off during the next clear spell. The minimum protection needed was the presence of stones or sticks underneath the lowest tier of bags, to keep them out of the mud.

From the point of view of a traveler, pemmican has a series of advantages over jerky and suet, or pounded meat and suet, that are kept separately but in practice are eaten together.

Jerky has the disadvantage that, although the lean has been reduced to one-sixth of its former weight, the bulk has not been reduced by nearly as much. For when strips of dried meat are tied into bundles the pieces will not fit smoothly against each other; there are wide open spaces between, as with a bundle of corrugated tree bark.

Another difficulty of jerky is that, although it will shed the water of a quick rain shower, it is not exactly waterproof. It will absorb moisture gradually, even from damp air, thus gaining in weight and bulk while at the same time it becomes susceptible to mold and decay. The difficulties with pounded meat are worse. It is still more bulky than the jerky from which it was made. It is less water-resistant and spoils even more easily.

Where prices are mentioned in connection with the fur trade, jerky is never quoted at more than half the pemmican rate per pound; but the tallow that was eaten with the jerky was sometimes priced as high as the pemmican itself. For it was a commonplace that jerky alone is not a complete food —there had to be fat with it if in a hunting country or cereals with it when agricultural products were substituted. Now and then a writer says explicitly, and the same is frequently implied, that no one would eat jerky if pemmican were available, unless to save the pemmican.

Still, many writers of the frontier are loud in praise of jerky in comparison with European preserved meats. One of these is Professor James Frank Dobie of the University of Texas, author of historical and other books on the early Southwest. After disclaiming special knowledge of pemmican, thus implying he has had no personal experience with it, he says in a letter of August 7, 1944: "Nothing will stay with a man longer than sun-dried beef. This packer-prepared 'chipped beef' is moonshine compared to good old jerky."

Pemmican combines all the advantages that jerky and pounded meat have over fresh or salt-preserved meat. It is less bulky than the separate tallow and jerky from which it is made. It is waterproof in itself. It excludes air through its own nature and, especially when protected by rawhide, is proof against weather and bacteria under most conditions of handling and of climate. It is easy to chew because the lean has been shredded and the shreds have been combined with fat.

That pemmican is a complete food, maintaining full
health and strength indefinitely, the Indians had doubtless
known for centuries before the Europeans first borrowed it
and made it their bread of the wilderness, the cornerstone of
success in exploring and developing the interior of this
continent.

The chief deterrent to the use of pemmican has always
been its costliness, in labor and time. The only lean suitable
was that which was so free of tendons and connective tissue
that it would powder or shred easily, and the process was so
long that some early writers say it required two buffalo to
feed the Indian's family and dogs while they made a single
piece of pemmican, ninety pounds. The common figure is
that a buffalo, weighing perhaps 1,000 pounds on the hoof,
would make one piece.

Naturally, then, pemmican was used only at feasts, on
journeys, or in time of famine. The food cheapest, as measured by the labor required, was eaten first. This was meat
that was fresh, either because recently killed or through frost
preservation. Next in order came jerky and pounded meat,
each supplemented with fat taken separately, as has been
described. The longest hoarded, last to be eaten, was the
pemmican.

In that pioneer movement of the nineteenth century which
colonized the middle and west of the United States and Canada, it was first the explorer, then the fur trader, last the
stock rancher and plowman. In the first and second of these
stages pemmican was a large factor, so that its nature, use
and influence are of consequence to those historians who
devote themselves to discovery and settlement. It is the frontier historians, then, who study the role of pemmican.

One of these historians, author of *The Year of Decision,
1846,* and many other books and articles that deal with the
early history of the Plains and the Rockies, is Bernard De
Voto, a Harvard man born in Utah and thus presumably

combining an understanding of East and West. Replying to
a questionnaire on pemmican, he wrote July 26, 1944, a
letter, some of which is used here, another part later:

"My notions about pemmican are . . . those of a layman
who has studied the plains Indians and more especially the
white trappers and traders, the mountain men, for a good
many years. Such as they are, I'm glad to set them forth. I
wanted to write to you a good many years ago, when your
experiments with an exclusively meat diet were published,
for it seemed to me that the history of the West confirmed
you up to the hilt. . . .

"Pemmican is by far the best concentrated food I've ever
heard about in detail. The only other one in American history that appears to have had any merit is the one, variously
named, which was made from pulverized parched corn. . . .
But it clearly was nothing to use steadily and it clearly caused
flatulence and digestive disorders. Absolutely certainly, pemmican was infinitely better.

"I should say that the historical evidence for pemmican is
overwhelming. A food used so universally and over so long a
period and by so many different kinds and conditions of
people must have been an excellent food. . . .

"[Pemmican] was by far the favorite meat of the (white)
mountain men, who except for a couple of weeks a year,
were exclusively meat eaters. . . . As soon as soldiers and
emigrants come into the West, they highlight the normal
good health of the trappers by developing dozens of ailments
—ailments that the trappers never suffer from. . . .

"Well, a good part of the time they were not living on
fresh meat. They regularly stopped to 'make meat' whenever
they encountered a buffalo herd. That is, they dried it, by
sun if possible, by gentle smoking if the weather happened
to be bad. My impression is that the trappers did not often
stop to make pemmican themselves, but they traded for it
very eagerly whenever they found Indians who had it, and

the Indians seem to have made pemmican almost as regularly
as they dried meat. . . .

"It is certain that both Indians and trappers lived on dried
meat or pemmican for very long stretches at a time, for
stretches repeated so often that in sum they amounted to a
very considerable fraction of every year. It is equally certain
that both Indians and trappers greatly preferred pemmican
to merely dried meat."

I find by a canvass of the literature that, as frontier historian, De Voto speaks for his craft. So it may appear that
there is need for no further witness. But there is need; for
we are discussing an American food invention which is now
so far forgotten by most of our countrymen, as to its origin,
nature and history, that many think it a food useful only in
cold weather and chiefly in polar exploration, if they have
heard of it at all. Therefore I supplement the presentation
of a historian, who has approached his subject more from
the human point of view, by quoting a biologist whose chief
interest was not in the men who used the pemmican but in
the animal that formerly produced it, the buffalo.

William Temple Hornaday (1854-1937), zoologist, was in
his later years director of the New York Zoological Park. He
was author of several books and lengthy reports, one of the
most important of which is *The Extermination of the American Bison, With a Sketch of Its Discovery and Life History.*
Later reissued separately, this work was first published by the
United States National Museum in its report for 1887. I
quote from page 447:

"Out of the enormous waste of good buffalo flesh one
product stands forth as a redeeming feature—pemmican.
Although made almost exclusively by the half-breeds and
Indians of the Northwest, it constituted a regular article of
commerce of great value to overland travelers, and was much
sought for as long as it was produced. Its peculiar 'staying
powers,' due to the process of its manufacture, which yielded

a most nourishing food in a highly condensed form, made it of inestimable value to the overland traveler who must travel light or not at all."

The study of the buffalo, from which this has been quoted, deals with the animal from Mexico City on the south to Great Slave Lake on the north. Hornaday is therefore not thinking in terms of winter, for there is little winter in some of the country he is discussing.

It is part of the history of the North American frontier that meat has been used to take the place of bread ceremonially as well as dietetically, and this would naturally happen also with that preparation from meat which is called pemmican.

In the famous Papal brief of 1492, doubtless written before the Pope heard about the return of Columbus from his West Indies voyage of that year, Alexander VI bewails the sorry straits of the church beyond the Atlantic, in Greenland; * for he possessed reliable information that among all the churches in this most remote of bishoprics there was only one corporal suitable for the celebration of the mass (doubtless the Pope thought of parchment or fur as unsuitable); and the poor people, having no grain in their whole country, had been forced to substitute dried fish and milk for bread and wine.

The Pope is not explicit, and it is possible to interpret the reference to mean that he is sorry the Greenlanders have to use dried fish and milk for food in place of bread and wine; but the whole tenor of the letter is that he worries over the spiritual rather than the mundane welfare of these remote Christians, and so he has been understood to deplore

---

* The Pope does not state, but historical sources, confirmed by archaeology, make it known that there were along the coast between Cape Farewell and the present Godthaab district sixteen churches, a monastery and a nunnery under a single bishopric, the seat of which was in the present Julianehaab district. For discussion, and for the text of this Papal brief, see *Greenland* by V. Stefansson, New York, 1942.

the inadequacy of the symbolism where fish and milk instead of bread and wine are used in the sacrament to represent the body and blood of Our Lord.

This document of 1492, published by the Vatican in connection with the Chicago World's Fair of 1892, is considered to embody the first known reference to the use of the flesh of animals in the New World to take the place of bread in sacraments of the Roman Catholic Church. As I have said, fur trade journals and other records speak of pemmican as "the bread of the wilderness," and this resemblance in use—indeed also a resemblance to black or brown bread in appearance—logically appealed as much to the early missionary as to the early merchant.

Perhaps not so very sound linguistically but of historical significance is the contention that the word "pembina," usually considered to be from the same root as "pemmican," meant "sacred bread"; for this harks back to the importance of pemmican to the early missionaries of the Plains country, chiefly Roman Catholic and usually French, and to their acceptance of pemmican as the frontier equivalent of bread.

After descanting upon this interpretation of "pembina" in connection with the trading post of Pembina, the "Pemmican Capital of the Fur Country," Linda M. Slaughter says in "Leaves from Northwestern History," published in the first volume of the Collections of the State Historical Society of North Dakota:

"In the absence of bread, the priests who came from Minnesota and Canada before the establishment of missions on this side of the line,* to accompany the half-breeds and natives on their annual hunts, used . . . pemmican as a substitute for bread in the administration of the sacrament of holy communion while out on the prairies."

In this quotation Mrs. Slaughter deals with the period

---

* "This side of the line" is an expression locally common in North Dakota and means, south of the United States-Canada boundary.

around and after 1800 in that section of present United States territory, the Red River Valley of Minnesota and North Dakota, which suffered together with the Prairie Provinces of Canada the bloody turbulence of the Pemmican War, which started in 1814.

10

The First Pemmican War

WE OVERSIMPLIFY when we say that the War Between the States was fought over slavery; it remains true that slavery was an important issue, though perhaps not the main one. We oversimplify, too, when we follow the historians and speak of the bloody seven-year feud of 1814-21 between the North West Company and the Hudson's Bay Company as the Pemmican War. More broadly it was a struggle between a legally entrenched London corporation, which gained access to North America's fur territories through Hudson Bay, and a Montreal corporation, or group of affiliated traders, who secured their wares from Europe through the Gulf of St. Lawrence.

Some consider that the North West Company, founded with Yankee participation at Montreal in the winter of 1783-4, was the first true organization of Big Business along modern lines, at least the first in North America, and that what followed was a competition between this new kind of force and an old-fashioned, chartered company that was, to an extent, an agency or extension of the British government. For the Hudson's Bay Company had many non-commercial rights, including, under certain conditions, the power of life and death.

The Company was not supposed to hang a man just because he was competing with it; but the belief is general that some who were punished, after due trial, suffered not so much for the crime with which they were technically charged as for having interfered with the trading privileges of the Company.

At the instance of a group of nobility and merchants,

under the formal leadership of his nephew Prince Rupert, King Charles II in 1670 had granted a charter to "The Governor and Company of Adventurers of England trading into Hudson's Bay." This document gave to the Company "the sole trade and commerce of all these seas, straits, bays, rivers, lakes, creeks, and sounds, in whatsoever latitude they shall be, that lie within the entrance of the straits, commonly called Hudson's Straits, together with all the lands and territories upon the countries, coasts and confines of the seas, bays, lakes, rivers, creeks and sounds aforesaid," and it set forth "that the said land be from henceforth reckoned and reputed as one of our Plantations or colonies in America, called Rupert's Land."

The Company's domain, Rupert's Land, was never exactly defined; or, rather, it was defined frequently and in a number of different ways. A minimum description is that the charter gave rights in the territory that drained into Hudson Bay. This would include much of what are now Quebec and Ontario, and westward nearly south to Lake Superior, with a projection into what is now the United States to cover the Minnesota-Dakota part of the Red River drainage; and then the valleys of the Saskatchewan-Nelson system to the Rocky Mountains, and of the Churchill and Thelon Rivers, draining most of northeastern Canada. The Company's territory was, in fact, much larger than this, for it had posts as far southwest as California and as far northwest as the center of Alaska. It took in the valley of the Mackenzie and eventually all of northern Canada, including many of the Canadian islands. However, some of this northern expansion took place after the Company had retreated from the extreme southwest and northwest, from California and Alaska. It did not finally surrender its powers as a quasi-government to the Dominion of Canada until 1869.

In addition to its legal position, the Hudson's Bay Company had the fundamental advantage over the North West

Company that the routes to the fur country from Britain and France were shorter and cheaper through Hudson Bay and Strait than through the St. Lawrence and the Great Lakes. This advantage did not apply to certain small sections, such as the immediate basin of the St. Lawrence, but it applied in most of the inland reaches where the rivals traded, even to where now are Winnipeg in Manitoba and Fargo in North Dakota.

But the Great Company, as it was called, or more often the Company, had the weakness of its strength. For a hundred years there was practically no competition, and the Company grew flabby as it grew fat. Its agents just established posts at the places most accessible from Europe and waited for the Indians to come to them.

In those days, and indeed for long after, the Indians could not grasp the European idea that time has value. It did not seem to them any particular hardship to spend weeks or months in coming a hundred and in some cases nearly or quite a thousand miles to trade for what were at first novelties, which later became necessities.

Prosperous and lethargic with easy gains, the Company did not even take real pains to carry out the most important obligation of its charter, its promise to the Crown that a search would be made for a practicable seaway around the north of America which would furnish Britain a short route to the Indies, the Northwest Passage. Indeed, the feeling seems to have developed early within the Company management that to find the Passage would be to their disadvantage; for, if successful, the route would bring in colonists. Those in charge were traders who saw themselves as mere dealers in fur. Indeed, it was not until within the time of men now living that the Company realized what a series of opportunities it had lost by not coming in on the ground floor on a lot of other developments that were inevitably replacing the fur trade. What it actually did for more than two centuries was to fight nearly every movement toward agriculture and similar progress, on the correct but limited view that farmers destroy the fur-bearing animals.

The one apparent exception to this rule of opposition to farmers is connected with the series of events that brought to a head the Pemmican War—Lord Selkirk's establishment of an agricultural colony near the present Winnipeg. The real motive here, except perhaps for Lord Selkirk's own attitude when he succeeded in getting control, was that the Company was trying to thwart its rivals, the Nor'westers.

In the century that was practically without competition, 1670 to 1770, the Hudson's Bay Company learned a good deal about the interior, although in the main it waited at its seaport trading stations for the Indian customers to straggle in. The Company did send Henry Kelsey west, or rather permitted him to join the Indians and wander off westward to where he saw the prairies and was first in Canada to report the buffalo. That was in 1690. In 1754 Anthony Henday (also called Hendry) reached the Saskatchewan and visited the Blackfoot Indians near the Rockies.

Around 1770 Hearne wandered off from Hudson Bay with the Indians, somewhat as the others had done, but northwest rather than southwest, and got to some point on the Coppermine River; it is a bit more than doubtful that he reached Coronation Gulf, which he claims to describe as an eyewitness but does describe more as if from hearsay.

Still, he was the first white man to reach the vicinity of the Polar Sea by an inland journey through North America.

These observations are leading up to the Pemmican War, and that struggle is to be considered mainly from the pemmican side; so the westward and northward progress of discovery and of the fur trade is here barely sketched, avoiding most of the other grave issues and considering in detail only the food situation.

The Company's *servants,* as their employees were called,

came mainly from Scotland and the Orkneys. In spite of their numerous good qualities, they were conservative, especially about diet, so that during the first hundred years they appear to have learned comparatively little about native foods. As if they had been still in Scotland, they lived in the main on porridge and bread, on salted fish and salted red meats. The fish might be locally caught and some of the meat was of local origin, but they imported along with their cereals a good deal of European salted pork, beef and other preserved meats, as well as some European fish.

Like many other parts of the world in those days, Hudson Bay had a good deal of trouble with scurvy. Nor do they seem to have held in the early years a belief that was prevalent among the Company's servants after 1800, that scurvy could be prevented and cured by fresh or dried local meat. Clearly the medical theories of the Company during its first century in America were like those of Europe, that scurvy was caused by such things as poor ventilation, idleness, lack of entertainment. There was a heavy moral side to the reasoning, the conviction that a man who was ill-tempered, lazy, without initiative, would develop scurvy in consequence. As I have said elsewhere, this is putting the cart before the horse; they observed mental symptoms which were in reality the effect of scurvy and mistook them for the cause.

Then, of course, they believed that salted meats were conducive to scurvy; for this view seems to have been universal in Europe and in the American colonies during the period.

It was an omen, though without revealed meaning for a hundred years, that the men who really started the Hudson's Bay Company were two French Canadians from the St. Lawrence region, Pierre Esprit Radisson and Médard Chouart, Sieur des Groseilliers, who sold the idea to Prince Rupert and his associates; for the competition which was destined to worry the Great Company so much, and which indeed became eventually a life and death struggle, originated from the St. Lawrence.

The French in North America were nearly everywhere more adaptable than the British, at least to the extent that they more readily adopted native ways. That makes travel easy, as had indeed been shown by Kelsey, Henday and Hearne, who simply joined up with groups of natives and tagged along after them, traveling without equipment, expense, hardship or danger. This adaptability tended to be exceptional with the British and to be the rule with the French.

In the 1730's Pierre Gaultier de Varennes, Sieur de la Vérendrye, traveled from Montreal with a small party, living by their own hunting or the hunting of the people whom they visited. They got as far as the Missouri River where now are the Dakotas. This and similar journeys were or might have been warnings to the Gentlemen Adventurers of London that one day they were going to have some real competition from Montreal. It did develop—slowly, at first, in part through French Canadians and in part through British colonials, Canadians as well as Yankees, who adopted native ways to a large extent and so traveled fast and far, or at least cheaply and far.

In the decades following the successful revolt of the Thirteen Colonies along the Atlantic seaboard, Free Traders (as competitors of the Hudson's Bay Company were called) were pushing aggressively west beyond Lake Superior and northwest across what are now the Prairie Provinces of Manitoba, Saskatchewan and Alberta. Indeed, the Revolutionary War still was far from over when a Connecticut Yankee, Peter Pond, established the first trading post in the Athabaska region, for that was in 1778. The valleys of the Athabaska and Peace, tributaries of the Mackenzie, became commercial tributaries to the merchants on the St. Lawrence. Instead of making long journeys to Hudson Bay, the Athabaska and

Peace River Indians now traded with merchants who brought European wares almost to the doors of the teepees.

The Hudson's Bay Company were not exactly caught napping, but the Nor'westers frequently beat them to the draw. For instance, when the Company sent Samuel Hearne in 1774 to build Cumberland House on the Saskatchewan, near the present western boundary of Manitoba, they found that the North West Company had a post there already.

Toward 1800 the competition had grown really severe. It had been gentlemanly at first, but was increasingly turning cutthroat as the Hudson's Bay Company felt itself slipping. The shares of the corporation, long a prized investment of Londoners, now went down and down.

The dividends of the Great Company dropped in 1801 from eight to four per cent, and continued so until 1808 when they ceased entirely, from 1809 to 1814. This is plausibly blamed by some on the Napoleonic Wars, in which the United States took part against Britain through what we call the War of 1812; others maintain that the inroads of the North West Company were largely responsible for the decrease and then the cessation of dividends.

In the period between 1720 and 1820 the number of Company shareholders varied from 50 to 109. These holdings were not widespread, accordingly; but a drop in income, and the struggle with the Nor'westers, still made a profound impression in Britain, for the shareholders were, generally speaking, the leading families, commercially, socially and politically.

There were on the side of the Company two main advantages in the competition with the Nor'westers, that they had a superior legal position and that it was, or should have been, cheaper per pound for them to bring in trade goods to the northern plains and to the upper Mackenzie basin—their mileage from Hudson Bay was far less than that of the Nor'westers from the St. Lawrence, and their transport routes were, on the whole, easier. The Company's great weaknesses were that it was not adaptable and that it was not enterprising. A partial cause of both troubles was that the Company was governed from across the Atlantic by a stodgy lot of financiers and nobility who had only the vaguest notion about the real problems; and who, to some extent, did not even want to understand the difficulties, feeling that the good old English way had succeeded in the past and would succeed again.

Lethargy in North America derived from a weakness in London; but there was the important further reason that the Company's servants were underpaid and did not have a profit-sharing arrangement with their employers. The traders of the North West Company were many of them partners rather than employees. In any case they had a great deal of freedom, each being permitted to develop his own opportunities in his own district pretty much as he saw fit. Then, insofar as they were governed from a distance it was only from Montreal; and it was chiefly by older men who had themselves in their youth traded for furs in the valleys of the Red, the Saskatchewan, the Athabaska and the Peace. They understood conditions, they knew the ropes.

The historians seem to agree that where the relative adaptability of the rival trading organizations counted the most was in methods of transportation and in provisioning. Transportation called for exploration, the discovery of the best canoe routes and portage routes, in which the Nor'westers excelled. Indeed, most of the great figures in the exploration of the period are men who, either at the time or thereafter, were affiliated with the North West Company—the mentioned Yankee explorers, chief of them Peter Pond and the two Alexander Henrys, and men of old country British stock like David Thompson, Alexander Mackenzie and the several Frobishers.

Mackenzie was the first to descend the river named after

him to the Polar Sea and the first in Canada to cross the
continent from east to west, which he did by way of the Peace
and Fraser Rivers. Scarcely less important were the journeys
of. Thompson, for their physical extent is equaled by the
literary and historical importance of the diaries he kept and
by the cartographic value of the maps he made, including
that of the Columbia River in our States of Oregon and
Washington, which he was the first to descend. *The Encyclopedia of Canada,* for instance, says of Thompson that "when
he left the western country in 1812, he prepared a map of it
which has been the basis of all subsequent maps."

The greatest single element working for the success of the
Nor'westers was that they adopted native foods. Unlike most
of the Hudson's Bay Company men, who felt they had to
have bread and porridge along with their meat, the Nor'westers, if there was anything to be gained by it, lived exclusively
by their own hunting or that of their companions. And insofar as the Hudson's Bay Company used native foods, it
tended to prepare them in the European way, which meant
that instead of wind-drying meats the men salted them. With
the added weight of the salt, the watery meat was several
times heavier and considerably more bulky than the dried
provisions of the Nor'westers, whose men used jerky in camp
and on short trips, pemmican on the long journeys. Besides,
as experience showed and as is discussed at length hereafter,
men sickened with scurvy on European-style corned beef but
kept their health and strength on the local jerky and pemmican.

It was a standard calculation of the fur trade that one
pound of jerky had the food value of six pounds of lean meat,
and they knew from experience that in order to remain
healthy and strong indefinitely they needed a pound of suet
to go with each six pounds of fresh lean, meaning they would
have to have a pound of suet for each pound of jerky.

It was considered that a man who worked hard needed per

day a ration of six or seven pounds of fresh lean and a pound of fat. Now pemmican is by weight half dried lean and half rendered fat; so the maximum daily pemmican ration was two pounds; some of the best authorities, among them Thompson, say the outside quantity was a pound and a half. This was for men who slaved at the hardest labor fourteen and sixteen hours per day, as when tracking canoes up swift rivers and carrying them and their loads on their shoulders across portages.

We find nowadays that when a man eats nothing but pemmican he requires only about three-quarters of a pound per day, if he is around town in somewhat the routine of the average business man, which means that he could do a good deal of muscular work on a pound. It is hard, therefore, to see how the voyageurs managed to get away with two pounds, but there seems evidence that some of them did. Then, eating was their chief enjoyment on the long journeys; they were mighty trenchermen, and proud of it.

By 1810 it was generally realized that the Nor'westers were decidedly getting the best of the contest with the Hudson's Bay Company. This was in the main through a superior transport. They had developed the best routes, the best travelers and the best travel methods. Their food, pemmican, was so much more compact and so much lighter that they could make considerably longer journeys, or carry bigger pay loads on trips of equal length. It is the pay loads that bring in the pay, the wages of employees and the profits of stockholders or partners. The partners of the North West Company were getting rich; the stockholders of the Hudson's Bay Company were on reduced income.

By the first decade of the nineteenth century the manufacture of pemmican had become big business. "Pemmican Capital of the Fur Trade" was the usual characterization of Pembina, on the Red River where now is the northeast corner of the State of North Dakota. The Dictionary of

American History says through a section written by O. G.
Libby, Professor of History in the University of that State:
"Pembina . . . was a strategic fur-trade point for the
North West Company in its war with the Hudson's Bay
Company. . . . Chaboillez, in 1797, . . . and Alexander
Henry, Jr., in 1801, successively occupied the post for that
company. It was also one of the best-known outfitting points
for the buffalo hunters of the prairies to the west and south.
Their Red River carts and ponies returned with loads of
pemmican, robes, skins and dried meat. The pemmican was
usually sold in Fort Garry or Winnipeg."

Now enters upon the stage Thomas Douglas, fifth Earl of
Selkirk, for whom it was something between a career and a
passion to settle Scottish Highlanders where they would be
less crowded than at home. In 1803 he planted a colony of
them in Prince Edward Island. Then he went about pur-
chasing shares of the Hudson's Bay Company—some say
merely to get control, others say to get a control which he
could use to make the Company give him, in his private
capacity, a concession in some fertile acres from their domain
as masters of Rupert's Land. By 1811 he was in control, and
got from the Company a concession of 45,000,000 of such
fertile acres, in the Red River valley of what is now North
Dakota, Minnesota and Manitoba.

Some think this was a move on the part of the Hudson's
Bay Company itself to plant an agricultural settlement in
the heart of the pemmican country, with a view to getting
the farmers to destroy the buffalo, which they would do to
keep these wild animals out of the grain fields, and also to
prevent their meat from competing with domestic beef and
mutton. Whatever the truth, the fur men on the ground,
whether Hudson's Bay Company or Nor'wester, took the
move as an attempt to ruin the North West Company by
depriving it of pemmican. That meaning was implemented

through an order issued by Miles Macdonell, Governor of the Red River Settlement, on January 8, 1814, forbidding export from the colony of pemmican and other dried provisions, meaning jerky and pounded meat.

This move, if successful, would cripple the Nor'westers, whose transportation system was based upon the use of light and compact provisions and who could not get these in sufficient quantity except in the prairies of what is now northern Dakota and southern Manitoba. True, there were buffalo elsewhere, and pemmican was made and sold throughout the buffalo country; but, as said, pemmican was now a big business; hundreds of thousands of pounds a year were required, and a single 1,000-pound buffalo would produce only 100 pounds. Great operations, such as those of the Nor'westers, could not be maintained full scale except on the basis of a continued main supply from the Red River valley to supplement local production at the various posts that now dotted the country from Minnesota to the Rockies and north to the Peace and Athabaska.

The contemporary authorities do not disagree; but it is nevertheless hard for most of us to grasp realistically the dependence on pemmican of the vast operations of the two great companies. The position, therefore, may be strengthened by quoting what can fairly be styled the official history of the Hudson's Bay Company, written by a member of the staff of the Canadian head office, Douglas MacKay, and published in 1936: *The Honourable Company.*

In his account leading up to the Pemmican War, MacKay makes the usual point that the business rivalry of the companies hinged on transportation, the question of bringing in the largest pay loads of trade goods and taking out the largest pay loads of furs over routes thousands of miles in length that involved ascending and descending swift and rapids-infested streams, with long and difficult portages from one river to another through connecting swamps and over dividing ridges. It was a material advantage of the Nor'westers that they had been in advance of the Honourable Company in discarding European foods, and European methods of food preparation, for the native foods and ways.

In this the adoption of pemmican was chief. On page 138, MacKay says that in 1814 Macdonell "asserted his authority by issuing a proclamation forbidding . . . the export of pemmican from Selkirk's territory of Assiniboia. Pemmican was the concentrated staple food of the fur trade, and Assiniboia was the richest pasturing ground of the buffalo. From these plains the half breeds hunted for both companies, and the food supply of the entire fur trade had become dependent upon the area."

So, practically speaking, the Nor'westers had to fight with guns or yield. They chose to fight.

It is agreed by the historians that both trading companies thought they had to have pemmican for the success, or at least for the easier success, of their transportation systems, as well as for stores to keep the Indians alive through seasons of scarcity. It has not been as widely recognized by the scholars, although clear from the documents, that one of the chief reasons for the supposed necessity of having enough pemmican was an opinion, common by 1810 to both rivals, that, in addition to being more nourishing for its weight and bulk than European foods, pemmican would also keep a man in better health, and, in particular, would save him from or cure him of scurvy. This is discussed hereafter.

Expressly and by implication the relation of the fur trade to pemmican at this stage is well stated by two of the chief figures of the northwestern fur lands, Mackenzie and Thompson.

In 1801 Mackenzie published at London his *Voyages from Montreal, on the River St. Laurence, through the Continent of North America, to the Frozen and Pacific Oceans: In the Years 1789 and 1793. With a Preliminary Account of the*

Rise, Progress and Present State of the Fur Trade of that Country. In his account of the trade Mackenzie says:
"The lean parts of the flesh of the larger animals are cut in thin slices, and are placed on a wooden grate over a slow fire, or exposed to the sun, and sometimes to the frost. These operations dry it, and in that state it is pounded between two stones: it will then keep with care for several years. If, however, it is kept in large quantities, it is disposed to ferment in the spring of the year, when it must be exposed to the air, or it will soon decay."

What Mackenzie has thus far described is the pounded meat that readily absorbs moisture to which it is exposed. He now describes pemmican:

"The inside fat, and that of the rump, which is much thicker in these wild than our domestic animals, is melted down and mixed, in a boiling state, with the pounded meat, in equal proportions: It is then put in baskets or bags for the convenience of carrying it. Thus it becomes a nutritious food, and is eaten, without any further preparation, or the addition of spice, salt, or any vegetable or farinaceous substance. A little time reconciles it to the palate.

"There is another sort made with the addition of marrow and dried berries, which is of a superior quality."

Thus we have from Mackenzie in 1801 a beginning of the debate as to whether it is better to use the plain article, the pemmican of lean and fat only, or to flavor with berries. This is part of a worldwide and ages-long debate between those who like their food with a natural taste and those who like it seasoned. It is essentially the debate on which is better, cake or bread, an argument that is not wholly a matter of personality but is, at least in part, dependent on whether you are thinking of an occasional food or of a steady diet.

Thompson's experience in the country was even more extensive than that of Mackenzie and differed from Mackenzie's, who was always in command and who, as expected with officers and gentlemen in his day, was favored on journeys through doing the least work and having the best of everything. Thompson, although sometimes in command, was less the commander who orders things done for him and more the worker and provider, hunter and fisher as well as leader.

In 1810, four years before the start of the Pemmican War, Thompson was on the north Saskatchewan River where stood Fort Augustus which, until eleven years before, had been the most westerly trading post of the Hudson's Bay Company, near what is now the boundary between the provinces of Saskatchewan and Manitoba. It was already more than twenty-five years since he left his native Scotland, and he was a man who had worked his way upward in frontier trade and travel. He gives in his diary entry for June 22, 1810, at once a picture of the staple food of the long distance traveler and of the role it played in the fur industry. I quote from pages 434-435 of *David Thompson's Narrative*, edited by J. B. Tyrrell, Champlain Society, Toronto, 1916:

"On the west side of these alluvials is Cumberland Lake, on the east bank of which is situated Cumberland House in Latitude 53° 56′ 45″ N Longitude 102. 13 West. This House was the first inland trading post the Hudson's Bay Company made, remarkably well situated for the trade of the fine Furrs: it serves as the general Depot for all the dried Provisions made of the meat and fat of the Bison under the name of Pemican, a wholesome, well tasted nutritious food, upon which all persons engaged in the Furr Trade mostly depend for their subsistence during the open season [i.e., when rivers are ice-free, during spring, summer and autumn.]"

Thompson now describes the pemmican he is talking about, raising some points that are new to this discussion: "It is made of the lean and fleshy parts of the Bison dried, smoked, and pounded fine; in this state it is called Beat Meat: the fat of the Bison is of two qualities, called hard and soft; the former is from the inside of the animal, which when melted is called hard fat (properly grease) the latter is made from the large flakes of fat that lie on each side of the back bone, covering the ribs, and which is readily separated, and when carefully melted resembles Butter in softness and sweetness.

"Pimmecan is made up in bags of ninety pounds weight, made of the parchment hide of the Bison with the hair on; the proportion of the Pemmecan when best made for keeping is twenty pounds of soft and the same of hard fat, slowly melted together, and at a low warmth poured on fifty pounds of Beat Meat, well mixed together, and closely packed in a bag of about thirty inches in length, by near twenty inches in breadth, and about four in thickness which makes them flat, the best shape for stowage and carriage . . .

"I have dwelt on the above, as it [is] the staple food of all persons, and affords the most nourishment in the least space and weight, even the gluttonous french canadian that devours eight pounds of fresh meat every day is contented with one and a half pounds per day: it would be admirable provision for the Army and Navy."

Except for Thompson's implying it is wholesome in a general way, I do not find in his extensive writings the view that pemmican will prevent and cure scurvy. So far as I know, this is first stated explicitly in 1812, then as part of a recommendation which is looked upon as one of the causes of the Pemmican War.

A. J. H. Richardson, of the staff of the National Archives of Canada in Ottawa, has examined for me some of the voluminous unpublished Selkirk documents that are in the Archives, and especially the papers of William Auld, who is looked upon as being, with Miles Macdonell and others, an instigator of the Pemmican War. Richardson wrote on April 8, 1944:

"I did some searching on my own account in the Selkirk Papers, and I'm enclosing notes on the only document that looked useful among those I had time to go through. It was written at the time of the 'Pemmican War' (which Auld and Macdonell themselves precipitated), and you might want its evidence on the superiority of pemmican to salted meat—and indeed its absolute necessity at the posts."

Attached to Mr. Richardson's letter was the following memorandum which is here copied exactly as written, including his footnote on Mr. Auld:

"Copy of Mr. Auld's * advices. May 13, 1814. Gives his reasons for advising Captain Macdonell to prevent the North West Co. traders from carrying 'the *Dried* Provisions' out of the lands ceded to Selkirk by the Hudson's Bay Co. Among them he states that the seizure of these provisions by the North-Westers the two previous years had led the Hudson's Bay Co., 'from our anxiety to promote the wellfare of the Settlers,' to 'give up part of the dried provisions collected by the Companys Servants,' as a result of which the Company 'are absolutely reduced to our English provisions in their stead, which it is the duty & interest of the Company's principal Officers to prevent, as being most injurious to the health of the people, who during the two preceding Winters have suffered much from Scurvey, a disease entirely occasioned by salted & weak food, & but too frequent especially at York Factory.' The lack of dried provisions had forced the Company to withdraw its servants from many posts this summer and 'the Canadians (i.e., the North West Co.) will drive (derive) all the advantages of the Trade, in consequence of their being allowed to possess themselves of the dried Provisions.' (Public Archives of Canada, Selkirk Papers, Vol. 4, pp. 1083-9)."

The conclusions arrived at by Auld, during or before the year 1812, and apparently common among his associates, that pemmican will prevent scurvy, can be derived from the whole history of the fur trade in the interior of North

* William Auld, H. B. Co. Superintendent at York Factory.

America, and likewise from the history of polar exploration since the northern travelers began to use pemmican.

Although the Pemmican War is considered to have started in 1814, with Macdonell's order handicapping the Nor'westers in their use of pemmican, the first serious bloodshed did not take place until June 9, 1816, in a small-scale battle near Fort Douglas between the Nor'westers and the Hudson's Bay Company men. In that "massacre" fell the representative of Lord Selkirk, Robert Semple, and with him twenty of his adherents. This was the largest single blood-letting of the war, but smaller fights occurred here and there, houses were burned, trade goods were destroyed.

How the Pemmican War looked from England while it was raging, appears with a slant favorable to the Hudson's Bay Company in a privately printed and anonymous book which appeared in London during 1817: *Statement Respecting the Earl of Selkirk's Settlement of Kildonan, etc.* I quote and paraphrase just enough to show the kind of "war" this was.

The book is dealing with the spring of 1816 on the Qu-Appelle River that flows eastward through southeastern Saskatchewan and southern Manitoba to the Red. Pambrun and Sutherland of the Hudson's Bay Company faction were proceeding downstream in five boats with twenty-two men, "loaded with a considerable quantity of furs, and about six hundred bags of pemmican," thus about 54,000 pounds. "On the 12th of May . . . they were attacked by an armed party, of about fifty of the servants of the North West Company . . . Mr. Pambrun and the rest of the party were taken prisoners . . . The party were forcibly detained for five days, and then liberated under the promise not to bear arms against the North West Company.

"About the end of May Alexander M'Donnell embarked in his boats with the furs, and the bags of provisions, which he had seized. He was attended by a body of Brûlés on horse-

back, which followed him along the bank of the river . . .
When the party arrived near the Hudson's Bay Company's
trading post of Brandon House, Cuthbert Grant was dispatched with twenty-five men, who took the post and pillaged
it, not only of all the British goods, together with the furs,
and provisions, belonging to the Company, but also of the
private property of their servants . . .

"After this exploit, M'Donnell divided his forces, amounting in all to about one hundred and twenty men . . . into
(four) separate brigades . . . When this organized banditti
arrived at Portage des Prairies, the plunder was landed from
the canoes, and the six hundred bags of pemmican were
formed into a sort of rampart or redoubt, flanked by two
brass swivels, which had formerly belonged to Lord Selkirk's
settlement.

"On the 18th of June, Cuthbert Grant, Lacerte, Fraser,
Hoole and Thomas M'Kay, were sent off from Portage des
Prairies, with about seventy men, to attack the colony at Red
River . . . On the 20th of June, a messenger returned from
Cuthbert Grant, who reported that his party had killed Gov-
ernor Semple with five of his officers, and sixteen of his
people; upon which M'Donnell, Seraphim Lamar, and all
the other officers, shouted with joy."

The book tells the story of the "Semple Massacre" according to a number of eyewitnesses, each story from a written
statement. About the shortest, and not the most gruesome,
is from the affidavit of Michael Heden:

"Boucher, the Canadian,* advanced in front of his party,
and, in an insolent tone, desired to know what he (Semple)
was about. Mr. Semple desired to know what he and his party
wanted. Boucher said, he wanted his fort. The governor desired him to go to his fort, upon which Boucher said to the

---

* As customary in narratives of the time, the adherents of the North West
Company are referred to as Canadians, Canada at that time being the region
of the St. Lawrence; the Hudson's Bay people are correspondingly referred
to as English, though more of them were Scots.

governor, 'Why did you destroy our fort, you damned rascal?' Mr. Semple then laid hold of the bridle of Boucher's horse, saying, 'Scoundrel, do you tell me so?' Upon this Boucher jumped from his horse, and a shot was instantly fired by one of Grant's party of horsemen, which killed Mr. Holt, who was standing near Governor Semple.

"Boucher then ran to his party, and another shot was fired, by which Mr. Semple was wounded. The governor immediately cried out to his men, 'Do what you can to take care of yourselves.' But, instead of this, his party appears to have crowded about him, to ascertain what injury he had met with; and, while they were thus collected, the Brûlés, who had formed a circle around them, fired a general volley among them, by which the greater part were killed or wounded. Those who were still standing, took off their hats, and called for mercy, but in vain:—The horsemen galloped forward, and butchered them."

The Semple Massacre was the most sensational episode of the Pemmican War. The story is told here to give an idea of the bitterness that underlay the whole struggle.

For seven years the Pemmican War was waged through a combination of gangster methods and the dirtiest business competition. The struggle ended through an amalgamation of the two companies, accomplished in London in 1821.

The Nor'westers had been winners in the business competition that preceded the Pemmican War, and they were to an extent victorious in the actual field struggles of that contest. But they lost out in the final settlement because of the entrenched legal position of the Hudson's Bay Company and because of the organizational weakness of a partnership, as compared with a stock company. The Nor'westers had built up no reserves; the partners became wealthy, each in his own right, while the corporation had little more than enough to go on from year to year. These wealthy partners were not all equally willing to put their money into the fight against the

Company, when it came to fire and sword. In any case, had the Nor'westers been completely victorious in all respects, the company resulting from the amalgamation would probably still have been known as the Hudson's Bay; for that company owned the charter.

The legal strength of the Company, if combined with the adaptability of the Nor'westers, could lead to success. It did.

Salt meat, bread and porridge were little used by the rejuvenated Hudson's Bay Company, except at the seaports, and at Winnipeg where salted domestic beef and flour were locally produced. With pemmican for food and goods for trade in their canoes and on the backs of whites and Indians who carried over the portages, the servants of the Great Company now extended its domain along the Mackenzie to the Polar Sea and across the mountains to the Pacific where they were stopped to the southwest by the Spaniards in California and to the northwest by the Russian American Company in Alaska.

11

The Romance of Pemmican

WRITERS who discuss pemmican in terms of romance are usually thinking of the period which followed the struggle between the two great fur companies. In the publicity sense, that is correct.

What keeps the writers from talking of romance before the day of the Nor'westers is no doubt the fact that pemmican was not then highly regarded by whites, through their tendency to look down upon anything that is the usual food of "savages." The immigrant was likely to consider American foods as of lower grade than European, just because they were native. Indeed, it seems usually to have required a famine, or other bit of tough luck, to get the colonists to go beyond tasting, and sneering at, the special dishes of native America. It was no doubt the semi-starvation around colonial Massachusetts Bay, and other parts of New England, during the first few years which broke down there the sales resistance of an immigrant people, who must have been through tradition at least as conservative as the Scottish servants of the Hudson's Bay Company.

Hunger taught the Puritans, and the rest of the New Englanders, to eat succotash, corn on the cob, maple syrup and roast turkey. We relish these now because we inherited the taste for them from our colonial ancestors. There seems to have been no pemmican east of the Alleghenies in the period when our national food tastes were being formed.

It has been shown that first it was the competitive necessity of the Nor'westers to find travel rations more portable and more preservable than those of the Hudson's Bay Company that swung them into line as pemmican users; and then it was the financial success of the Nor'westers that compelled the Hudson's Bay Company to follow suit. True, an occasional Hudson's Bay Company traveler used pemmican even before there were any Nor'westers, especially those who joined Indian bands and tagged along with them; but they were the exception.

However it may be for the early period, there certainly was romance in the story of pemmican after 1800. Now it was attracting long-distance attention from the nobility and gentry of Britain, whose most typical and reliable investment was shares in the Hudson's Bay Company, and who realized that the extent of the territories from which they could draw revenue in North America, and the size of the pay loads of their trading expeditions, depended upon the lightness and goodness of this travel ration. It was in the same period that the poets, the essayists, the historians, the speechmakers in Parliament, began to develop those uses for the word given in my quotation from the Oxford Dictionary, where pemmican became a figure that symbolized strength in small compass, where "the very pemmican of thought" was a phrase to signify "the very pith of language."

The romance of diamonds is perhaps more readily apparent to us from a distance than to the Kaffirs and poor whites who seek them through pit and tunnel on the African Rand. And so it may have been with the local Indians and "Canadians" who paddled and poled the boats upstream in the service of the fur trade and who carried them and their cargoes with back-breaking toil over portages that varied from a few yards to scores of miles. No one could hold a job in these labor battalions on the portages unless he could carry at least a piece, meaning ninety pounds of pay load, a distance of fifteen to twenty miles a day, in addition to his food, bedding, and such other gear as he thought he needed.

A sample of a long portage was the Arctic mountain crossing from McPherson, on the Peel, directly west to the Bell (when the Rat River portage was not used). The routine was that one left McPherson in time for a three-hour carry before supper, then he carried his loads four whole days, and arrived at the Bell about the middle of the forenoon of the sixth day, thus making about eighty miles in four days and a half.

I carried over that portage myself in 1907, and that is why I take it as a specimen case. As we plodded ahead with our burdens, we had the choice of stepping directly into the mud cracks between the hummocks of vegetation, when we sank halfway to the knee, or attempting to place a foot upon the middle of each hummock, in which we succeeded about three times out of four. The fourth time we would slip, with such a discomforting result that we were likely to conclude it was simpler not to be so choosy. The tendency was to pick footing the first few hours of each day and to stop being selective when you got tired.

I did this portage in September, when the mosquitoes were gone. During the height of the fur trade they usually did it in June, with heat and flies at their worst.

Imagine, then, the worst of possible Arctic summer days, with a steaming temperature of about 90° in the shade, and at least 20° hotter than that in the sun, with the mosquitoes in such swarms that they would fill a man's nostrils and interfere seriously with his breathing, if he did not wear a head net that interfered with his breathing also, though to a less extent. The entire body would have to be densely clad so as to prevent insect bites. Buckskin gloves * were worn, and leggings. At a minimum a man carried a pound a day of pemmican for the six days, in addition to his ninety-pound pay load; and then, as said, would come any gear that he thought he needed.

* A northern traveler, who has read this book in manuscript, objects to the implication that ordinary buckskin gloves would protect against the Arctic mosquito. The critic is right; they sting through an ordinary buckskin glove. But we used to grease ours and get them caked with mud, whereupon they became mosquitoproof.

When I carried over the Peel-Bell portage, John Firth was still in charge at McPherson. He had been there since Lapierre's House and Rampart were active ports on the Bell, decades before. Firth said that in the good old days there were very few of the portagers who carried only a single piece; more than half of them carried two pieces, and three or four of the best men would carry three pieces each, meaning 270 pounds of pay load, in addition to their food and personal belongings.

It is easy to see the importance of a condensed ration, like pemmican, in business of this sort; it is not so easy to see romance from the point of view of the working man. But the romance was patent from beyond the Atlantic where the dividends were rolling in upon the British stockholders.

In judging the romance of the fur trade, from the angle of the working man, it must be remembered that journeys were chiefly made in summer or, as Mackenzie puts it, "during the open season," when the rivers were free from ice. That was the warmest time of year.

The belief is common that the summers, as well as the winters, are cooler the farther north one goes; so we had better refresh our memories on how cool July was in the pemmican country.

When it comes to actual danger from heat prostration, it is not the average temperature for the year that matters, or even the average for the hottest month. Rather it is the temperatures of the hottest days and their excess above normal, the factor of chief importance apparently being unusually high temperatures persisting for several days at a time.

The length of the daily sunshine period matters a great deal, also. In the tropics, where the night is always practically as long as the day, the earth has time to cool off during a long spell of darkness. This cooling period gets shorter as the summer nights get shorter with increased northing, so that on the mentioned Peel-Bell portage, or at Fort Yukon on the Yukon River, there is no complete cessation of heat delivery by the sun, even at midnight. This moves the hottest period of the day later and later into the afternoon, until within the Arctic Circle it is likely to be somewhere between five and seven P.M.

Consider, for instance, how the summer was in 1847 when Alexander Hunter Murray came over from Fort McPherson, about sixty miles north of the Arctic Circle, to establish the Hudson's Bay Company post at Fort Yukon, which is about six miles north of the Circle.

According to Murray's *Journal of the Yukon,** published at Ottawa, 1910, he found it cool at the very crest of the Peel-Bell divide, "although calm and oppressively hot below." When he reached the location on which he was about to build Fort Yukon he said, for June 25:

". . . we put ashore at the entrance to a small lake at ½ past 9 o'clock for the purpose of encamping, but the mosquitos seemed determined we should not . . . I have been in the swamps of Lake Pontchartrain and the Balize, along the Red River (Texas) and most parts of the 'Gullinipper' country, but never experienced anything like this; we could neither speak nor breathe without our mouths being filled with them, close your eyes, and you had fast [between the eyelids] half a dozen, fires were lit all around, but of no avail."

Summarizing the experience of the first month he spent at Fort Yukon, Murray says:

"July was oppressively warm . . . I never before spent a summer so far north and could scarcely have credited others had I been told, that, on the banks of the Youcon, not far from the Arctic circle, the thermometer was, at 2 o'clock on the afternoon of July 10th, 90 degrees above zero."

According to this, Murray was really having a cool sum-

* Edition of L. J. Burpee.

mer; for the United States Weather Bureau, under the ordinary conditions of its scientific observation stations, has recorded at Fort Yukon 100° in the shade. There is almost necessarily a high humidity, for the country is one steaming swamp; the traveler is necessarily in heavy clothing, for he must keep out the mosquitoes; and his breathing is interfered with by a net over his face, for otherwise the mosquitoes would be filling his nostrils as they did Murray's. Take all this together with the midnight sun, which means a complete absence of the restful coolness of a dark night, and you have one more angle on the romantic life of the pemmican eater.*

Although length of the sunshine day and extreme humidity are conducive to heat prostration, there are not many accounts of this from the fur trade. And that has a bearing on the merits of pemmican, at least to those who believe that what one eats, and how much he eats, will condition him to the effect of heat.

An enlightening case of heat prostration in the North, striking because of the man to whom it happened, is that of Buffalo Jones, as told through apparently verbatim diary quotation by Colonel Henry Inman in his *Buffalo Jones' Forty Years of Adventure*, Topeka, Kansas, 1899.

Charles Jesse Jones was born in Illinois, where the summers are warm at times; he spent a good many of his years in northern Mexico and in the southwest of the United States, where temperatures run pretty high in midsummer.

---

* The "pemmican-eater" was the veteran of the fur country. A "pork-eater" was a greenhorn, a newcomer, one who did not know the ropes. This was from the circumstance that near the eastern seaboard, whether on the St. Lawrence or on Hudson Bay, salt pork was much cheaper than pemmican and was accordingly substituted; and, besides, men new to the country were used to salted meats and wanted the food to which they were accustomed. Salt pork was a standard element of the provisioning of the fur brigades as they set out from headquarters, and remained so as long as navigation conditions were favorable. Salted meats were replaced by pemmican when the brigades reached the difficult country, where canoes took the place of York boats, where rivers were swift and portages numerous.

He had traveled in equatorial Africa, and in many other places.

On his way toward a search for musk oxen in the Canadian Arctic, Buffalo Jones found himself on July 25, 1897, rowing alone in a boat on the Athabaska River, just south of Athabaska Lake, about as far north as the south tip of Greenland. He had been rowing hard to keep off a sandbar, had cleared the bar and had ceased rowing. Inman quotes him: ". . . in another hour was floating down the river northward again. At this juncture I lost all consciousness, and when reason returned I found my boat lodged near the north end of a long island. I had over-exerted myself, and the result was a slight sunstroke.* Realizing in some way what had happened, I managed to get hold of a towel, and with it applied water to my head. I recovered sufficiently to enable me to think, although my brain was in a measure paralyzed."

So far as I have been able to learn from a biography of 469 pages, this was the only heat stroke that Buffalo Jones suffered in his whole career. The experience came to him in the sub-Arctic, just about where (in the old days) buffalo pemmican was replaced by the fur brigades with caribou pemmican. It does not appear that Jones was using this food; for by 1897 the time was long past when it could be purchased from Hudson's Bay Company traders, or from the Indians, unless perhaps if you gave them a year's notice.

It is not necessary to go north beyond the Arctic Circle, or even north as far as the lower Athabaska, to be in danger from heat prostration. True, the risk increases with the length of the sunshiny period of each day and with the increased humidity, both of which factors are larger the farther north one goes; but it is also true that there is still greater heat in the more southerly reaches of the pemmican country.

* Jones does not say how hot it was, nor do we have available any figures of the Weather Service of Canada to show how hot it can get right where he suffered the sunstroke. But at Fort Smith, about 150 miles farther north, the Service gives a maximum of 103° in the shade.

Some maintain that the true pemmican region does not run farther south than Kansas, believing that in Texas,.Oklahoma, and Missouri, it was jerky they ate, with tallow on the side, or pounded meat dipped into melted grease. Take it, then, that the pemmican users did their long journeys in the temperatures that prevailed from Kansas north.

Consulting the Department of Agriculture Yearbook for 1941, *Climate and Man;* and, as heretofore, dealing only with extreme records, I find that it can be as hot as 121° in the shade in Kansas, 118° in Nebraska, 120° in South Dakota, 122° in North Dakota, with no great drop when on crossing north into Canada, where the top records are 112° for Manitoba, 113° for Saskatchewan and 115° for Alberta. These records are not attained, of course, more than once in a lifetime; still they mean that ordinary summers can be pretty warm in the pemmican lands. Keeping in mind the dictum of Mackenzie that pemmican is used during the summer, it is evident how little historical foundation there is for the belief that the Indian invented pemmican as a cold-weather ration and that the white man borrowed it from him with midwinter particularly in view.

True, there was the winter use of pemmican, but that was seldom for journeys; then it was to tide over a famine period, when usually the pemmican eaters stayed in camp, avoiding exertion as much as possible and sitting around the fire to keep warm.

In spite of heat, mosquitoes and grueling labor, there was romance in the work of the fur brigades. Or at least it seemed so to the European servants of the Company who traveled with the brigades, as we shall now see.

One of the classics of the fur trade is *Hudson's Bay,* which has the sub-title "Every-day life in the Wilds of North America, During Six Years' Resident in the Territories of the Honourable Hudson's Bay Company," by Robert M. Ballantyne. I use the second edition, Edinburgh, 1848.

In September, 1841, Ballantyne was practically fresh from the old country when he left York Factory on Hudson Bay for the Red River:

"The Portage la Loche brigade usually numbers six or seven boats, adapted for inland travelling where the navigation is obstructed by rapids, waterfalls, and cataracts, to surmount which, boats and cargo are carried overland by the crews. These carrying places are called *portages*, and between York Factory and Red River there are upwards of thirty-six, of various lengths. Besides these, there are innumerable rapids, up which the boats have to be pushed inch by inch, with poles, for miles together; so that we had to look forward to a long and tedious voyage."

He says, however, of his companions: "These hardy Canadians and half-breeds are accustomed to such voyages from the age of fifteen or sixteen, and think no more of them than other men do of ordinary work."

That Ballantyne saw romance in the journey we read in his description of the second day out from the seaport of York Factory:

"Upon the occasion of our first breakfast in the woods, we were fortunate. The sun shone brightly on the surrounding trees and bushes; the fires blazed and crackled; pots boiled and cooks worked busily on a green spot, at the side of a small bay or creek, in which the boats quietly floated, scarce rippling the surface of the limpid water. . . . The whole scene was indescribably romantic and picturesque."

On the shores of Hudson Bay pemmican was much more expensive than European food; things like flour could be unloaded cheaply from British ships right on the dock at York Factory, but pemmican had to be brought by canoe and portage hundreds of miles from Winnipeg—and, as things went then, was costly even at the point of origin. Accordingly, the cheaper European foods were used, especially during the first part of the westward journey, to sup-

plement the various forms of dried meat. Ballantyne says
for the trip being described that "the provisions of the men
consisted of pemican and flour." Farther on he describes
the work of the pemmican eaters:

"The men used to row for a space of time, denominated a
pipe, so called from the circumstances of their taking a
smoke at the end of it. Each *spell* lasted for nearly two hours,
during which time they rowed without intermission. The
smoke usually occupied five or ten minutes, after which they
pulled again for two hours more, and so on. While travelling in boats, it is only allowable to put ashore for breakfast; so, about noon, we had a cold dinner in the boat; and,
with appetites sharpened by exposure to the fresh air, we
enjoyed it pretty well.

"In a couple of days we branched off into Steel River, and
began its ascent. The current here was more rapid than in
Hayes River; so rapid, indeed, that, our oars being useless,
we were obliged to send the men ashore with the tracking
line. Tracking, as it is called, is dreadfully harassing work.
Half of the crew go ashore, and drag the boat slowly along,
while the other half go to sleep. After an hour's walk, the
others then take their turn; and so on, alternately, during
the whole day."

This journey was at an ideal time of year. The mosquitoes were gone, the days were no longer very hot and the
nights were pleasantly cool. The following year Ballantyne
made the same journey by canoe during the mosquito season. He says:

"I did not take a tent with me, our craft requiring to be
as light as possible, but I rolled up a mosquito-net in my
blanket, that being a light affair of gauze, capable of com-
pression into very small compass. Such were our equipments;
and on the 23d of June we started for the interior."

As they left the cool sea coast behind, the climate changed
rapidly. They were twenty or thirty miles inland:

"The day, which had hitherto been agreeable, now became oppressively sultry; not a breath of wind ruffled the water; and as the sun shone down with intense heat from a perfectly cloudless sky, it became almost insufferable."

The night over, "breakfast consisted solely of pemmican and flour, boiled into the sort of thick soup dignified by the name of *robbiboo*. As might be expected it is not a very delicate dish, but is, nevertheless, exceedingly nutritious; and those who have lived long in the country, particularly the Canadians, are very fond of it. I think, however, that another of their dishes, composed of the same materials, but fried instead of boiled, is much superior to it. They call it *richeau;* it is uncommonly rich, and very little will suffice for an ordinary man."

In the account of this canoe journey Ballantyne has a good deal to say about mosquitoes. For instance, at the close of one of the ordinary fifteen-hour working days they stopped for the night:

"We soon had our encampment prepared, and the fire blazing; but hundreds of mosquitoes were, as usual, awaiting our arrival, and we found it utterly impossible to sup, so fiercely did they attack us; so we at last went to leeward of the fire, and devoured it hastily in the smoke, preferring to risk being suffocated, or smoke-dried, to being eaten up alive.

"It was certainly amusing to see us rush into the thick smoke, bolt a few mouthfuls of pemican, and then rush out again for fresh air; our hands swinging like the sails of a windmill round our heads . . . In this manner we continued rushing out of and into the smoke, till supper was finished, and then prepared for sleep.

"This time, however, I was determined not to be tormented; so I cut four stakes, drove them into the ground, and over them threw my gauze mosquito-net, previously making a small fire, with wet grass on it, to raise a smoke and prevent intruders from entering while I was in the act of putting it on; then, cautiously raising one end, I bolted in after the most approved harlequinian style, leaving my discomfited tormentors wondering."

Such was the romance of canoe transportation when pemmican was king.

The commercial role of pemmican has been described, of necessity, by most historians of frontier development in the Plains section of North America, and by every historian of the fur trade. Rather than attempt to summarize them all, or to average their opinions, I quote from a single writer extracts sufficient to cover the ground fairly well.

One of the most extensive users of pemmican, among business men famous enough to leave a marked impression on history, was Sir George Simpson, who for a long generation, about a century ago, was practically emperor of half of North America. In his writings, as published by the Champlain Society and others, there are innumerable references to pemmican, but without any good description; for one does not ordinarily tell much about things that are commonplace, and to the wilderness traveler of his day pemmican was what bread is to us—taken for granted and seldom mentioned unless bad or unless one ran out of it. I cannot find, then, a pertinent quotation from Sir George himself; but Frederick Merk, Professor of American History at Harvard and editor of Simpson's journal, published in 1931 as *Fur Trade and Empire,* says on pages 346-347 of that work:

"Pemmican was almost ideal voyaging provision. It occupied little space in a canoe, for it is one of the most concentrated of foods, a fact which commends it still to Arctic explorers. It was convenient to pack into canoes or to carry over portages by reason of its bag form. When properly protected from wet and mold it could be kept indefinitely. It could be eaten cooked or uncooked, which recommended it particularly for long canoe voyages where haste was necessary. For all these reasons it was an item of major importance in fur trade economy.

"Pemmican made possible the development of the interior communication system of the North West Company, and it was on this foundation, also, that Simpson built the remarkable transportation system of the Hudson's Bay Company."

The remark of Professor Merk that pemmican "occupied little space in a canoe" is occasion for a digression on the canoe and York boat freighting which, with its river portages, was the characteristic thing about fur trade transportation.

Many rivers had rocky rapids in which canoes and other boats would sink, not only when there was a mishap running them going down stream but also, less frequently, when tracking up stream. Then was it of importance to have goods and provisions that would not spoil in a dipping, that could be rescued either afloat in the river or sunk to its bottom.

Oatmeal and coarse flour are bad, from this point of view, for water penetrates throughout a bag and watertight barrels are difficult as back loads for men to carry across the portages. Fine wheat flour is good; for when a bag of it lies submerged in a river a week, or a year for that matter, only about half an inch all around the outside spoils; this forms a dough layer through which there is no further penetration of water. Pemmican was still better, for the water did not penetrate at all—even chunks that had no rawhide cover were impenetrable to water and would dry in a few minutes when rescued from the stream.

In this relation jerky was not so good, for water would penetrate gradually, and drying was then a problem. Pounded meat was as bad as oatmeal, for, being in shreds and powder, it got wet through immediately and was nearly impossible to dry.

The Yankees who contributed to the swelling fortunes of the North West Company during the last quarter of the eighteenth century, such as Pond and the two Alexander Henrys, make frequent references to pemmican in journals of the period of 1775-1800, but usually as taking it for granted, assuming that everyone knows its characteristics so they need not be described. The first Yankee I have discovered who gives a forthright characterization is Harmon.

Daniel Williams Harmon (1778-1845) was born at Bennington, Vermont. In 1800 he joined the North West Company; in August of that year he was near the mouth of the Winnipeg River on his first journey to and through the pemmican country. I quote from *A Journal of Voyages and Travels in the Interior of North America,* using the New York, 1922, edition, pages 22-23:

"Sunday, 3 (August) . . . This is the first day which I have ever spent, since my infancy, without eating either bread or biscuit. As a substitute for bread, we now make use of what the Natives call *pimican,* which consists of lean meat, dried and pounded fine, and then mixed with melted fat. Pimican is a very palatable, nourishing and healthy food; and on it, our Voyagers subsist, while travelling in this country."

By the time of Harmon, and indeed before, the North West Company, when once in the land of difficult transportation west of the Great Lakes, was depending mainly on the buffalo as food; they lived nearly or quite exclusively on meat when traveling, chiefly on meat when at the posts. These provisions were secured by purchase, through Indian hunters who worked for the whites or through the prowess of the white men themselves, a few of whom were good hunters. The Harmon narrative, like the rest, brings out the fact that in a stationary summer camp, or at a post in winter, the diet was fresh meat when available; the hoarded foods, in sequence, were jerky, pounded meat, pemmican. Except at feasts, pemmican was not eaten in camp if other food was available; it was treasured for use on the road.

On the trail the food sequence was the same. Fresh meat was eaten first, because it was heavy and would not keep; then came jerky, pounded meat, pemmican.

Thus far, the geographic background of discussion has been mainly the western plains of the United States and of southern Canada. Now turn to the use of pemmican in the Arctic.

In the south, and indeed by fur trade usage as far north as the delta of the Mackenzie River, hard by the Polar Sea, pemmican had been a summer food because most journeys depended largely on canoes that required ice-free rivers. In the extreme north, the sledge took the place of the canoe, and journeys were largely in winter, when the rivers are ice boulevards and the sea frozen and walkable, which eventually made pemmican there a winter food.

However, the first exploration of northwestern Arctic Canada was done by canoe and boat in summer. The considerable use of pemmican for summer travel in Arctic exploration started in the third decade of the nineteenth century.

The Hudson's Bay Company played a large part in the overland exploration of the Arctic between 1820 and 1860. The company had been using pemmican before 1800; but not, as I have said, in the systematic way of the Nor'westers, nor much on winter journeys.

In 1819 Hudson's Bay Company officers in London believed that their representatives in Canada would be able to supply the expedition which, as the Dictionary of National Biography has it, the British Government was sending out "with the general idea of amending the very defective geography of the northern part of America." Sir John Franklin was to be the leader, with Sir John Richardson as medical officer and chief scientific observer. But when the party reached Cumberland House in 1820, they found (again quoting the Dictionary) "that owing to the rivalry, amounting almost to war, between the two trading companies which disputed the territory, no supplies were available." This scarcity of pemmican is usually considered one of the reasons for the great hardships of that expedition the following year, when some of the party died of hunger and some killed others to eat them. If this be part of the romance of pemmican, it has a gruesome slant.

When Franklin's second expedition came along, 1825 to 1828, the Pemmican War was over and supplies were again available. With pemmican as the chief ration, Franklin now descended the Mackenzie to its mouth and himself surveyed the Arctic coast westward as far as Beechey Point, just east of the Colville, while Richardson, in a remarkably successful and easy journey, mapped the coast eastward from the Mackenzie to the Coppermine, ascending that river and crossing to Bear Lake. This whole journey was made in spring, summer and autumn.

Between 1836 and 1840, supplied with pemmican by the Hudson's Bay Company, Thomas Simpson went down the Mackenzie and west along the Arctic coast beyond Sir John's farthest, to complete the mapping of the north coast of Alaska by attaining Point Barrow. Later pemmican took him eastward, so that he practically completed the delineation of the Arctic coast of the mainland, discovering the long-sought Northwest Passage.* These were also summer expeditions.

Pemmican was now, upon occasion, made in England. It was the recognized food of explorers, and this was the beginning of the great age of polar discovery. Those who became familiar with pemmican in the North used it on

---

* For details of the use of pemmican by these expeditions, and of the extent to which this condensed ration was supplemented by European foods and by the hunt, see the original narratives listed in the bibliography. For a brief statement, see the chapters on Franklin and on Simpson in Vilhjalmur Stefansson: *Unsolved Mysteries of the Arctic*, New York, 1938.

other journeys and for a variety of purposes. Sportsmen began to take it up.

With the possible exception of Sir Edward Sabine in the field of mathematics and physics, the greatest scientist who was engaged in northern exploration for the British government during the first half of the nineteenth century was Sir John Richardson, doctor of medicine from Edinburgh, friend of Burns and teacher of Huxley. He accompanied Franklin on his first and second expeditions, as I have mentioned, and led one of the search parties when Franklin, with two ships and 128 men, had disappeared on the third venture led by him.

Alone, or in collaboration with other distinguished scientists, Richardson wrote a series of works on botany, zoology and related subjects. He contributed to the narratives of the Franklin expeditions and published the story of his own journeys. It is, then, possible to epitomize both the use of pemmican in the exploration of the time, and the opinion generally held of it around the middle of the nineteenth century, through quoting from his *Arctic Searching Expedition,* Vol. I, pages 36-40. Incidentally, this is the best description I have found of pemmican-making in Britain, as distinguished from the Indian practice described heretofore:

"In April, 1847, I had the advantage [says Richardson] of a personal interview with Sir George Simpson, Governor-in-chief of Rupert's Land, who was then on a visit to England. . . . He informed me that the stock of provisions at the various posts in the Hudson's Bay territories was unusually low, through the failure of the bison hunts on the Saskatchewan, and that it would be necessary to carry out pemican from this country, adequate not only to the ulterior purposes of the voyage in the Arctic Sea, but also to the support of the party during the interior navigation in 1847 and 1848.

"I, therefore, obtained authority from the Admiralty to manufacture forthwith, the requisite quantity of that kind of food in Clarence Yard; and as I shall have frequent occasion to allude to it in the subsequent narrative, it may be well to describe in this place the mode of its preparation.

"The round or buttock of beef of the best quality, having been cut into thin steaks, from which the fat and membranous parts were pared away, was dried in a malt kiln over an oak fire, until its moisture was entirely dissipated, and the fibre of the meat became friable. It was then ground in a malt mill, when it resembled finely grated meat.

"Being next mixed with nearly an equal weight of melted beef-suet or lard, the preparation of plain pemmican was complete; but to render it more agreeable to the unaccustomed palate, a proportion of the best Zante currants was added to part of it, and part was sweetened with sugar. Both of these kinds were much approved of in the sequel by the consumers, but more especially that to which the sugar had been added.*

"After the ingredients were well incorporated by stirring, they were transferred to tin canisters, capable of containing 85 lbs. each; and, having been firmly rammed down and allowed to contract further by cooling, the air was completely expelled and excluded by filling the canister to the brim with melted lard, through a small hole left in the end, which was then covered with a piece of tin, and soldered up. Finally, the canister was painted and lettered according to its contents.

"The total quantity of pemican thus made was 17,424 lbs., at a cost of 1s. 7-1/4d. a pound. But the expense was somewhat greater than it would otherwise have been from the

---

* The men to whose taste Richardson here refers were chiefly British sailors who were initiated into the use of pemmican on a journey that occupied only a few months of one year. Beginners are nearly always reported as preferring the cakelike holiday pemmican to the more breadlike standard variety.

inexperience of the labourers, who required to be trained, and from the necessity of buying meat in the London market at a rate above the contract price, occasioned by the bullocks slaughtered by the contractor for the naval force at Portsmouth being inadequate to the supply of the required number of rounds. . . .

"As the meat in drying loses more than three fourths of its original weight, the quantity required was considerable, being 35,651 lbs."

Richardson then gives "Particulars of the estimated expense of pemican, manufactured in the Royal Clarence Victualling Yard, in Midsummer quarter, 1847:

	£	s.	d.	£	s.	d.
Fresh beef 35,651 lbs. at 6-¾d. per lb........	979	10	1			
Lard— 7,549—at 88s. per cwt.	296	11	4			
Currants— 1,008—at 84s. per cwt.	37	16	0			
Sugar— 280—at 31s. 2d. per cwt.	3	17	11	1,317	15	4
Oak slab 46 fms. at 22s. 6d. per load	47	5	0			
Hire for labourers	59	8	8			
Hire of kiln and cartage	8	1	0	114	14	8
				1,432	10	0
Deduct for scraps of fat sold				35	18	1
				1,396	11	11

Quantity of pemican manufactured 17,424 lbs.; average cost per lb. 1s. 7-¼d.

As a by-product of his work with the first and second Franklin expeditions, Richardson had before this edited and had largely written (though there were several learned collaborators) the magnificent four-volume quarto *Fauna Boreali-Americana,* which had been published with the support of the British Government by John Murray, London, 1829-37. In the volume on quadrupeds, when discussing the caribou, he had given his view on pemmican as made by the Red Indians of the sub-Arctic and Arctic forest, that "from the quantity of nourishment it contains in small bulk, it is perhaps the best kind of food for those who travel through desert lands."

It is of special interest here, and fits in with the evidence presented in the chapter "Living on the Fat of the Land," that Richardson gives a smaller fat component for the most northerly native pemmican than is given by the usual authorities for pemmican as made in the section between Kansas and Manitoba. Note, also, that whereas the native Arctic pemmican, as described by him, had only a third of fat against two-thirds of lean, Richardson tells us, above, that when he himself was making pemmican in England he used nearly as much fat as lean, therefore perhaps 45 per cent. Thus he was following approximately the high-fat formula of the buffalo pemmican of the fur trade rather than the comparatively low-fat Arctic formula.

The 1818 naval expedition of Sir John Ross and the 1819 overland expedition of Sir John Franklin began an epoch of polar exploration in which the British were supreme, as, indeed, they had been in some previous epochs. It was not yet time for Norway and the United States to begin that contest with Britain for supremacy which was at its height around 1900.

The first use of pemmican on a winter (sledge) journey in polar exploration seems to have been by Dr. John Rae of the Hudson's Bay Company the winter of 1846-7 in north-easterly Canada, west and north of Hudson Bay. In general, pemmican may be said to have come into winter use with the numerous expeditions that searched for the lost Franklin party through more than a decade following 1846, of which series Dr. Rae's was the first.

It is usually considered that the greatest man Britain ever placed in the field of northern exploration was Admiral Sir Francis Leopold McClintock, 1819-1907. He distinguished himself more than any of the other numerous commanders during the Franklin search expeditions that ran

from the late forties to the late fifties of the nineteenth
century; it was he who finally discovered enough relics and
documents to cause the Franklin Search to be considered as
having come to an end with his voyage in the *Fox*. From
1848 to 1859 he served in four Arctic expeditions, of which
he commanded two. He made the longest Arctic sledge
journey prior to 1900, indeed the longest sledge journey ever
made by Arctic explorers who depended on pemmican or
other provisions which they hauled with them—longer journeys have since been made by explorers who lived mainly
or wholly by hunting.

When a new era of Antarctic exploration was more or
less deliberately planned by the British, at the turn of the
century, under the formal leadership of the Royal Geographical Society of London, the most distinguished living
polar explorers were secured as collaborators on *The Antarctic Manual*, a book of 586 pages, London, 1901. Mc-
Clintock contributed the article "On Arctic Sledge-Travelling." On page 297 he says of pemmican that it should consist of nothing but lean and fat, that "no salt or preservation
of any kind is used," and that it is the most concentrated
food known.

Like the fur traders of the Pemmican War period, around
1810 and 1820, McClintock believed fifty years later that
pemmican would prevent and cure scurvy.

In 1877 Sir George Nares was on semi-formal trial in
London for having had scurvy on his 1875-76 expedition,
at which trial it appeared that they had used lime juice
in winter quarters but not on the sledge journeys. The
findings of the tribunal criticized Nares for not having used
enough lime juice, which angered McClintock, who wrote
denouncing men who paid so much attention to those dietetic theories which happened to be in vogue during a given
year and paid so little heed to opposed testimony from the
experience of large numbers of people who had lived for

long stretches of time on the foods which the current theory condemned. He gave his own experience as typical:

"I have myself made several sledging journeys, varying in length from 20 to 105 days each, without either lime-juice or scurvy in any of my parties; and the experience of my brother officers in the Franklin Search agreed with my own.

"Briefly, we lived upon pemmican, and enjoyed sound health."

With the California Gold Rush of 1849 began a period when the writings of newcomers to the fur country take the place of journals kept by the old masters—the Ponds, Henrys, Thompsons, Frobishers. The Forty-niners had heard much of pemmican before they went into the West. A few are disappointed to find this much-praised travel ration below their expectation in palatability; some are even disgusted with it.

However, most of the tenderfeet complain not really against pemmican, as such, but rather against methods of preparation which were being used, or which they thought were used. They object to finding in it things like buffalo hair, gravel, human hair. Some writers say that gravel and hair were exceptional; others seem to believe them common ingredients.

Those of long experience agree that there was "pemmican and pemmican"—with as wide a quality range as in almost any other food.

In a study of opinion on pemmican which I made for the Office of the Quartermaster General of the Army I copied out from books perhaps a hundred thousand words of testimony. Instead of trying to summarize this bulky evidence here, I quote at length from two writers, one of them nearly the least and the other nearly the most favorable of those who traveled the Plains shortly before the buffalo disappeared, but while pemmican was still in common use.

About the most condemnatory of those who printed their opinions in this period was a Scottish nobleman, James Carnegie, Earl of Southesk (1827-1905), who made a journey during 1859-1860 from the Mississippi River northwest through Canada almost to the Pacific coast, and back by a different route. The account of this expedition, *Saskatchewan and the Rocky Mountains*, was published at Edinburgh, 1875.

November 20, 1859, the Southesk party were on the middle Saskatchewan:

"Had 'berry-pemmican' at supper. That is to say, the ordinary buffalo pemmican, with Saskootoom berries sprinkled through it at the time of making. . . . Berry-pemmican is usually the best of its kind, but poor is the best.

"Take scrapings from the driest outside corner of a very stale piece of cold roast beef, add to it lumps of tallowy rancid fat, then garnish all with long human hairs . . . and short hairs of oxen, or dogs, or both,—and you have a fair imitation of common pemmican, though I should rather suppose it to be less nasty.

"Pemmican is most endurable when uncooked. My men used to fry it with grease, sometimes stirring-in flour, and making a flabby mess, called 'rubaboo,' which I found almost uneatable. Carefully-made pemmican, such as that flavoured with the Saskootoom berries, or some that we got from the mission at St. Ann, or the sheep-pemmican given us by the Rocky Mountain hunters, is nearly good,—but, in two senses, a little of it goes a long way."

The book contains many references which show that the party, like most travelers of the period, depended in the main on pemmican. But Lord Southesk himself ate little of it.

"I always took my meals alone, unless now and then when M'Kay joined me on special invitation. Breakfast, dinner, tea or supper—whatever the name of the repast—it con-

sisted much of the same materials,—tea, flour-cakes, and
such meat as happened to be available. At this particular
time my own dish was generally supplied with slices of beef,
cut from huge joints brought from one or other of the Forts.
Sometimes I chose dried meat for a variety, but pemmican
—the chief food of the rest of the party—I seldom cared to
taste."

Thus to a noble Scot pemmican was "nasty," and seemingly he did no more than taste now and then the chief
food of his traveling companions. Fourteen years later a Scottish commoner, destined for leadership in Canadian public
life, journeyed through the country without having his meals
specially prepared and living on the same food as the rest
of his party. He is cited here for contrast.

George Monro Grant, D.D., LL.D. (1835-1902), was Principal of Queen's University, Kingston, Ontario, from 1877
to 1902. He was educated at Glasgow University and was
ordained a minister of the Church of Scotland. During his
career as head of Queen's University he was looked upon
as outstanding both in education and in politics. The most
famous of his several books, one that continues to be re-
printed, is *Ocean to Ocean,* Toronto, 1873, an account of
the preliminary work that led to the extension of the Canadian Pacific Railway from Ontario to the Pacific.

The overland expedition described in *Ocean to Ocean* was
commanded by Sir Sanford Fleming (1827-1915), one of the
most distinguished of Canada's railway builders, for whom
Grant was acting as secretary. The whole journey, from
Toronto to the Pacific, was accomplished between July 16
and October 14, 1872. They reached what had been the
pemmican country when they arrived at Fort Garry, now
Winnipeg, August 1; but the buffalo were gone from that
region and I find no reference to pemmican as in use by the
party until they were well on their way from Winnipeg to
Edmonton, on August 13.

Dr. Grant's personal experience of pemmican was not, so far as this narrative is concerned, more than five weeks, but on the journey he associated with or met a number of Europeans who had used it much longer; to some members of his party, and to many at the various stations they passed, it had been "the bread of the wilderness" from childhood. It is clear, as one analyzes the comments, that Grant was depending for his views upon a combination of his own experience with what he heard and saw.

Most travelers who have described journeys of similar length in the buffalo country have referred to pemmican only a few times in their publications. That Grant refers to it more often than any other writer I have examined, is perhaps because most of the others have summarized their impressions when the books were being written, while Grant published what in large part is a reproduction of diary entries set down in the field. Thus, each passage conveys Grant's knowledge and feelings as they were at a specified date. He says on page 24 of the London 1877 edition: "Our notes are presented to the public, and are given almost as they were written so that others might see, as far as possible, a photograph of what we saw and thought from day to day."

The first pemmican reference I have discovered is not, however, from Grant's diary but from his reflections on the development of the Province of Manitoba:

"The fertile plains along the Red River, the Assiniboine, and the two Saskatchewans ought to have been opened up by the Empire and formed into Colonies long ago: but their real value was not known. It was not the business of the [Hudson's Bay] Company to call attention to them as fitted for any other purpose than to feed buffalo: for those plains were their hunting grounds, and their posts on them were kept up chiefly for the purpose of supplying their far northern posts with pemmican or preserved buffalo-meat. The

Company did what every other corporation would have done, attended simply to its own business."

August 9, 1872, the party was leaving the country of the Assiniboine River for that of the Saskatchewan, and there are references to the first buffalo, the first jerky. The regular use of pemmican did not begin until August 16, when they reached Fort Carlton on the North Saskatchewan and "dined with Mr. Clark on pemmican, a strong but savoury dish, not at all like 'the dried chips and tallow' some Sybarites have called it. There is pemmican and pemmican however, and we were warned that what is made for ordinary fare needs all the sauce that hunger supplies to make it palatable."

After leaving Fort Carlton on their way up the North Saskatchewan to Edmonton, Grant's entry for August 19 says:

"Terry gave us pemmican for breakfast, and, from this date, pemmican was the staple of each meal. Though none of us cared for it raw at first, we all liked it hot. . . .

"Pemmican and sun-dried thin flitches of buffalo meat are the great food staples of the plains, so much so that when you hear people speak of provisions, you may be sure that they simply mean buffalo meat, either dried or as pemmican."

August 22: "At the camp, the Chief treated them with great civility, ordering pemmican, as they preferred it to fresh buffalo."

August 26: "Camped before sunset within twenty-seven miles of Edmonton, and in honour of the event brought out our only bottle of claret. As we had no ice, Terry shouted to Souzie to bring some cold water, but no Souzie appearing he varied the call to 'Pemmican.' This brought Souzie, but great was his indignation when a bucket was put into his hands, instead of the rich pemmican he was never tired of feasting on."

August 31 they left Edmonton and headed westerly for

Jasper House. On September 6 they "halted for dinner at the bend of the river, having travelled nine or ten miles, Frank promising us some fish, from a trouty looking stream hard by, as a change from the everlasting pemmican.

"Not that anyone was tired of pemmican. All joined in its praises as the right food for a journey, and wondered why the Government had never used it in war time. . . . As an army marches on its stomach, condensed food is an important object for the commissariat to consider, especially when, as in the case of the British Army, long expeditions are frequently necessary.

"Pemmican is good and palatable uncooked and cooked. . . . It has numerous other recommendations for campaign diet. It keeps sound for twenty or thirty years, is wholesome and strengthening, portable, and needs no medicine to correct a tri-daily use of it. Two pounds weight, with bread and tea, we found enough for the dinner of eight hungry men.

"A bag weighing a hundred pounds is only the size of an ordinary pillow, two feet long, one and a half wide, and six inches thick. Such a bag then would supply three good meals to a hundred and thirty men. Could the same be said of equal bulk of pork? But as Terry indignantly remarked: 'The British Gauvirmint won't drame of pimmican till the Prooshians find it out.' *

"Frank came back to dinner with one small trout though Beaupre said that he and his mate last summer had caught an hundred in two hours, some of them ten pounds in weight. Perforce we dined on pemmican, and liked it better than ever."

September 17: "This was an entire reorganization, and again Terry was the only one of the old set that remained

---

* Apparently the "Prooshians" did find it out; for, according to the (United States) *Cavalry Journal* of Jan.-Feb., 1941, the German Army was using pemmican in World War II.

with us. . . . Beaupre's only consolation was that he would get pemmican again, for he declared that life without pemmican was nothing but vanity; and we had made the huge mistake of exchanging our pemmican with McCord for pork.

"The next day and every day after we rued the bargain, but it was too late. Beaupre and Valad had suffered grievously in body from the change, and for an entire day had been almost useless. The Doctor was reduced practically to two meals a day, for he could not stand fat pork three times.

"Indeed all, with the single exception of Brown, lamented at every meal, as they picked delicately at the coarse pork, the folly of forsaking that which had been so true a stand-by for three weeks."

Ocean to Ocean was published in 1873. For any possible change in views during the next several years I have examined a series of three articles "The Dominion of Canada," which Dr. Grant published in *Scribner's Magazine* during 1880, but have discovered only a single reference, one however that fails to indicate any change of attitude:

"More than the potato to the Irishman, or the date-palm to the Arab, is the buffalo to Indians and half-breeds. By 'provisions,' in the Northwest everybody means pemmican, or buffalo meat preserved in a pounded and triturated state."

Grant appears to have considered pemmican only as a travel ration, since he recommends it for British troops in view of an assumption of their special need for mobility. Many soldiers have recommended pemmican for the use of soldiers. There are also cases where soldiers have recommended pemmican for civilian use. For instance:

John Wesley Powell (1834-1902) was born in New York State. He graduated from Illinois Wesleyan, was LL.D. from Columbia and Harvard, Ph.D. from Heidelberg. He lost his right arm at the battle of Shiloh and was retired from the United States Army with the rank of major. He was first to descend by boat the Grand Canyon of the Colorado, 1869. He was director both of the United States Geological Survey and the United States Bureau of Ethnology, and was author of works on the arid regions of the southwestern United States and on the North American Indians.

In his twenty-third annual administrative report, as Director of the Bureau of American Ethnology, Major Powell has a general discussion of the Indian, including references to the indebtedness of the white man to him in certain respects. I quote from pages xi and xii:

"It is well known that aboriginal America gave the world corn, the potato, certain beans and squashes, tobacco, two varieties of cotton, and the domestic turkey; it is not so well known that the native tribes utilized various other natural resources which might well be introduced into the dietary and commerce of Caucasian peoples; and still less is it realized that various prepared foods habitually used by the Indians are of unsurpassed excellence—for while succotash and hominy have come into general use, the far superior pinole, tamale and pemmican are only locally used by whites, and many other desirable dishes are entirely neglected."

Powell lived to see the tamale widely popular throughout the United States; in our Southwest it has attained nearly the position of a national dish. Pinole is less used, but seems to be gaining.

In thinking well of pemmican Major Powell was by no means a pioneer among soldiers of the United States; the early military explorers of the buffalo country seem to have agreed generally with the fur traders. There is, for instance, the "Report on an Exploration of the Territory of Minnesota by Brevet Captain (John) Pope" which was published in Senate Executive Document 42 of the 31st Congress, 1st Session. In connection with an account of the buffalo, the Report says that pemmican "is of the richest and most nutritious character. . . . It is very palatable, and from its exceeding richness, but little is required to satisfy the appetite."

Captain Pope has in mind the plain pemmican, not the berry sort; for his detailed description of how it is made speaks of only two ingredients, lean and fat. On palatability, the Captain is evidently giving us his own verdict; as to long-term usefulness he relies upon observation and, no doubt, upon common knowledge, where he says:

"The half-breeds make all their long voyages . . . with this sole article of food; and they march further, and with far less of baggage and supplies, than any people I have ever seen." *

Grant's book on his transcontinental journey of 1872, from which I have quoted, tells of almost the last summer during which pemmican was of consequence to the fur trade.† It had always been a costly food, in terms of labor and of the number of buffalo required. The use of an expensive condensed ration paid dividends only while transportation was difficult. The railways were coming in and good highways, with steamboats on the navigable rivers and on the big lakes. Salt meats were cheaper now, in the long run, irrespective of their weight; pemmican was no longer required as a scurvy preventive, for health could now be maintained through the use of vegetables that were raised in gardens at nearly every post.

It was, then, not so much the disappearance of the buffalo as the coming in of the farmers' beef and potatoes, with the associated development of transportation facilities, that caused the disappearance of pemmican from the frontier

---

* Information regarding Captain Pope's report supplied by the Library of the Army War College.

† Hornaday considers that the last buffalo pemmican (in appreciable quantity) was sold at Winnipeg in 1883.

markets, even way down north * in the sub-Arctic. The gardens of the missionaries and the post managers worked in with the cattle herds of the ranchmen to produce cheap foods locally. Around the turn of the century there was a flour mill on the Peace River. Even before that, the successful garden at Fort Good Hope on the Mackenzie, only a few miles south of the Arctic Circle, was shipping potatoes and other produce both up and down stream.

But when pemmican disappeared from the fur territories it appeared in New York and London, on the shelves of outfitters that catered to wealthy sportsmen for journeys to the north woods, for mountain climbing, for fishing excursions, and for weekends.

Ballooning was one of the great sports before the coming of the airplane. The balloonists in Europe do not seem to have used pemmican; unlike the European polar explorers, they somehow were not in the tradition. But the Americans knew and used pemmican. Many of that generation are gone. One of the most distinguished of those who remain is Augustus Post, who has kindly replied (March 9, 1944) to a letter asking about his use of pemmican:

"David Abercrombie, authority on camping and formerly a member of Abercrombie & Fitch, sporting and expedition outfitters, and member of the Campfire Club of America, suggested and provided Pemmican for our balloon trips, also for automobile trips to the woods of New Brunswick, hunting big game.

"On my balloon trip in 1907, the International Balloon Race from St. Louis, with Mr. Alan R. Hawley, President of the Aero Club of America, we used Pemmican sewed up in raw hide bags holding five pounds, which was the way it was put up in Canada.

* The expression "down," referring to a point of the compass, depends in North America on the flow of the main rivers. It is down east along the Atlantic seaboard, down south in the Mississippi valley, down north in the basin of the Mackenzie.

"We used it again in our balloon trip from St. Louis in 1910 when we won the International Gordon Bennett Balloon Race Cup. . . . We found it invaluable as a food and superior to canned or 'iron rations' as they were called—as issued to the army.

"The package was easily handled and the raw hide could be used after the bag was empty much better than a can. We made straps and thongs of the raw hide and could pack instruments and delicate things to be carried, after landing, through the forest. I liked it and relished it stewed. . . . I believe it was only an improvement on jerked or dried meat extensively used by the Indians and early trappers and hunters.

"Dan Beard had Pemmican for his boys' camp at Hawley, Pa., and the boys carried it on 'hikes' when they stayed away from camp. . . .

"It keeps well and does not spoil. I do not know about its [present] use in aviation but would think that its exceptional properties would make it of the first importance, for an emergency food as well as a regular article of diet where ease of preparation and maximum nutrition were desired. It can be eaten without cooking or stewed in boiling water, in which case other things can be added, like dehydrated vegetables, etc."

By the middle of the nineteenth century the tropics and temperate zone were pretty well mapped and the real explorations were mainly in the polar regions, Arctic and Antarctic. At this time the United States began to compete seriously in the field of exploration. The chief use of pemmican from then on was, therefore, among the polar explorers.

Rear Admiral Robert Edwin Peary (1856-1920) is usually considered the greatest of modern Arctic explorers, or as sharing that distinction with Fridtjof Nansen. In sledging he far outranked Nansen, and he is no doubt the greatest sledge traveler in the entire history of polar exploration.

A graduate of Bowdoin, Peary began his field work in the

tropics. He was assistant engineer of the Nicaragua Ship Canal survey, 1884-85, and was in charge of the Nicaragua Canal Surveys, 1887-1888.

Peary's first Arctic journey was a reconnaissance of the Greenland Inland Ice in the summer of 1886. He wintered first during 1891-92, and spent in the Arctic altogether nine winters. On some of the longest sledge journeys in history, depending mainly on pemmican as food for men and dogs, he determined the insularity of Greenland, discovered Peary Land, explored Ellesmere Island, and made several journeys out on the drifting ice of the Polar Sea, culminating in his attainment of the North Pole on April 6, 1909. This was accomplished by a round-trip sledge journey, from land to the North Pole and back to land again, where about nine hundred miles were covered in sixty-three days, the men not only walking but at times pulling with the dogs or otherwise working to support the sledges or push them ahead. That journey is the longest on record where dependence was on pemmican.

Peary retired from active field work in 1909. There were then available only two techniques that made long polar journeys feasible; one to live by hunting, the other to carry the things needed. Peary was the unquestioned master of the second technique. It seemed to his explorer friends, as it did to his publishers, that he ought to write a book explaining his methods so that they would not be lost to future generations. The result was *Secrets of Polar Travel*, New York, 1917. I quote from pages 78-79:

"Too much cannot be said of the importance of pemmican to a polar expedition. It is an absolute *sine qua non*. Without it a sledge-party cannot compact its supplies within a limit of weight to make a serious polar journey successful. . . . With pemmican, the most serious sledge-journey can be undertaken and carried to a successful issue in the absence of all other foods.

"Of all foods that I am acquainted with, pemmican is the only one that, under appropriate conditions, a man can eat twice a day * for three hundred and sixty-five days in a year and have the last mouthful taste as good as the first.

"And it is the most satisfying food I know. I recall innumerable marches in bitter temperatures when men and dogs had been worked to the limit and I reached the place for camp feeling as if I could eat my weight of anything. When the pemmican ration was dealt out, and I saw my little half-pound lump, about as large as the bottom third of an ordinary drinking-glass, I have often felt a sullen rage that life should contain such situations.

"By the time I had finished the last morsel I would not have walked round the completed igloo for anything or everything that the St. Regis, the Blackstone, or the Palace Hotel could have put before me."

During the twenty-three years from 1886 to 1909, Peary had been almost continuously either traveling within the Arctic or preparing at home for new Arctic journeys, so what he tells us in 1917 of pemmican is the opinion of a man who has used this food through so many years that one may think he has forgotten what he thought of it during the first and second years. Accordingly, I quote a British traveler who was a member of only two expeditions, a total of three Antarctic seasons, during which time the sledging on which pemmican was used probably did not cover much more than a total of six months. For in camp they would naturally use little pemmican, since these expeditions, like practically all others, were short on condensed foods and used them, therefore, only where other foods would not serve because of their too great bulk and weight.

Raymond E. Priestley was a member of the scientific staffs of the first Shackleton expedition, 1907-09, and the second Scott expedition, 1910-13. He served with distinction through

* On sledge journeys Peary used only two meals. morning and evening.

the First World War, and among his books is a *History of the* [British] *Signal Service in France*. He has been Secretary General of the Faculties of the University of Cambridge, England; Vice-Chancellor of Melbourne University, Australia; and has been since 1938 Principal and Vice-Chancellor of the University of Birmingham, England. In his book *Antarctic Adventure*, New York, 1915, he refers to pemmican frequently in terms of its being a standard food. I quote only what he says on page 344:

"Our pemmican consisted of 60 per cent. of fat * and 40 per cent. of shredded meat, and was an ideal food for sledging.

"Under ordinary circumstances, when one first starts on a journey one's full allowance is seldom eaten, but, as time passes and the work and the keen air take effect, one becomes hungrier and hungrier, until the sledging allowance of pemmican is not sufficient to satisfy the cravings aroused. It is then that pemmican is truly appreciated at its full worth. Nothing else is comparable with it.

"I have taken all sorts of delicacies on short trips when the food allowance is elastic, I have picked up similar delicacies at depots along the line of march, and I have even taken a small plum-pudding or a piece of wedding-cake for a Christmas treat, but on every such occasion I would willingly have given either of these luxuries for half its weight of the regulation pemmican.

"It can therefore be imagined how we looked forward

* The pemmican of the first Scott expedition, of which Shackleton was also a member, had the usual North American Indian proportions of half and half, by weight, rendered fat and dehydrated lean. Apparently both Scott and Shackleton came to the conclusion that this fat percentage was too low; for Scott provided for his own second expedition, and Shackleton for the first expedition he commanded, pemmicans that had by weight 60 per cent of rendered fat, 40 per cent of dehydrated lean. This is the highest fat percentage I have found in any of the exploration records and is considerably higher than that of any pemmicans recently made, so far as I known, by United States packers.

to a resumption of pemmican after a six months' enforced abstinence."

If Priestley, who had lived on a ration that was mainly pemmican for probably less than a year all together was eager to resume it after "a six months' enforced abstinence," it might be surmised that those who had lived on pemmican for years would long for it correspondingly. That is, indeed, the case, when one talks to the addicts; but not many of them have placed this in print, except as in saying that they were glad to be on the road again for they would once more be eating pemmican. But there are some striking cases on record, among them that of the Beaver Club.

The Yankees, Scots and others, who were the pioneers of the North West Company, in many cases retired to Montreal when they became wealthy, and lived there in grand style. A part of the style was the fabulous Club where they feasted on pemmican that had been brought expensively by canoe and man-packing a distance of two thousand miles. Douglas MacKay says in his book *The Honourable Company: A History of the Hudson's Bay Company,* New York, 1936:

"In Montreal the full-blooded lives of these men found outlet in the Beaver Club where hospitality was famous. The club was founded in 1785 with nineteen members who qualified by having wintered in the northwest, 'the *pay de'en Haut.*' Later the membership numbered fifty-five men. The club met fortnightly in winter; fines such as six bottles of Madeira were imposed for neglect of exacting rules and ritual. Members wore large gold medals on club nights. . . .

"Pemmican . . . was brought from the Saskatchewan to be served in the unfamiliar atmosphere of mahogany, silver and candle glow."

12

Pemmican in Transition

THE last chapter saw pemmican near the top of the social ladder, with the magnates of the Beaver Club, pioneers of Big Business in the New World, fetching it from the remote prairies, at great cost, to be the chief dish at their banquets. Nostalgia for youthful days on the frontier was no doubt at the back of their longing for the bread of the wilderness; but at least the association with it must have been pleasant in their memories or they would not have longed for it. And it must have tasted good, even amid delicacies imported from Europe, or they would not have maintained its dominance at their sumptuous dinners.

But pemmican is not by nature a mere delicacy, like caviar; more nearly it is a richer, more compact, roast beef. There was no great future in its use at banquets, since it belongs in the class of staples. The need for it in the fur trade grew less as roads and railways were built that brought in cheap foods at low transportation cost and took furs to market at an equally cheap rate. The traders were businessmen and, though they might pay at a high rate for a little pemmican for their own delectation, they would see to it that their staffs, and particularly their laborers, ate the cheaper meats, fresh or salted.

There was coming along a small-scale use in polar exploration and ballooning, and there were sportsmen who felt they needed condensed rations on hunting or mountain climbing jaunts. Only one *possibility* of a grand-scale need was on the horizon, military outfitting. War is a natural market for provisions that are nourishing and wholesome and which have in addition the qualities of being light, compact, easily preserved and easily prepared—or, best of all, like pemmican, demanding no preparation but still well suited to be an ingredient in cooked dishes when circumstances allow.

Military requirements did not, however, seem likely to open a large market; for the period during which roads and railways were destroying the North American frontier market for concentrated foods was also a time of peace. In this country the Rebellion was ten years in the background and men were feeling confident that there would not be another civil war in the United States. Throughout the world, or at least throughout the white man's world, prevailed the feeling that wars were an anachronism and the confidence that we were moving steadily toward an era of brotherhood. The spread of Christianity was to create a universal love of man for his fellow.

The suitability of pemmican as a military ration did not, then, promise a market to justify its routine industrial production by the meat packers. No doubt those of them who were familiar with pemmican kept it in the backs of their minds, during the eighties and nineties of last century, that if a war came they could readily turn their facilities to the manufacture of this concentrated ration.

For a while the Utopians seemed right. Wars were few and small; and some of them, like the Russo-Japanese, were far away from where pemmican had been known; and, partly also through being short, these remote wars did not develop any large market for concentrated foods.

There were mobile campaigns in which pemmican would have been useful, and in one of these, the Boer War, pemmican was indeed used, as was also the South African biltong, similar to the jerky of the American Indian. The high local reputation and the convenience of local production led Briton and Boer alike to the use of biltong, a fact that has long been known.

That pemmican also was used is less well known; indeed, the news that it was a stand-by ration is likely to come as a surprise to most students of the Boer campaigns. For testimony as to its use we are indebted to that able and colorful soldier and explorer, Major Frederick Russell Burnham, who served in the Boer War as chief of scouts of the British Army in the field, a post for which he was eminently qualified. In the 1880's he had been cowboy, miner and guide in the western United States, and had acted as scout in the Arizona campaigns against the Apaches; during the five-year period 1893-98 he combined exploration of Rhodesia with military scouting for the British forces in the Matabele War. From Africa he went north for two years to operate gold mines in Alaska and the Klondike, whence he was summoned in 1900 by Lord Roberts for the Boer campaign. In his book *Scouting on Two Continents,* New York 1927, Burnham says of pemmican:

"In the North, the great stand-by of Indians and trappers is. pemmican. This is dried meat, finely powdered and put up in animal fat. In the Boer War the iron ration given us was made of four ounces of pemmican and four ounces of chocolate and sugar. On this a man could march thirty-six hours before he began to drop from hunger."

In response to a letter asking for further details of Major Burnham's experience with pemmican, Mrs. Burnham kindly replied on his behalf (September 9, 1945), prefacing the information about the Boer War with the remark that the Major could "cite reams of instances of its [pemmican's], use during his many treks." Of his African experience Mrs. Burnham says:

"The Major states that in Africa they used biltong in all its forms, but that it is not generally known that the iron ration which they used in the Boer War was pemmican, and was the last ration which was "pulled" and only then when ordered by the commanding officer. The ration was prepared in two small tins (soldered together) which were fastened inside the soldiers' belts, and composed of 4 ounces of equal amounts of chocolate and sugar in one tin, and pemmican in the other (4 oz.). This ration was supposed to maintain full vitality for thirty-six hours, and from some of his own experiences the claim was justified."

The feeling of the Canadian soldiers, who participated in the Boer War, that pemmican proved a good ration in Africa, shall be documented presently in a quotation from their chief in that campaign, General Steele.

In the long run the Utopians proved wrong about war markets. Wars, it turned out, were destined to grow bigger, and two large ones were destined to occur in quick succession. The need for a compact military ration developed not merely through the great numbers of combatants involved in World Wars I and II but still more through a new transportation device, the airplane, which could travel so fast that its speed made up in part for its drawbacks as the carrier of heavy loads. Through air freighting there grew up a sudden and special need for compact foods, the very need that pemmican had been invented to fill.

Today it is being said that if there is a third world war the need for concentrated foods is going to be even greater. This is implied, for instance, by the statement of Lord Swinton, head of the British delegation to the air congress of 1944 in Chicago, where he said that if there is another war the troops for an invasion will not come by sea; they will come instead by air. If troops move by plane their food will also, meaning that heavy weight and large bulk are going to be such drawbacks as they never were before—if there is a World War III.

In the lull that has come after World War II, the statesmen and soldiers of the Powers are saying to each other and to the public, with the greatest amity and amiability, that the United States intends to maintain a high pitch of military strength to safeguard the peace of the world, that the Union of Soviet Socialistic Republics is going to do the same thing for the same purpose, and thus down the line of the countries which are or hope to be militarily strong.

There is, then, a promising market for concentrated foods; and pemmican still remains, in 1946, the leader in that field.

World War II involved maneuvers of rapid advance and swift retreat where men had to carry their own food and were not able to cook, the very conditions under which pemmican functions at the top of its qualifications. But the central consideration of the future is that while the role of the airplane grew in World War II, it will be paramount if there is a World War III. In any case, maintaining that readiness for war which has been said to be a guarantee of peace and world stability by Churchill and Montgomery, Roosevelt and Eisenhower, Stalin and Zhukov, will necessarily involve maintaining war technique at the highest level. This means, among other things, the development of air transport and of those supplies, including foods, which are most readily carried by air.

This is the time, then, to study pemmican, with other condensed foods, in relation to a military strength that depends on air transport. The following paragraphs examine, therefore, the theories and facts which apply to pemmican as a military ration.

It has been suggested that in combat flying an exclusive pemmican diet has a characteristic valuable to aviators in that it produces no gas within the intestines. For on mixed diets high-altitude fliers complain of difficulty through the expansion of gas in the digestive tract that results in upward pressure against the diaphragm, causing discomfort that lessens fighting efficiency; in extreme cases the pressure may interfere with heart action. For some this trouble begins to be obtrusive at 16,000 or 17,000 feet, becoming serious above 20,000 feet.*

It is of course true that to avoid gas in the intestinal tract it is not necessary to use pemmican; the same result can be attained by an exclusive diet of fresh meat, using the lean and fat in the proportions desired by each person at a given meal.

A flier would have to confine himself to pemmican, or exclusive meat from another source, for about three days before a flight. In actual service this would mean that he would have to be on the diet the whole time—no hardship to those who are used to it but difficult the first few days to inexperienced men of strongly established mixed diet food habits.

Some army physiologists, who believe in numerous advantages of a meat diet with a high fat content, nevertheless do not favor its use in high-altitude flying, which indicates a canceling disadvantage mitigating against the advantage of getting away from a carbohydrate diet that produces intestinal gases. It would seem that this difficulty has never been reported by balloonists who used pemmican, but it has been complained of by mountaineers as serious above 15,000 feet —for instance by Belmore Browne in his *Conquest of Mt. McKinley.*

A physiologist who has been in charge of instruction for high-altitude work in World War II puts it that if a high fat-protein diet is fed to aviators "immediately before as well as during flight, the capacity to tolerate oxygen lack and to work at high altitudes is reduced. On a high carbohydrate diet similarly taken a definite increase in altitude tolerance is observed. The results are probably due to the fact that, in comparison with carbohydrates, proteins and fats require for

---

* In high-altitude flying the expansion of gas in the circulatory system is more serious—the so-called bends. Against that condition no special merits for pemmican are as yet claimed by even the most enthusiastic fans.

use relatively larger amounts of oxygen, which is less available at high altitudes."

In trench warfare, and in a number of other military situations at moderate altitudes where oxygen is plentiful, there can be a considerable advantage in the low-residue nature of pemmican, which reduces the frequency of bowel movement by several hundred per cent—the period would be changed from once every day or two on a mixed diet to once every five to eight days on an exclusive pemmican diet. This would also be of some post-operative importance in certain types of surgical cases.

The feces of an exclusive meat eater, whether the diet is pemmican or fresh meat, are without disagreeable odor. Since this allegation is hard for many to believe, I refer again to the experience of Professor John C. Torrey, specialist in the study of intestinal flora at the Cornell Medical School of New York City, who has found this difference in comparing the feces of mixed-diet eaters and those who live on exclusive meat. The mixed diets produce odors with which all are familiar, and which few like; Dr. Torrey testifies that with meat eaters the odor is very slight and not disagreeable, being of an acid type, reminding of vinegar.

Apart from the provisioning of war parties by the Plains Indians, the chief uses of buffalo pemmican were peaceful— to make possible the long journeys of the fur trade and to store food from years of plenty against a time of scarcity. The campaigns of the United States Army against the Plains Indians did not come along until the buffalo pemmican era was near its end. Only in the Plains section of Canada did white troops use pemmican in campaigns against the Indians.

But, apart from official adoption by white armies, recommendations for the military use of pemmican are traceable back more than a century. These derive from men who had lived in the buffalo country, from Texas to the Saskatchewan, and from others who had used caribou pemmican thence north to Great Bear Lake.

So far as I have discovered, the first man to recommend pemmican specifically for the use of armies was the famous overland traveler, David Thompson, previously quoted. He described it in 1812 as a "wholesome, well tasted nutritious food, upon which all persons engaged in the Furr Trade mostly depend for their subsistence during the open season." After a detailed and favorable discussion, he says:

"I have dwelt on the above, as it [is] the staple food of all persons, and affords the most nourishment in the least space and weight; . . . it would be admirable provision for the Army and Navy."

The second specific recommendation of pemmican as a military ration which I have found is in the previously referred to *Ocean to Ocean* by Dr. Grant. I have quoted at length what he wrote in 1872 concerning the use of pemmican during a hot-weather journey when his party was living almost exclusively on it. From these entries, which the reader has seen in their proper sequence, the remarks that bear on army use are now extracted and brought together.

"Pemmican is good and palatable uncooked and cooked . . . It has numerous other recommendations for a campaign diet. It keeps sound without being canned or salted for twenty or thirty years, is wholesome and strengthening, portable, and needs no medicine to correct a tri-daily use of it . . . All joined in its praises as the right food for a journey, and wondered why the Government had never used it in war time. . . . As an army marches on its stomach, condensed food is an important object for the commissariat to consider, especially when, as in the case of the British Army, long expeditions are frequently necessary."

However, Thompson was a geographer and businessman, Grant a doctor of divinity and a university president. From an army point of view the recommendations of army men are more pertinent. We turn to them.

As said, the Indian wars of the United States in the prairie West came at the stage when the buffalo was disappearing, and with it the making of pemmican; so only a few army men had a chance to use this food. Some of them report that it did not taste particularly agreeable on first trial, but they usually add that you like it when you get used to it.

In another connection I have quoted Major J. W. Powell, veteran of the Civil War, who recommended pemmican as better than several other Indian foods the use of which by white men was by then widespread. However, Powell was apparently thinking of it for civilian rather than army purposes.

A soldier who made a special study of pemmican, using it and making inquiries about it, was Hiram Martin Chittenden, who graduated from West Point with the class of 1884 and (after a varied service including the Spanish-American War) became a Brigadier General in 1910, soon after which he was retired for physical disability.

Both while in the army and later, Chittenden devoted his leisure to scholarship. He wrote several books which rank high, each in its sphere. His *The American Fur Trade of the Far West,* published in 1902, is generally recognized as the great work in the field. A full reprint was issued at New York in 1935, for the original had become scarce. I quote from Vol. II, pages 801-802:

"It was not always, however, that the hunter or traveler had the buffalo with him, and it became necessary to provide in times of plenty against the times of deficiency. This was ordinarily done by the process of jerking or drying the meat. . . .

"The Indians had another process of curing buffalo meat, equal, if not superior, to the most approved canning processes, and wholly free from the use of chemicals. . . .

"This was the much used pemmican . . . it would last indefinitely and was always ready for use without cooking. It formed a very palatable as well as nutritious food."

Unlike those of the United States, Canada's military struggles with the Plains Indians came, as has been said, at a time when the buffalo, although no longer numerous within the territory of the United States, was still abundant where now are the Prairie Provinces and where the Canadian government had those troubles with the Indians which are known as the Riel Rebellions. One of Canada's most distinguished soldiers received his training there.

Major General Sir Samuel Benfield Steele (1849-1919) had a military career throughout. Born at Purbrook, Ontario, he obtained a commission at the age of seventeen as ensign in the 35th Regiment of Militia. He served during the Fenian Raid of 1866 and in the Red River expedition of 1870. *The Canadian Encyclopedia* says:

"In 1873 he became a troop sergeant-major in the Royal North West Mounted Police; and in 1885 he became superintendent in command of this force. He commanded the cavalry during the North West rebellion of 1885. During the South African War he commanded Strathcona's Horse; and from 1901 to 1906 he was in command of the South African constabulary. In 1907 he returned to Canada and in 1915 he was appointed to the command of the Second Canadian Contingent in the Great War, with rank of major-general. In 1916 he was made general officer commanding the Shorncliffe area; and he died at London, England, on January 30, 1919."

It may be that no soldier has ever been better qualified than Steele, by his own experience and by that of his associates, to judge pemmican. He received his training far enough east so that pemmican was unknown, or at least unused; he was not, therefore, habituated to it from childhood, as were some of the fur traders and explorers who have been quoted. He began to serve on the plains at the age of 21, and continued there until the beginning of the South African War, 1899. Thus he was familiar with the use of pemmican by the regular army (both old country British and Canadian), and by the Northwest Mounted Police through the service of which he rose until he was its chief. During his African command of the famous Strathcona cavalry in the Boer War he became equally familiar with biltong, a ration as common there as pemmican was on the Canadian prairies.

General Steele's *Forty Years in Canada* was published at Toronto in 1915. It contains a number of passing references to pemmican and two comparatively extensive passages, in Chapters V and VI.

In Chapter V Steele has finished his years of apprenticeship on the plains that began with the Red River Expedition of 1870. He is now describing the organization of the Northwest Mounted Police (which later became the Royal Northwest Mounted Police, and still later the Royal Canadian Mounted Police). The party had left Winnipeg and were traveling westerly across the prairies:

"On the Salt Plain we met several brigades of carts driven by hunters, freighters and traders with packs of buffalo robes, dried meat and pemmican. Inspector Jarvis bought a supply of pemmican, which is the best food in the world for the traveller, soldier and sailor . . ."

In Chapter VI, Steele is telling of the Edmonton country, the valley of the Saskatchewan. He describes a buffalo hunt and then the manufacture of pemmican:

"The winter hunt was for robes and meat; the spring and summer hunt for pemmican and dried meat. . . .

"Pemmican would keep in perfect condition for decades. I do not know what the record is, but I have seen sacks of pemmican which had been worn smooth by transportation, not a hair being left, and yet it was as good as the best made within the year. It is first-class food for travellers, hunters or soldiers, and, now that the buffalo no longer roam the plains, it can be made from the meat of the domestic animal, and is much superior to the 'biltong' of South Africa."

Major Frederick Russell Burnham, whom we have quoted a few pages back on the use of pemmican in the Boer War, confirmed in September 1945 that he is in agreement with General Steele's views on pemmican and biltong.

The regular pemmican sources dried up when the buffalo disappeared. Thereafter beef pemmican was made for the Mounted Police on special occasions—notably a large quantity at the time of the Klondike gold rush, 1897-99.

Getting beef pemmican became increasingly difficult, and the quality deteriorated as the people died who had known how to make it from buffalo meat. Although the packing industry never took on the regular manufacture of pemmican, they made it up in small quantities at high prices for sportsmen and explorers, and usually or always on special order. The packers felt then, as they apparently still do, that in their general business they can make more money selling the ordinary salted and canned meats. With the development of transportation, weight and bulk of such things as canned corned beef ceased to be of consequence to the average buyer; cans and salt do keep meat from spoiling, no matter how much water it contains.

The explorers who needed pemmican grew fewer because the unknown lands were steadily contracting. The sportsmen who wanted pemmican grew fewer because their journeys were now shorter. Remained only one form of grand-scale human activity, war, in which it was still crucially important to have food that was light, compact, easy to preserve and convenient to eat without utensils or cooking if necessary. In battle, in a swift pursuit or retreat, a man still might have to carry his own food for several days. In case of siege, or for distant outposts, food might have to be transported by airplane. In crash landings or on bailing out, where men might have to wait long for rescue or be forced to walk, it would be important to have a ration that would keep them strong for the longest time on the least weight. In ships of limited storage space, like destroyers and submarines, bulk and weight are also of consequence, and even more so with life rafts.

It might be supposed, then, that the United States Army and Navy would have placed large orders for pemmican on the day after Pearl Harbor, if they had failed to do so before. But this was not done, nor even a year after Pearl Harbor; and the few officers who were able to secure pemmican, for the special use of their commands, had to fight battles of red tape to get it. The reasons were numerous, but the chief trouble was that there had grown up a cult of "modern" dietetics, according to which pemmican is not a good food.

As is common with disputes, the really serious difficulty on pemmican was that both factions were sincere, each with complete faith in its own kind of evidence. The controversy became so emotional and bitter that it has been called the Second Pemmican War.

13

The Second Pemmican War

THE Second Pemmican War, an internecine strife within the framework of the Second World War, appears in retrospect to have been primarily a struggle between theory and testimony.

At the beginning of World War II, those familiar with the history of the American frontier, whether in the United States or Canada, took it for granted that in a war of global scale, which necessarily involved difficulties of transportation, one item in our plan would be to make use of that strikingly American invention, pemmican, so as to provide our troops with the lightest and most compact of known emergency rations.

There was talk of food winning the war and of air power winning it. A plane could carry victuals for a larger number of people than otherwise if chief dependence were put on this food which had carried the early explorers across the continent, had sustained the fur trade, had taken balloonists to Gordon Bennett Cup victories and Peary to the Pole. It seemed particularly logical that where men would have to carry their food on their backs they would be supplied with a ration small in bulk, light in weight, hard to spoil, easy to prepare if you have a fire and needing no preparation if you have none—a food which, as Admiral Peary had said, you could eat at every meal for a year and not become tired of it.

But to the bewilderment and consternation of these disciples of the history of human diet, it was announced in 1942 that "the dietitians" had ruled pemmican unsuitable for the use of army or navy in any of their services and that the higher-ups in Washington were refusing to honor requests from officers in the field, for instance in the Air Transport Command, that pemmican be issued to them so that, through lighter provisions, they might be able to carry in each plane more men or strategic materials.

Indirectly, the Second Pemmican War may have cost lives through want of the best emergency rations in planes and at the front; but it differed from the First in that there were no outright massacres. However, feeling ran so high and the struggle, though chiefly of the verbal and wire-pulling sort, was so bitter that the designation, the Second Pemmican War, is at least figuratively justified.

A basic difference between the two pemmican wars lay in their objectives. The First was a rebellion of businessmen against the dominance of a corporation and was in defense of the right of the Free Traders to use pemmican; the Second was a revolt of modern dietitians against the traditional dominance of pemmican as an emergency ration and was in defense of the right of laboratory technicians to prefer the results of their experiments to the testimony of experience.

The technicians felt they knew from its chemistry that pemmican was not a good food; they had tasted it and did not like the taste. It was their duty as they saw it to protect our soldiers against this unscientific and disagreeable ration.

The position taken by the nutritionists was, to say the least, bewildering to students of frontier history, which appeared to show that pemmican had moved from one success to another through more than three hundred years of rigorous trial while it supported our plainsmen and became in the fur trade a mainstay of big business. There seemed an inexplicable contradiction between the testimony of thousands through centuries and the alleged discoveries of the dietitians. But we can see now, when we take stock, that the revolt against what had long been a staple food was not the sudden flare-up that it appeared to be but instead had been in the making for a long time.

So, before going on to describe the Second Pemmican War it will be good to look for its antecedents, tracing them as far back as possible, to show that the declaration of a full-scale war on pemmican in 1942 was the result of a protracted and in a way logical development.

The first and deepest root of the Second Pemmican War grew in the soil of a racism which developed slowly with Europe's growing consciousness that through the mastery of gunpowder as a killing device the whites were a master race, holding direct or indirect sway over all lands and peoples that were backward in the use of pistol, musket and cannon. From this gun-engendered sense of power developed the idea that we are a better race than the others, and that our things are better things than theirs, as a rule.

The Red Man of the Americas was obviously far inferior to us, for he did not even have inferior guns; he had no guns at all unless we sold them to him. Through this and a number of other causes he and his way of life were looked down upon. We looked down upon his food and his methods of preparing it. So when we encountered his pemmican on the Western plains we were predisposed against it.

To the avoidance of native foods there was in colonial days a notable exception, or a notable series of them, in early New England. The Plymouth Rock and some other groups of settlers came so near starving that they were forced to eat the food of the local natives. Hunger is such a good sauce, and the New Englanders had so much of this sauce, that the Indian victuals tasted good. The scarcity lasted so long that before it was over the use of the foods of the New England Indian had acquired the force of an established food habit; their use became a national heritage. Roast turkey, corn on the cob, corn bread, pumpkin pie, maple sugar, succotash, and a number of other dishes of the lowly savage, had been adopted. Their use spread throughout our territory as the whites moved westward.

To a less but nevertheless material extent there was hardship the first years among various of the other seaboard colonies, from Nova Scotia and Quebec south to the Carolinas and Georgia. Local foods were adopted somewhat as in New England; their use spread westward as the pioneers advanced.

But pemmican was not one of these foods, for it did not exist along the seaboard. It was a discovery or invention of the Plains Indians and had not as yet penetrated east across the Appalachians though it had, in places, crossed the Rockies. Our people did not come in contact with it, therefore, during that early period when hunger was an ever-ready fillip—a period, too, in which the colonists were, to an extent, receptive to new things. They realized they were in a new world and so had an inclination to taste new fruits and learn if they were good.

In the time before the Louisiana Purchase only a few of our hardiest and most adaptable crossed the Appalachians and reached the prairies, chiefly to buy furs and to hunt the buffalo. It has already been shown how readily these took to jerky and pemmican when they discovered them among the buffalo Indians.

However, it seems likely that the earliest of these Western pioneers may have been the first to launch against pemmican as a condensed food the sort of attack that has, in the long run, been the most effective against it.

The pemmican Indians were, in the main, exclusive meat eaters, in the sense that if they had enough meat they ate little or nothing else. By contrast, the Indians along the Atlantic seaboard were largely agricultural. Upon landing, the European colonizers, who were agriculturists, had found themselves among people who depended on corn and beans and squash. With the exception of the turkey, the unfamiliar foods with which the Indians sustained the colonists through the first years were in their nature chiefly agricultural.

So when the pioneers reached the buffalo-hunting and

pemmican-using Western prairies they brought with them European tastes, slightly modified by the Indian type of agriculture. They were used to eating potatoes and bread with their never very abundant meat, and to them it would not seem right to follow the custom of the plains and to eat straight buffalo, whether fresh or as jerky and pemmican.

Here reference must again be made to the contention of some that before the whites entered the buffalo country the Indians had no berry pemmican but used only two ingredients, dried lean and rendered fat. If that was so, if there was no berry pemmican in Nebraska when the New Englanders and Virginians arrived, they would almost certainly have invented it, introducing berries as a flavoring to make the pemmican seem more familiar through an increased resemblance to suet pudding.

But their finding berry pemmican already in use seems the more probable, for the exclusively buffalo eating tribes had been, some of them, to a considerable extent agricultural before they obtained the horse from the Spaniards and became so successful as mounted hunters that they saw no further need to piece out their beef meals with garden truck.

With their general fondness for mixed dishes, the whites would naturally have encouraged the Indians to make more berry pemmican, giving a higher price for it in exchange for trade goods.

Mincemeat, plum duff and suet pudding are the foods that English-descended Americans were most used to in colonial times, of those that resemble pemmican. None of these is made of suet and lean meat alone, flavored with berries or other fruit; they also contain cereal ingredients. Pemmican could therefore be made more like what the Europeans were used to if cereals were mixed in. So we begin to hear, although not to any extent until past the middle of the nineteenth century, that some pemmicans had corn meal in them.

Many of those who are used to plain pemmican are fond

of it, as I have brought out in quotations. But still and all, pemmican is not by nature a dessert or a confection, it is in chief a condensed food, a ration for wayfarers and warriors who need to travel light so they can move fast and go far. Its claim to excellence is that it gets the maximum energy from minimum weight and bulk. That end is attained by having in it no more protein than is required for optimum health, deriving all the rest of the energy units from fat, one ounce of which is as good as two and a quarter ounces of either a protein or a carbohydrate.

For permanent good health there is required an irreducible minimum of protein, furnished by the pemmican through its shredded or powdered lean meat. The fat element, however, can be replaced by a carbohydrate, meaning starch or sugar, without impairment of health; but this substitution cannot be made without decreasing the merit of pemmican as a condensed ration, because every ounce of fat removed will need to be replaced by more than double its weight of starch or sugar. With dried fruit, such as berries or raisins, the case is worse; for it takes far more than two ounces of raisins to make up in nourishment for an ounce of fat.

So there we have the attack on pemmican revealed. By progressively adding more and more fruit, by adding sugar or flour, to make the food more nearly European style, the Europeans tended to increase the bulk and weight, which meant decreasing the advantage that pemmican has over other foods in being lighter and more compact for a given energy value. A so-called pemmican that contains raisins, shredded coconut, pea meal, sugar, and the like, is no longer very light or very compact in proportion to energy value, and ceases to have the true pemmican's great advantage over other food.

The first step, then, that led to the Second Pemmican War, the struggle of 1942-45 for the overthrow of pemmican as a dominant condensed ration, was taken by the first European, whoever and wherever he was, who told the first Indian that pemmican would be "better" if it had more fruit in it.

The attack of the adulterators upon the pure travel ration was more serious than has thus far been indicated. For pemmican had a great merit other than portability in being the most preservable of foods. It is the true pemmican, made exclusively of dried lean and rendered fat, concerning which we have testimony that it was as good after twenty or thirty years as the day it was made. Pemmicans which had dried berries in them did not keep well, in comparison. The "modern" pemmicans that contain ground-up bacon, shredded coconut, butter, pea meal, and the like, spoil quickly. They cannot be used on long summer journeys, unless canned.

The double attack of the adulterators upon the portability and the preservability of pemmican has been increasing in its effectiveness to the present, and has been one of the chief weapons in the hands of the revolutionaries of the Second Pemmican War. As shall be shown later, by quoting a letter from the Surgeon General of the Navy, it has even been possible during World War II, first, to give the name "pemmican" to a candy bar which contained not only a great deal of sugar, vegetable oil and peanuts but even had chocolate to take the place of the lean beef—and, then, to get a ruling passed by the Navy, on the basis of this candy mixture, that pemmican shall not be used because it is thirst provoking!

A few pages back I made the point that Europeans, after becoming lords of the earth through the skilful use of gunpowder, developed the racist idea that we whites are better than folk of other colors, we looking down upon the colored peoples as generally inferior and upon their food as of a lower grade. I now return to that argument, considering how pemmican was affected by the idea that it was derived from a people socially beneath us, and that it was therefore a food which it was beneath us to use.

Women, at least European women but no doubt women generally, are sticklers for the proprieties. The first whites who reached the Plains were generally single men and frequently of the extremely adaptable Kit Carson type who took readily to the ways of any people among whom they traveled or lived. A good biography of Carson, any good book on the lives of the mountain men and plainsmen of his period, shows them living in the best of health and in full content on an exclusively meat diet for the larger part of each year. They took readily to pemmican, which became their staff of life, that and jerky.

But after the true plainsmen came the agricultural pioneers. They brought their women who, in turn, brought with them the idea that Indian food was not good enough for them. They insisted it was not good enough for their husbands, either, and certainly not for their children, who were not going to grow up like savages if their mothers could help it.

One of many writers who bring out this attitude of the second-string pioneer women is Irene D. Paden. I quote from her excellent book *The Wake of the Prairie Schooner*. She has been talking about diet standards of the Plains which were satisfactory to the men, and goes on: "Women, on the other hand, were invariably prejudiced in favor of a better variety of food. They carried potatoes and squash, eggs safely packed in corn meal which would be used up as the eggs vanished, rice, preserves, pickles, and other imperishable commodities. Breadstuffs were often carried in barrels." These things, under the firm social guidance of the women, took the place of the buffalo steaks and roasts, the jerky and pemmican, that had been the daily food of the Kit Carsons of the early West.

Europeans are used to having fresh meat, and so the use
of fresh buffalo meat was in line, and was not strongly opposed by the women. But pemmican was distinctly not European. It was an invention of savages, and the white women
found it an "unappetizing concoction." Mrs. Paden sums it
up: "Pemmican was the standby of the plainsman, but not
so often used by polite society—even in wagon trains. . . .
This confection was used after other supplies were gone, but
it is said that a man could do a harder day's work on pemmican than on any other food."

Bernard De Voto, historian of the frontier who was quoted
two chapters back, thinks women responsible for a gradual
spread throughout the West of the idea that it was not the
thing to eat native foods. His previously mentioned letter
of July 26, 1944, says: "I know of no complaint about the
taste of even the plain dried meat until there are women in
the West, after which remarks about its palatability, or more
often its unappetizing appearance, are common enough. . . ."

Placing responsibility not on the women but rather on
newcomers in general, who bring along their old food habits,
Miss Anne M. Henderson of Winnipeg, secretary of the Lord
Selkirk Association of Rupert's Land, agrees that pemmican
ceased to be used when families began to move into the
plains country, instead of the single men who had come
earlier. She thinks that, as a result, local health suffered,
particularly as to scurvy. In a long and valuable letter on
the food of the pioneers she said in 1944:

"A friend, whose family pioneered in Saskatchewan in the
early 80's, remarked that scurvy was always a nightmare to
them. . . . These people, coming in from Eastern Canada,
bringing their own customs with them and insisting upon
following them, of course did not use pemmican."

The first attacks on pemmican, then, were along the line
of making it less nourishing and less preservable through
blending it to make it conform more nearly to the established

food habits of the early whites. Then came attacks based on sociological and psychological grounds. White women, when they appeared on the plains, opposed it specially. Both men and women tended to oppose it because it was of low native origin. The immigrants were considered, by themselves, to be of a higher mold.

Sad to say, the next and one of the most effective attacks came from the best friends pemmican has recently had, the polar explorers. Quite unintentionally, but the more effectively for that, they introduced the notion that pemmican is specially suited for use in cold weather. From this was drawn the complementary inference that it is not well suited for use in summer or in the tropics.

First to fall in with the new attitude were the navies of the United States and Britain. Army men, like General Chittenden of the United States prairies and General Steele of the Canadian prairies, knew pemmican from the Indians and the fur trade, so they recommended it in their books without qualification as to season, doubtless thinking of it really as a summer food, their experience with it having been mainly in that season.

Unlike the army, the navy heard of pemmican, it seems, first from the polar explorers, thus with the implication that it was primarily a cold weather diet. This idea was destined to spread wide and deep and to become a serious theoretical handicap to pemmican as an all-year and all-climate food.

I have quoted the British polar authority Admiral McClintock as saying that he and the rest of the explorers of the middle nineteenth century just ate pemmican and kept in good health. Sir Clements Markham, president of the Royal Geographical Society of London, who looked upon himself as a naval man, criticized the diet of the second Scott expedition as not having had a large enough percentage of pemmican. The literature is full of similar cases. So the British Navy was definitely favorable; but they were always, as far as I have been able to discover, thinking of pemmican *as a winter food* and commending it in those terms. The case is the same with the United States Navy.

Rear Admiral Winfield Scott Schley (1839-1911) graduated from Annapolis in 1860 and served through the Civil War but is most widely known in connection with the Spanish-American War. During 1884 he was in command of an Arctic expedition for the rescue of Lieutenant (later Major General) A. W. Greely. Of this operation he made an official report, and also a popular one through a book, *The Rescue of Greely,* which was signed jointly by Schley and by Professor J. R. Soley (1850-1911), who graduated from Harvard in 1870, was head of the Department of History and Law at the United States Naval Academy 1872-1882, and was Assistant Secretary of the Navy 1890-1893. I quote from page 132: "The pemmican, which is always the most nutritious food in the most compact form for Arctic work, was packed in one and two-pound cans and boxes. . . . It is palatable and wholesome, and may be eaten from the can, or cut into cakes and fried."

A good many sportsmen were buying pemmican and continuing its summer use; the like may be said of a few balloonists. But the general public heard little of this and much of one polar explorer after another who varied from the discreetly lyrical to the dithyrambic in praise, but always in connection with cold weather, for that was when sledge journeys were made. Indeed, the belief spread among the polar explorers themselves that pemmican was a cold-weather food, primarily.

Moreover, there grew up in the late nineteenth century, or was much strengthened, a view which has continued gaining prestige in the twentieth, that foods rich in fat are not suitable for warm weather. That view was discussed in the chapter "Living on the Fat of the Land," where it was shown that this folk belief is not merely of recent origin, and confined geographically to certain districts, but also that it is contradicted by the general knowledge of the very people who hold the belief. In any case, we of the United States, Canada and northern Europe are passing just now through a phase of "modern" dietetic theory in which it is commonly accepted that fats are not desired in summer, and that they are not desirable in summer, or in the tropics, where it is always summer.

When the standard blends derive from 70 per cent to 90 per cent of their energy units from fat, it is obvious that no one is going to favor pemmican as a summer diet if he believes that fat is undesirable in warm weather. But it follows that these same people are going to think it comparatively good as a winter diet. The errors are reciprocal, to think that fat is particularly undesirable on a hot day and to think that it is particularly desirable on a cold one.

This theoretical attack, however, merely demoted pemmican from an all-year food to a winter food. Other theoretical attacks proved more serious in that their condemnation did not fluctuate with the season.

During the last two or three generations there has been a growth and spread of the belief that, in order to be healthy, one needs a varied diet. According to this view, as it stands now, one should have each day, or at the least each week, a little fruit, a little cereal, a little egg, a little milk, a little green vegetable, a little yellow vegetable, a little red meat, a little fish, and so on.

Now there is no variety in pemmican—no cereal, no fruit, no milk—so, by the current theory, one cannot be healthy on it. Testimony that thousands of people a year for hundreds of years have been healthy on pemmican does not mean a thing to a person if he is sufficiently convinced, as most people are, that a varied diet is essential to health. So one dismisses as fiction the alleged facts of those who say it is feasible to remain in good health permanently on exclusive meat; or he explains them away, feeling there must have been this, that or the other modifying condition.

Then, when one has proved to himself, by reviewing the theory, that pemmican is not a good exclusive food, he feels inclined to extend the reasoning and conclude that neither can it be much good as an element in a mixed diet.

One of the acclaimed discoveries a few decades back was crystallized by the slogan: "Fat burns only in the flame of the carbohydrates." This was interpreted to mean that the human body could not utilize fat without the help of carbohydrates; amplified, it meant that if one ate a lot of fat he had to eat a lot of carbohydrates to help use up the fat.

This doctrine turned out to be a foundation for the most serious of all the theoretical attacks on pemmican. For the standard blend of the fur trade contains no carbohydrates, except the tiny amount that is in meat; so that the fat which from the chemist's point of view represented 75 per cent or 80 per cent of the energy units was scarcely usable at all, by the theory, because of the lack of carbohydrates with which to "burn" the fat. An extreme deduction would be that about all the energy the human body can obtain from pemmican is what it can get out of the lean, the body thus being able to utilize only 20 per cent or 25 per cent of the theoretical energy contained in a unit of pemmican. In the emotional heat of the Second Pemmican War some of its dietitian opponents have been taking this very stand.

In a sense it is an outgrowth of the "fat burns only" theory to claim that acidosis, or ketosis, will develop when there is "too high a percentage" of fat in pemmican. Dietitians the last few years have varied in their estimation of what "too high" means in this connection. Some say that 30 per cent is permissible, while others go to 40 per cent or 50 per cent; those who consider themselves very liberal permit 60 per cent of energy units derivable from fat. Even that liberal top estimate falls well below the fat content level of the fur trade pemmicans.

Here I repeat what has been said in another connection, that when two of us were living at the Russell Sage Institute on an exclusive fresh meat diet, and when we chose at each meal between fat and lean according to our taste at the moment, with nothing to choose between except lean and fat, we selected our food so that, in the opinion of the supervising technicians, we were deriving 75 per cent to 80 per cent of our calories from fat, the remainder from the lean. Thus, by trial and error, we arrived in New York at the same proportion of fat and lean which had been arrived at in the same way by the Plains Indians in their compounding of pemmican centuries before.

But, as said, this means nothing to those who are really convinced, as most dietitians are, that a high percentage of fat in meals is not desirable.

However, it should be noted that, although much of the current opposition to pemmican is traceable to the theory that "fat burns only in the flame of the carbohydrates," it is also true that the theory itself began to give ground a few years ago. A leading physiologist (who does not seem to admire dietitians as a class) told me while I was composing this chapter that he considers even a dietitian blameably slow on the uptake if he held this theory later than 1942— he should have dropped it somewhat earlier.

For a nutritionist who holds to "fat burns only," there appears to be no way of escape open if he tries to reconcile his theory with the experience of pemmican users and of exclusive meat eaters generally. However, once that theory is jettisoned reconciliation can be attained by suggesting that the diets on which ketosis troubles have been observed, when fat gave only 40 per cent or 50 per cent of the total number of energy units, were diets which contained carbohydrates as well as fats. The carbohydrates could then be made the villains of the piece, by saying that instead of being useful in handling the fats they are as a matter of fact harmful—that fats are more effectively usable when there are only two main elements in the diet, fats and proteins, than when there are three—fats, proteins and carbohydrates.

This appeared such a common-sense idea that letters were written to several leading physiologists to get their views on it. Most of them replied that they did not as yet fully understand the interrelations of fats, carbohydrates and proteins in human alimentation. They were also inclined to feel that, since ketosis has often been reported troublesome on mixed diets when no more than 50 per cent or 60 per cent of calories are derived from fat, but not troublesome on an all-meat diet, even when the fat yielded 75 per cent to 80 per cent of the calories, it seemed likely that the presence of carbohydrates does interfere with the utilization of fat; or, putting it the other way, that replacing the carbohydrates in a meal with protein may facilitate the body's use of fat.

Most of the communications received are, on this point, fairly summarized in a paragraph from a letter written April 17, 1944, by a commanding authority in the field, Dr. Walter B. Cannon, Harvard professor emeritus of physiology and former president of the American Association for the Advancement of Science: "It seems to me possible that the specific dynamic action of protein may accelerate metabolism to such a degree as to permit (in an all-meat diet) a larger intake of fat without ketosis than is possible with a mixed diet."

It seems permissible also to suggest that, while there is an indispensable thing in diet, protein, the two other chief elements of the conventional modern diet, fats and carbohydrates, are not both of them needed but are reciprocal, in the sense that the less carbohydrates one eats the more fat he has room for, and vice versa.

The impression must not be given that the 1942-45 war

against pemmican was fought solely by army and navy dietitians and nutritionists. They were supported, for instance, by some of the chemists and biologists of the meat industry. It appears that in recent years notable advances have been made in the study of enzymes, one of the conclusions being that rancidity will develop in beef tallow if the air has access to it, particularly, it seems, if no salt is used as a preservative and if the weather is warm. So when the packers were asked to furnish unsalted and uncanned pemmican they demurred, for their technical men "knew" that it would not keep. One of the leading scientists of the industry went on record in support of one of the leading scientists of the Quartermaster General, to the effect that, until they discovered a method of controlling certain enzymes, pemmican would have to be canned to keep it from going rancid during summer.

There was, however, no such unity, real or seeming, among the scientists of the meat industry as among those of the army —perhaps a matter of discipline—for there were men high in Chicago positions who questioned the infallibility of the enzyme conclusions of the research workers.

There was, for instance, Colonel Edward Norris Wentworth, Director of Armour's Livestock Bureau. He knew of an unsealed container of rendered mutton fat which had remained on a shelf in a Florida home for more than twenty years without going rancid.

Colonel Wentworth thought beef fat might do almost or quite as well; so he kept open in his office several cans of beef pemmican which his company made in 1942. He meant to keep them there indefinitely, but wrote me in 1944 that inadvertently he got them emptied, through his own nibbling at the contents, and that of his friends. However, the last open can did not become empty for more than a year— of Chicago summer heat and ordinary winter office temperature. The final chunk he nibbled at showed no sign of rancidity.

Nevertheless, the last word received from the Office of the Quartermaster General, in 1944, was that they would not countenance the use of uncanned pemmican until some method had been discovered for controlling enzyme action in rendered beef fat.

In the summer of 1943, when emotions generated by the row within the United States Army between the theory school and the experience school regarding pemmican were at or above the prevailing June temperatures, one of the tropical advisers of the Quartermaster General, Earl Parker Hanson, found himself in hot water (to keep up the warm similes) over his belief, gathered through many years of travel and residence in different parts of the tropics, that people are just as likely to enjoy fat in weather which is hot and humid as in any other climate. We asked him for a statement, which he kindly supplied through a letter dated February 29, 1944. Because it seemed even more interesting on the side of general principles than in its specific bearing on pemmican, I used the full text in the chapter "Living on the Fat of the Land." I comment on the letter here from the pemmican side.

The test covered nine weeks in June, July and August. Some of the time was spent in New York but most of it in Washington, which at that time of year is one of the most distressingly hot and humid places in the United States. So this was a trial both of pemmican as an exclusive food and of its suitability in a climate which in previous years Hanson had found a little warmer than, and quite as damp as, anything he had ever seen in two full years spent going up and down the Orinoco and Amazon.

The Hanson letter refers to a trait of pemmican, which I have indeed emphasized, that in beginning its use, even when one has eaten so much that any more would produce nausea, the stomach (large through the habitual use of bulky foods) still craves more as a filling. This tends towards over-eating, with resulting nausea.

Then there is a visual difficulty about realizing that what you are going to eat is really a square meal. As Peary has it, "When the pemmican ration was dealt out, and I saw my little half-pound lump, about as large as the bottom third of an ordinary drinking-glass"—then he could not realize that he was going to get a square meal, even though he had frequently been satiated by like amounts in the past. "By the time I had finished the last morsel I would not have walked round the completed igloo for anything or everything that the St. Regis, the Blackstone, or the Palace Hotel could have put before me." The tiny lump always did satisfy him, no matter how hungry he was, but it was hard for him to remember this the next day.

The trouble with inexperienced men in Peary's situation is that they eat more than he did, perhaps a lump as big as two-thirds of a water tumbler, and then they are nauseated. Hanson solved the difficulty by eating small amounts, each of which would temporarily satisfy him.

After five or six days on exclusive pemmican and unsweetened tea, Hanson found himself eating per day about three-quarters of a pound of a blend that derived 80 per cent of its calories from beef fat, the remainder from lean beef. With this quantity in those proportions he felt well fed and at ease. He tried another blend, where the calories were 60 per cent from fat and the rest from lean; of this he ate a full pound a day, four ounces more than of the other, and had a vague discomfort which he came to recognize as a sign that he needed a higher fat ratio. He recovered his sense of well-being when he shifted to a quarter pound less of the 80/20 blend.

If any reader wishes to follow up with close attention to detail, he had better review the full Hanson text on pages 135–42.

That there is likelihood of overeating when men are unused to pemmican has always been the chief trouble while
it is being introduced. For instance, in the Blue Books of
the British Government, which tell about the Franklin search
expeditions of the middle of the nineteenth century, there
are reported frequent complaints by sailors, novices to this
food, that when they ate a little pemmcian it took away
their appetite, both for more pemmican and for other food
—which they understood to show that pemmican was not a
suitable diet.

There are complaints in the Blue Books also that when
the full ration assigned to the sailors was consumed the men
were nauseated. This is hardly a wonder. Mr. Hanson found
that he could do moderately hard work on nine-tenths of a
pound a day, and nothing else but water; but some of these
British rations were as high as 1¼ pounds of pemmican,
with other food in addition which brought the total up to
around 2½ and even 3 pounds. The sailors were inclined
to eat the whole ration, for its bulk was no more than what
they were used to having in their stomachs, doubtless somewhat less; but by the time they had filled the accustomed
space they had eaten too much.

One of the reasons sometimes assigned for nutritionist opposition to pemmican within the army is that it requires an
excessive drinking of water. I have corresponded on this with
a number of the more prominent physiologists, several of
whom have answered to the effect that we have not the necessary information to say whether a ration composed, for
instance, of nothing but pemmican made by the usual 80-20
formula, would call for more or less drinking water than an
army K-ration.

At this stage in the inquiry it was called to my attention
that the United States Navy had issued an order against the
use of pemmican, on the ground that it required excessive
water consumption. There were press dispatches about it

which had wide circulation and which may have had a number of sources, perhaps some of them outside the Navy. One form of the statement was:

"During the process of digestion of foods such as pemmican and chocolate certain salts are formed that require considerable water for their elimination, thus increasing the rate of dehydration of the body. Therefore it is requested that the following changes in aeronautical emergency food rations be accomplished soon as practicable. Remove all pemmican and chocolate . . ."

On the basis of this press release a letter was written to the Bureau of Medicine and Surgery of the Navy Department. A reply came which was signed by Vice Admiral Ross T. McIntire, Surgeon General of the Navy, dated March 16, 1944:

"This letter is an answer to yours of March 3, 1944. In it you ask concerning the reason for removing 'pemmican' and chocolate from the Navy aircraft emergency ration. You also ask for the formula of this 'pemmican' and inquire why the Navy uses this term for the product.

"The statement which you quote concerning the reason for the removal of the 'pemmican' and chocolate from the aircraft emergency ration appeared also in Naval Aviation News for March 1, 1944. The reason presented therein is not the correct one. Actually, these two items were removed from the ration because the majority of reports indicate that the 'pemmican' is difficult to swallow when the mouth is dry, and that the chocolate increases thirst, as well as being distasteful to some. . . .

"One 3¾ ounce can of each of 3 slightly different types of 'pemmican' was formerly provided in the aircraft emergency ration. The formulae for these 3 types follow (Schedule 5217, Bureau of Supplies and Accounts). . . . The figures given in the table represent parts by weight of the ingredients:

	Class 1	Class 2	Class 3
a. Rendered kidney fat	9	9	9
b. Prime oleo oil	6	6	6
c. Seedless raisins	30	30	30
d. Evaporated apples	15	..	..
e. Crisp bacon	..	15	..
f. Peanuts	..	..	15
g. Dextrose	15	15	15
h. Shredded coconut	25	25	25
i. Vanilla extract	1.5	1.5	1.5
j. Salt	1	1	1

[Here we omit further specifications as to the required grade of each ingredient.]

"It is not clear from our records whether the designation 'pemmican' was given these products by the Navy, or whether the experimental samples were already so designated by Armour and Company when they were first supplied to this Bureau in 1938."

This letter shows, then, that the Navy had not been using pemmican at all, in the sense of an exclusive meat preparation, but had been using instead a sort of candy bar which was, no doubt, the invention of some dietitian, and to which the name of pemmican had been given by somebody. That is the danger with a famous name of good repute—it is likely to be taken and used for the promotion of new things, which may or may not turn out to be good but which, in any case, are not the same thing as the original.

As mentioned, I had been corresponding with physiologists, trying to find out why pemmican was so commonly alleged to be thirst-provoking, and had received letters from several of them to the effect that not enough was known about pemmican and the applicable physiology to make a decision, for or against. Newspaper reports made it seem that the Navy actually had made the needed studies; but Admiral McIntire's letter shows that what the Navy had been working on was not pemmican; that the concoction found by them hard to swallow was instead a mixture wherein raisins, shredded coconut and dried apples were, by weight, the chief ingredients; and that *the food specifically charged by the Navy with being thirst-provoking was not any meat preparation but chocolate.*

During the early part of the Second World War, when recommendations were first made to the Office of the Quartermaster General that pemmican be issued as a meat component of mixed rations, and also for exclusive use in survival rations, there developed the situation which I call the Second Pemmican War. The nutritionists vetoed pemmican and set about inventing substitutes, "condensed" rations which proved far bulkier and more complicated but which met the current dietetic theories through having much variety, little fat, and usually not much lean meat either.

In the Army pemmican dispute, one of the big issues was in reality only a difference in point of view, as to the degree of palatability desired in a survival ration.

The opponents of pemmican said that it was tasteless and unattractive, and that even a life-and-death ration should be appetizing. The pemmican advocates took the opposite stand, maintaining that when you are on a limited allowance, getting less to eat than you would like, and are constantly hungry, then it is folly to make the little you do get tantalizingly attractive. They maintained that in such case a ration should be only mildly agreeable, like roast beef, bread or pemmican; there should be no confectionery sort of appeal but only that urge which derives from need. The moral strain of saving rations against the morrow, they contended, is always serious with a hungry man; it should not be further increased by a deliberate appeal to the palate.

The suggestion has been made that for the average taste pemmican is improved by adding to it about 1 per cent of salt. The fans oppose this; first on the ground that, for an emergency ration, increasing the palatability is a disadvantage; and secondly, because the pemmican might be needed on a life raft or in a desert, whereupon saltiness would be harmful.

But, they point out, if pemmican is being used as an ingredient in a mixed ration, and when conditions allow, then it can be seasoned to taste, and will naturally be flavored by whatever additions there are to it, as, for instance, onions when available and desired.

In the early part of World War II some army officers, chiefly those familiar with the history of pemmican on the plains, in the fur trade and in exploration, requested it for the use of their own commands.

One case was that of a colonel who during 1942 sent in a requisition for pemmican and was told that a much better ration would be forthcoming. When months passed, and no ration came which seemed good enough to be a reasonable substitute, he made a second request, with the same result—information that pemmican was not suitable and that a better ration would be supplied.

In 1943, when the colonel had become a general, he made a third request, whereupon Washington ordered from Chicago something like 20,000 pounds. However, the order specified that second-grade beef should be used, and directed that information describing the contents as of second-grade material should be plainly marked upon each container.

Those familiar with pemmican were surprised to see what a satisfactory reception this lot received when it was delivered. The experts had had two main fears. Some were afraid the men would be prejudiced against the batch on account of the "second grade" stamp which appeared large on every can; others thought it an even more serious drawback that the fat component was extremely oily. The manufacturers, with the best intentions in the world, had deliberately used oily fat, their theory being that the pemmican would be for extremely cold weather, and would not be so difficult to handle as if made with a harder fat.

What this commanding officer wanted with pemmican, it seems, was to increase the pay load of his transport airplanes; for he was in the Air Transport Command, where the regulations required that each plane had to carry a ten-day supply for every man aboard. There is a really material difference between a ten-day pemmican ration of ten pounds per man and a ten-day K-ration of more than twenty pounds, when the saving per man is multiplied by the number of men aboard a large army transport, crew and passengers alike counted. I have forgotten how many more passengers per day the general told me he could carry on the average, when he had shifted from K-rations to pemmican, but it was a heartening figure.

The complaint about too soft a fat in the mentioned lot of pemmican brought forth comment from one of the representatives of the packing industry—it seemed strange to him that, with regard to other foods, the War Department had frequently requested the industry to make tests on desirable blends and desirable methods of packaging, but that no such request had ever been made, so far as he knew, with regard to pemmican. In fact, whenever the industry received an order for pemmican, so far as he knew, it was always a hurry-up order, and each small lot had to be made under conditions which were not as good as if more time had been allowed; especially, the results were not as good as if tests had been made to determine optimum preparation methods, blends and packaging.

This scientist from the packing industry took a position with regard to beef pemmican that was common with the users of its buffalo prototype; he emphasized that "there is pemmican and pemmican," as wide a range of quality as in any other ordinary food, and as much thought and care needed for good results.

Those who favored the use of pemmican by the United States Army in World War II made recommendations of various sorts; but they all had this in common, that they considered pemmican a well known food, of which large amounts should be ordered immediately, on one or more of the standard formulas, and that the pemmican should be sent out for use in any country at any season wherever transportation was an important factor.

Countering this the army nutritionists maintained the position that, so far as the Army was concerned, pemmican was an unknown food. It would be necessary to determine whether soldiers liked it, whether they could keep their health on it, etc. In any case it had the drawback, they maintained, that it was unsuited for summer use and for the tropics.

Those who wanted pemmican to be used did not want the proposed tests made; for they believed them to be stalling devices, with the dietitians hoping that the men would overeat and be nauseated, then testifying that the food made them ill, and things of that sort. Anyway, said the proponents, what can you learn in a few days or weeks by tests on a few men that you do not already know from the century-long experience of thousands?

Generally, those nutritionists who tasted pemmican said that they disliked it as much as they disbelieved in its alleged merits. They felt sure that soldiers would refuse to eat it, and proceeded to the testing with that confidence.

The tests bore them out; and conclusions were formed by the nutritionists at the end which resembled the theories which they had held at the beginning. For the United States Army they were somewhat qualified, however, as will appear through a letter from the Office of the Quartermaster General, dated 26 July, 1944. From this I quote the applicable sections:

"This will acknowledge your letter of 15 July requesting

information on the reasons for the rejection of pemmican for use by the Army of the United States.

"The results of the ration tests which you mentioned are classified information and they cannot be released for publication.

"Probably the most important reason for not including pemmican in the special or emergency rations by the Army is its lack of palatability. Our experience thus far has been that most troops do not like pemmican and in many cases they will go hungry rather than eat it. The chief purpose of a special ration or an emergency ration is to provide soldiers with food in a compact form which will keep them in a condition to fight and work when ordinary food cannot be provided. Obviously this purpose is not achieved when the men fail to eat their rations. . . .

"From a nutritional standpoint, other reasons might be mentioned for not including pemmican in Army rations. Some of these reasons may be controversial and a consideration of such reasons in this letter is unnecessary, since the lack of palatability of pemmican, in our opinion, is sufficient reason for its rejection."

At this point the main concern is to bring out the striking difference of recent test results from those of previous experience.

As has just been shown, the verdict against pemmican by the Quartermaster was based on lack of palatability; so, for purposes of contrast, reference is again made to Chittenden, a general in the United States Army, who, after decades of experience, said it "formed a very palatable as well as a nutritious food"; and to Admiral Peary of the United States Navy, who said, after pemmican had taken him during several different expeditions to the far tip of Greenland, to the North Pole, and to many other places, that it was the only food known to him that a man can enjoy at every meal every day for a year "and have the last mouthful taste as good as the first. And it is the most satisfying food I know."

There is no doubt—I know it, for instance, from conversations with several officers who have been in charge of the tests —that the nutritionists of the Army have been able to find a considerable number of men who say they do not like the taste of pemmican and some who have gone as much as three days on short rations rather than eat it. Now the testimony I have adduced for the palatability of this food is mostly from books, and therefore from men the majority of whom belong to past generations. It has been suggested, though hardly in conformity with ordinary views of human evolution, that a physiological change may have taken place the last decades through which sons do not like and cannot maintain their strength on foods that were palatable, wholesome and sustaining to their grandfathers and even to their fathers. With this in mind I looked around for somebody comparatively young who nevertheless has had a wide experience with pemmican, and found him in the Harvard class of 1933, thus belonging to an age group which has furnished a preponderance of majors and colonels in World War II.

Prentice Gilbert Downes was in 1944 a civilian topographer for the United States Army Corps of Engineers. During the preceding decade he had made several frontier journeys. These, since he is a teacher by profession, were during the summer vacations that are customary in American colleges, so they were summer journeys. Those of them on which he had most occasion to use pemmican were in the forested country west of Hudson Bay where summers are hot and filled with mosquitoes and with portages that subject the canoe traveler to the severest drudgery, as described in a previous chapter through quotations from Ballantyne.

Here was a man of the Eastern college type, a traveler in the pemmican section of Manitoba, who was of an age comparable with the soldiers that were reported by the dietitians

as disliking pemmican. So, for possible testimony, I con-
sulted a book written by Downes, *Sleeping Island,* which had
been published when the war was already in progress, thus
contemporaneously with the army ration trials. I did find
on pages 190-191 a description of pemmican and a discussion
of its qualities. Downes says in conclusion:

"The pemmican is an important staple of this part of the
North. . . . It is the most delicious and sustaining food for
the trail that exists . . . in the early days of the fur trade,
the voyageurs existed almost solely on pemmican. . . ."

Except through what is implied by saying that the fur
traders used to live almost wholly on pemmican during their
summer journeys, Downes has nothing in his book on
whether pemmican is wholesome and sustaining in the long
run. So I wrote him on this point. He replied at length in a
letter dated from the Office of the Chief of the Air Corps of
the United States Army, May 9, 1943. From this I take extracts that bear directly on the two main issues, palatability
and the maintenance of health and strength.

"I always made every effort to secure pemmican. . . . It
has been my experience that nothing else is so practical and
satisfactory. The Chipewyans made two grades, a coarser with
less fat content and a finer with more fat content. This latter
is of course the choice and most nourishing. . . .

"My own use of pemmican has always been somewhat con-
strained by lack of supply.* I have never been so fortunate as
to have enough (that is, all I wanted and enough for four
meals in the working day). It was customary to eat available
fish and use the pemmican when I felt my energy lagging.
[We ate] pemmican, if possible, at the night meal. We would
also eat pemmican at any time of day if a big portage or very

* Downes explains elsewhere in the letter that in northeastern Manitoba
pemmican was hard to find and, in a land where other foods were cheap,
Indians would buy it from each other at relatively exorbitant prices. In
his own case, he found at Brochet, Manitoba, that in the 1938-43 period it
cost "a dollar a pound IF you could get it."

bad stretch of poling was anticipated. . . . It was splendid for restoring both strength and ambition. I think the mental effect of pemmican, at least in my own experience, is more important than we usually associate with food and I am firmly convinced of its peculiar mentally stimulating qualities. . . .

"On the Nueltin Lake trip, when we had some pemmican, I never experienced fatigue sufficiently serious to really impede me. . . . Later I made a return trip and used the best of available civilized food, going out with a freighting outfit of Indians, and experienced extreme fatigue. There may have been other factors but I know my own feeling was very strong for pemmican. . . .

"An important thing with pemmican is that it seems to have a relatively quick point of satiety. This is very important where both quantity and nutrition are a consideration. In contrast to any known dry [condensed] food, pemmican is a working food that goes a very long way."

So Downes, a man in his young thirties, is in agreement with Dr. Priestley, who was quoted on page 259 as saying when he was in his thirties, thirty years ago, that he would not have exchanged a serving of pemmican for twice its weight of any other delicacy—in agreement, too, with Admiral Peary, who was about thirty years ahead of Priestley, and so on with the whole sequence of pemmican enthusiasts back to the eighteenth century who have been quoted here, together with many others whom I did not quote for want of space. It would seem, then, that the liking of frontiersmen, explorers and sportsmen for pemmican has remained the same through all the generations back to the fur trade.

How explain, then, the letter quoted from the Office of the Quartermaster General of the United States Army with regard to soldiers, which says that "lack of palatability of pemmican, in our opinion, is sufficient reason for its rejection"?

Still more difficult is it to reconcile these things with the results of a test that was made during World War II on men of the Canadian Army under the supervision of a group of scientists which was international in the sense that they represented both the States and Canada. For the report of this test shows that soldiers who were using pemmican under the watchful eyes of nutritionists found both that the food is prohibitively unpalatable and that those who eat it cannot keep their strength on it.

I acknowledge gratefully the permission which has been given me to quote from the report of this test, though under the handicap that I must not reveal when or where the testing was done nor by what scientists.

No report of an experiment could well be more convincingly set up than the one which is about to be reviewed.

The document carries the names, academic degrees and military rank or civilian status (connection with respected institutions) of those who supervised the tests and arrived at the conclusions. There is precise information on almost every conceivable phase of the trials. There are tables of the results, and graphs.

The report, it is stated on its first page, is not official: "The views expressed . . . are those of the authors and are not to be construed as officially endorsed by any governmental agency." The title of the document is: *Defects of Pemmican as an Emergency Ration for Infantry Troops.* I quote with certain omissions, indicated by dots, using enough of the document, I feel, to bring out its true spirit and its main conclusions.

"METHODS. The maneuvers were held . . . in January and February. Temperatures ranged from —31° F. to +33° F., with a mean of —3° F. for the whole period. . . . The troops were from a seasoned rifle regiment, and the platoon which tested pemmican was particularly chosen because of its exceptional showing in physical fitness tests and in morale

during previous maneuvers in the same area. The command
ing officer was an excellent leader, skilled in bushcraft.

"The platoon was provided with and knew how to use
adequate arctic protective clothing and equipment. They
bivouacked throughout the test in a single spot, returning
each evening after the day's problems. . . . Energy expenditure in work was estimated to average about 4,500 Cals.
daily.

"The ration consisted of food for one man for one day:
Pemmican made of dehydrated prime beef with added suet,
four aluminum-wrapped blocks, 27 oz.; tea in bags, 6 bags;
cigarettes (5 per pkg.), 2 pkg.; matches, safety, 1 box;
matches, book, 1 book; instructions for using ration, 1 sheet.

"The calories were 70 per cent from fat and 30 per cent
from muscle. By analysis the pemmican contained no
ascorbic acid and only traces of riboflavin and thiamine. No
extra salt had been added.

"The instruction sheet read as follows:

" 'Four packages of dehydrated prime beef with added suet
—⅜ lb. each. A concentrated ration. Must be eaten in small
amounts.

" 'This ration is the most concentrated food known to
man, and so there is danger of overeating. *If taken in too
large amounts at any one meal* it may nauseate you.

" 'Do not overeat. If you choose you may carry the ration
in your pocket and nibble at it on the march.

" 'Hot black tea will keep you alert and warm. Drink fairly
large quantities of hot tea with meals. The ration is usually
eaten cold, not necessarily frozen. Heating, which separates
the fat from the lean, makes it difficult for some people to
eat the ration, or digest it properly.

" 'On days when heavy work is not done you will not eat
all your ration. Do not discard any part of it; return what
you do not eat to the Quartermaster. The ration is expensive.'

". . . In order to avoid prejudice, the word 'pemmican' was never mentioned in front of the troops.

"A variety of observations was made during the test. . . . Control observations were made on 3 other platoons which were subsisting on adequate field rations but undergoing the same rigors of environment and work as the platoon on pemmican.

"RESULTS. The work of the first day was hard and tiring. . . . The men tried conscientiously to follow instructions, nibbling at the pemmican throughout the day. Some heated it in boiling water but the majority took it cold. At the end of the day morale was not high, there were complaints about the food, and 11 of the 17 men complained of nausea.

"The second was a trying day, with the men hauling fully loaded toboggans 13 miles in deep snow over bush and trail. In contrast to their usually cheerful adaptation in previous tests the troops showed very poor morale and felt the cold so keenly that wood fires had to be started at the noon halt. The platoon ate very little. One soldier vomited early in the morning, one was dizzy all day, 4 were nauseated all day, and 12 felt weak and tired. Pathological fatigue was evident and it took 4 men to haul a toboggan even on level snow, when only 2 would ordinarily be required.

"The third day brought the platoon to the point of disintegration as a military unit. A 15-mile reconnaissance was scheduled. One man vomited twice before starting, and 4 others were so weak and exhausted during the morning that they had to be taken back to camp in a truck. At the noon halt the commanding officer decided that to complete the day's objective would risk too many casualties, so he turned back for camp. All of the men were very weak and exhausted. . . .

"A meeting of all test personnel was held to decide what to do with the platoon. It was agreed that they had started out 3 days before in excellent physical condition and with fine morale but had deteriorated to exhausted, unfit troops useless for military purposes. The line officers of the company agreed that if there had been actual combat between any of the other 3 platoons and the platoon eating pemmican, the latter would have all been casualties by the end of the second day. As the platoon was totally useless operationally, it was taken to base camp for 36 hours for study.

"On the morning of the fourth day, physical examination revealed a group of listless, dehydrated men with drawn faces and sunken eyeballs, whose breath smelled strongly of acetone. Neurological changes were present in several; tendon jerks were asymmetrical or absent. No other positive findings were recorded.

"Balance with respect to calories, water, salt and vitamins showed striking changes. The average weight loss was 7 pounds in 3 days. Average caloric intake had been 1,500 Cals. daily with a range from 800 to 3,800 and estimated average daily expenditure had been 4,000, 5,200 and 3,800 Cals. The platoon suffered from dehydration, low chloride reserves and low vitamin C reserves; but showed no significant changes in vitamin B_1, vitamin B_2 or niacin as measured by Factor F_2. The platoon was and had for 2 days been suffering from a severe acidosis as evidenced by gross ketonuria and ketonemia. During these 2 days medical examiners had already noticed acetone in high concentration on their breath.

"Physical fitness was at a very low ebb, as was shown both by performance in the field and by short tests. One week previous to eating pemmican they all had finished a route march of 47 miles in 36 hours. After 3 days of pemmican they were unable to finish a 15-mile reconnaissance. As measured by the 'pack test' their fitness was extremely poor.

"The diagnoses were clearly caloric deficiency, with associated ketosis; dehydration; salt depletion; and ascorbic acid depletion. The chief difficulty was caloric deficiency with associated ketosis, as was shown by feeding the platoon a high caloric carbohydrate diet consisting of toast, jam and hot sugared tea with added condensed milk, breakfast being at 8 A.M. and lunch at 12:30 P.M. Figure 6 [a group photograph] shows the extremely rapid improvement in fitness and decrease of ketonuria. Symptomatic recovery was equally rapid. The average voluntary caloric intake on this one day was estimated to be about 7,500 Cals."

Thus did a rigidly controlled scientific test demonstrate in three days that those had been misled who had inferred from records of the fur trade, and from current tests such as that of Earl P. Hanson given in Chapter 6, that soldiers, like sportsmen and explorers, could remain in good health and full strength for long periods on pemmican as the sole food.

The supervising committee now faced allegations that pemmican is a good chief item in a mixed diet. Admiral Peary, for instance, has testified in his books that men have done well for at least three months on a ration of three factors only, a pound of pemmican a day, a pound of hardbread, and tea. This would be a ration where substantially more than half of the calories were derived from pemmican. The "Drawbacks of Pemmican" report deals with such allegations as Peary's:

"On the fifth day, the platoon was transported again to its bivouac area, and was offered, with considerable misgivings, a ration containing:

"Pemmican, 13.5 oz.; pilot biscuits, 10 oz.; rolled oats, 5 oz.; evaporated milk, 5 oz.; sugar, 3 oz.; tea, 6 oz.; salt, 1 oz.; matches, 2 pkgs.; cigarettes, 10.

"Approximately 5,000 Cals. a day were offered to each man. Much to the surprise of the observers, who thought that the troops had such a distaste for pemmican that they would never touch it again in any form, the men made hot mixtures of pemmican with biscuits or oatmeal and found them fairly acceptable for the next 6 days. They remarked repeatedly that they appreciated very much having sugar for their tea and salt for their pemmican, neither of which had been issued during the first 3 days.

"Considering their extreme weakness and general uselessness on the third day [of the exclusive pemmican diet], the men performed fairly well for the rest of the test, and all completed a forced march of 46 miles in 35 hours at the end. They seemed to have enough energy to complete all of their problems almost as well as the other 3 platoons but were usually very tired at night. Many of the soldiers complained that they never did feel normally fit; and in fact, they did not recover their normal physical fitness until they had been rested for a week on a good garrison ration. Morale in the last 6 days of the test was good; performance and energy picked up tremendously; physical fitness improved; and at the end all medical and nutritional abnormalities had disappeared.

"DISCUSSION. The chief evidence of the proponents of pemmican as an emergency ration is the performance of explorers in cold climates. We have made a complete search of the literature in order to determine exactly how pemmican has been used. . . . To the best of our knowledge no party has ever reported living on pemmican alone; it has always been used along with a variety of other components, commonly including biscuits and cereal products. . . . The results of the thorough literature search indicate clearly that pemmican has never been used as the sole component of an emergency ration and that it has proved unsatisfactory when used as a major part of the ration. . . .

"Present experience leads to the conclusion that pemmican is undesirable as a component of military emergency rations."

In the face of so clear-cut a verdict by dietitians who have conducted so rigorous an experiment as is here described, running three days on exclusive pemmican and six on pemmican as one of several ingredients, it is of only passing interest to mention a few anomalies.

The report says, for instance, that "The chief evidence of the proponents of pemmican as an emergency ration is the performance of explorers in cold climates." This is a remarkable allegation; for most or all of the "proponents" known to me have emphasized that pemmican was originally in the main a summer ration. More pemmican was surely used in one summer by the fur trade than has been used in a hundred winters by all the polar explorers.

The report says: "We have made a complete search of the literature in order to determine exactly how pemmican has been used." But the bibliography submitted in support of this statement is of less than a hundred books, none of which contains any extensive discussion of the use of pemmican by the fur trade, or indeed by anyone except polar explorers. Thus the "thorough literature search" is based on works that cover only one or two per cent of the total known use. Nor is it a fair sampling of the literature, since the small fraction examined was taken from a restricted group, the polar explorers, omitting such other groups as fur traders, overland explorers, sportsmen.

A striking illustration of the manner in which trained scientists can discover things to which the layman is blind, appears in a long table which is based on the mentioned "complete search of the literature." I, for one, suffer with a feeling of bewildered incompetence when I find the committee of nutritionists analyzing my own reports and arriving at conclusions the opposite of mine. However, this is perhaps not so very strange, for traveling parties of which I have been a member lived in the main by hunting, so we had little occasion to use pemmican.

The truly remarkable thing is how the scientists, by a study of Admiral Peary's records, arrive at conclusions opposite to his. What Peary's were, the reader can remind himself by turning back to pages 257–58 of this volume, or, better, through reading the entire pemmican section in Peary's own *Secrets of Polar Travel*, pages 77-83. Let it be noted here that Peary's verdict includes his saying that to him pemmican was the only indispensable food, that he and his men never got tired of it though they ate it at every meal for months, and that "it is the most satisfying food I know."

How far in the wrong Peary was in his conclusions, according to at least some nutritionists who have read his books, appears in the analysis of his experience with pemmican by the report under discussion. It finds that, as a result of using pemmican for the chief ingredient in a ration the other elements of which were biscuit and tea, Peary's men showed "exhaustion, accumulated weariness, suffered from cold, insomnia."

The report does not specify on what food a party would not suffer from accumulated weariness, for instance, toward the end of Peary's North Pole journey, when he and his men had traveled 900 miles and more in 63 days, not merely walking over the drifting floes of the Arctic sea but, for part of the time, helping the dogs to drag the sledges. Nor does the report enter into the detail of what food Peary should have used to avoid suffering from cold—ignoring the point that he claims his men suffered less from cold than usual in polar work. As to the insomnia, Peary dwells on this especially for the periods when he was just approaching and just leaving the Pole, as well as while he was there. This insomnia the analysis of the dietitians traces to the pemmican that was being eaten. Peary had thought it due to mental suspense, when he was about to reach the goal of his life work, and to excitement following the attainment of what had been his main purpose throughout all the years from 1886 to 1909.

But even if the scientists were wrong in their interpretations, and Peary right, that would not be much of a point. The fact would remain that, through a rigorous demonstration of nine days, the nutritionists arrived at a conclusion irreconcilable not merely with the experience of Peary and the other explorers but with the far longer and broader experience of the fur trade.

The scientists who conducted the test, on which the "Defects of Pemmican" report is based, may have been ever so unaware of the history of pemmican and ever so careless in their use of the limited collection of books of which they were aware (to judge by their bibliography). They made up for all this through being meticulous about their field studies. For instance, "In order to avoid prejudice, the word 'pemmican' was never mentioned in front of the troops." Then the camera was used to reinforce what we might otherwise have found it hard to believe, and we are shown a photograph of a sturdy young man flat on his back to confirm, as the legend says, that "On the second day excessive fatigue was apparent."

In view of all this and more, "The line officers of the company agreed that if there had been actual combat between any of the other platoons and the platoon eating pemmican, the latter would have all been casualties by the end of the second day." With such a condition facing them, what else could military nutritionists do but find against pemmican as a military ration?

We are in a dilemma, then, between two clear-cut and diametrically opposed verdicts. The one in favor of pemmican was arrived at by historians, primarily from evidence of the fur trade and secondarily from the testimony of explorers and sportsmen. The verdict against has been arrived at by scientists from the testimony of soldiers, buttressed by what the nutritionists and the camera have seen in confirmation.

We might speculate on resolving this dilemma. It has been suggested that explorers and sportsmen welcome pemmican as a diet because they are interested in what they are doing, and willing if not eager to use whatever food serves their ends most satisfactorily; while it is assumed the soldier is not interested in his job and is therefore less willing, if not definitely unwilling, to change from accustomed food.

There has been the suggestion, too, that the tests made by the explorers and the fur traders are truly physiologic in their nature, psychology playing a minor part—and a favorable one, since these men before they ever tasted pemmican were predisposed for it by what they had read and heard. That soldiers are supposed to be predisposed against pemmican is indicated by the report I have quoted, where it says that the supervisory officials were careful not to mention the word "pemmican" in the presence of the men, in order to avoid prejudicing them. However, it is difficult to see whence the food could have received a bad reputation, since nearly everyone who has written about it, from the earliest times to the present, has been favorable on immediate satisfactoriness for a day of hard work, upon long-term satisfaction when months on end were required, and especially upon palatability.

It has been suggested that pemmican is thought by soldiers to have been invented by Eskimos, which is supposed to antagonize them. This is on the assumption that soldiers, like the nutritionists who handled the Canadian test, believe pemmican to be, historically speaking, a cold-weather food only.

Since none of these solutions appears satisfactory, the debate remains impaled on the horns of a dilemma.

However, the military tests that resulted in unfavorable verdicts have been so far only cold-weather tests; and pemmican was originally a summer food, used by the fur trade of the Plains during the open season when the rivers were flowing and when temperatures would soar to 100° in the shade, with the men laboring under a burning sun. From this angle possibly significant evidence has come recently to the effect that businessmen and engineers are deeply concerned about the lack of energy shown by Europeans in a tropical climate, and that they think they may have found a solution. It appears that many from these two groups, and some physiologists and medical men, are increasingly of the view that the lack of energy observed among white men in the tropics, as compared with natives, may be due not to an effect of the climate, as such, upon the European but may instead be caused by his dietetics—his belief that meat, lean and fat, but particularly the fat, should be avoided.

Accordingly, we learn that some of the larger rubber plantations in Africa, and elsewhere, are thinking of increasing experimentally the meat element in the diets of their white employees, giving them both more lean and more fat, but particularly more fat.

It may be, then, that pemmican, temporarily successful in cold weather among the polar explorers, is about to return to its original function as a hot-weather diet.

Postscript

WHEN our book was in page proof, too late for material changes, a friend sent in the October, 1945, issue of *Nutrition Reviews*, published by the Nutrition Foundation of New York City, which contains a summary, "Defects of Pemmican as an Emergency Ration for Infantry Troops," covering an article in *War Medicine* which would appear, from this abridgment, to be substantially like, if not identical with, the secret report of the Canadian Army trials which we have been discussing on pages 303-313, *ante.* The secrecy as to where the pemmican tests were made, and who supervised them, would thus appear to have been lifted, and the reader will be able to examine the considered verdict, whether as a synopsis in the above-cited issue of *Nutrition Reviews* or as a full-scale contribution to *War Medicine* for June, 1945.

It seems, then, that the nutritionists who were in charge of the Canadian trials have not changed their minds. This is confirmed through a dispatch from Churchill, Manitoba, signed by David M. Nichol, Daily News Foreign Service, which was published in the Chicago *Daily News* of February 12, 1946:

"One more Arctic myth has been exploded in the preparation for Exercise Muskox, the Canadian Army's 3,200-mile march through the North.

"Pemmican, the Arctic food that appears in all the novels, is not sufficient by itself. A platoon fed with it alone disintegrates within three days into a group of useless men.

"Two weeks were required to restore the group to full

physical fitness, according to a series of tests run by the Canadian Medical Corps and the Fatigue Laboratory of Harvard University.

"Pemmican is dried and pounded caribou meat or beef over which boiled fat or suet has been poured. It will keep for long periods and has a consistency like pate de fois gras. The natives pack it in skins.

"Explorers like Stefansson had urged it as an exclusive Arctic diet * for soldiers. Trials demonstrated its inefficiency, however.

"Careful check of Arctic literature showed that expeditions which depended for their food on 40% or more of pemmican headed for grim tragedy."

According to this, most if not all of Peary's sledge journeys, among others, should have "headed for grim tragedy," since his ration, especially on the longer and harder trips, came nearer 80% than 40% of dependence on pemmican for their food energy units. Nor is it easy to grasp how Peary was able to sum up his views on provisions in 1917 by saying that pemmican was the "absolute *sine qua non*" of foods for long and hard journeys where transportation difficulties indicate the need for concentrated rations. How could he do that, if each of his own numerous long journeys, afoot, from 1886 to 1909, was "headed for grim tragedy" as the result of his more than 40% dependence on pemmican?

So far as accuracy in reporting the nutritionist verdict is concerned, the February 12 dispatch just quoted from the daily press is suspported by an article in the magazine *Life* for March 11, 1946, which says:

"This [Exercise Muskox] is probably the first arctic expedition which does not carry pemmican. Medical tests

---

* Actually, the "explorers like Stefansson" urged that pemmican be used (a) as the meat element in a complicated ration such as the Army's K or Monopac, (b) in a simple combination like the Peary ration, or (c) by itself, as in the Earl Hanson test, described *ante*. The recommendation was not limited to the Arctic or to winter but was for all zones and seasons.

proved that men who ate pemmican over long periods were weak and despondent."

This coupling of psychologic with physical weakness even sharpens the debate; for numerous civilian travelers have credited pemmican not merely with special excellence in maintaining full strength through long periods but also with promoting an energetic and optimistic frame of mind. One of these, Downes, whose book and letter we have quoted on pages 300-302, wrote in 1944 on the basis of experience in the very region where the February, 1946, part of "Exercise Muskox" was conducted and emphasized findings that are the reverse of the despondency charge of the Army nutritionists: "It [pemmican] was splendid for restoring both strength and ambition. . . . I am firmly convinced of its mentally stimulating qualities."

So we are able to close this postscript March 15, 1946, as we closed our manuscript six months earlier, upon a note of persisting contradiction—the testimonies of history and of laymen on one side against those of current nutritionists and their military experimental subjects on the other.

Bibliography

This is a list of works quoted or referred to. In the case of the author's own writings, only those are included which have a direct bearing on matters discussed in *Not by Bread Alone*.

Abruzzi, Duke of the (Luigi Amadeo): *On the "Polar Star" in the Arctic Sea,* London, 1903.

Anonymous: *Hints to Travellers,* London, 1938.

———: *North Dakota: A Guide to the Northern Prairie State,* Fargo, 1938.

———: *Statement Respecting the Earl of Selkirk's Settlement of Kildonan, etc.,* London, 1817.

———: Symposium of Nutrition Surveys, Federation Proceedings. Federation of American Societies for Experimental Biology, September, 1945, 4:252-281.

Alton, James J.: *See* Kennicott.

Anson, George: *A Voyage Round the World in the Years 1740-44.* New edition, with prefatory notes, by G. S. Laird Clowes. Boston and London, 1928.

Army War College: Memoranda of February 9 and February 19, 1944.

Bagshawe, Thomas Wyatt: *Two Men in the Antarctic,* New York and Cambridge, England, 1939.

Ballantyne, Robert Michael: *Hudson's Bay, Or Life in the Wilds of North America,* Edinburgh, 1848.

Bancroft, Hubert Howe: *History of the Northwest Coast,* San Francisco, 1884.

Barnes, Joseph: Dispatch in New York *Herald Tribune,* May 30, 1944.

Bartlett, Robert A., and Ralph T. Hale: *Northward Ho! The Last Voyage of the Karluk,* Boston, 1916.

Belcher, Admiral Sir Edward: *Last of the Arctic Voyages*, London, 1855.

Belden, A. L.: *The Fur Trade of America*, New York, 1927.

Bell, Charles Napier: *See* Kelsey.

Bernacchi, L. C.: *See Polar Book.*

Bertram, Colin: *Arctic and Antarctic. The Technique of Polar Travel*, Cambridge, England, 1939.

Bible. King James version.

Billingsley, L. W., Royal Canadian Air Force. Letter of July 4, 1944.

Branch, E. Douglas: *The Hunting of the Buffalo*, New York and London, 1919.

Bryce, George: *The Remarkable History of the Hudson's Bay Company*, New York, 1900.

Bureau of Ethnology, 14th Annual Report, Washington, 1896. George Parker Winship's translation of the account of the 1540-42 Coronado expedition.

Burnham, Frederick Russell: Letter of September 9, 1945.

————: *Scouting on Two Continents*, New York, 1927.

Burpee, Lawrence Johnston: *Search for the Western Sea*, New York and London, 1908.

————: *See* Murray, A. H.

Burr, George O.: Letter of July 27, 1944.

Butler, Lieutenant General Sir William Francis: *The Great Lone Land*, London, 1872.

————: *The Wild Northland*, London, 1873.

Cameron, D. R.: *See* Tache.

Cameron, William Bleasdell: "The Romance of Pemmican," *Canadian Magazine*, Vol. XVIII, No. 5, March, 1902.

————: *See* Moberly.

Camsell, Charles: Letter of April 13, 1944.

Cannon, Walter B.: Letter of April 17, 1944.

Carnegie, James, Earl of Southesk: *Saskatchewan and the Rocky Mountains*, Edinburgh, 1875.

Catlin, George: "The George Catlin Indian Gallery," *Annual Report* of the Smithsonian Institution to July, 1885, Washington, 1886.

Chappell, Lieutenant Edward: *Narrative of a Voyage to Hudson's Bay*, London, 1817.

Cheadle, W. B.: *See* Milton.

Cherry-Garrard, Apsley: *The Worst Journey in the World*, London, 1922.

Christian Science Monitor: News story of September 25, 1944.

Clowes, G. S. Laird: *See* Anson.

Collins, Henry B.: Letter of August 10, 1939.

Coronado: *See* Winship.

Coues, Elliott: *See* Henry.

Cowie, Isaac: *The Company of Adventurers, A Narrative of Seven Years in The Service of the Hudson's Bay Company During 1867-1874 on the Great Buffalo Plains*, Toronto, 1913.

Cullen, William: *First Lines of the Practice of Physic*. New Edition, Boston, 1790.

Curtin, Jeremiah: *Hero Tales of Ireland*, Boston, 1894.

Dall, William Healy: *Alaska and Its Resources*, Boston, 1870.

De Long, George Washington: *The Voyage of the Jeannette*, Boston and London, 1883.

Denig, Edwin Thompson: "Indian Tribes of the Upper Missouri," *46th Annual Report* of the Bureau of Ethnology, Washington, 1928-29.

D'Eschambault, Rev. Antoine: Letter of March 23, 1944.

de Trobriand, General Philippe Regis de Kerredern: *Four Years with the Army of the Potomac*, Boston, 1889.

———: *Army Life in Dakota*, translated from the French by George Francis Will, Chicago, 1941.

De Veer, Gerrit: *The Three Voyages of William Barents to the Arctic Regions*, Hakluyt Society, 2nd ed., London, 1876.

Dictionary of American English, Chicago, 1944.

Dictionary of American History, 6 vols., New York, 1940.

Dictionary of National Biography, London, 1885-1930.

Dobie, James Frank: Letter of August 7, 1944.

Dodge, Colonel Richard Irving: *Our Wild Indians*, Hartford, 1883.

Doughty, Arthur G.: *See* Kelsey.

Downes, Prentice Gilbert: *Sleeping Island*, New York, 1943.

Du Bois, Eugene F.: "The Control of Protein in the Diet," *Journal* of the American Dietetic Association, September, 1928.

Du Bois, Eugene F.: *See* McClellan.

Encyclopaedia Britannica, 14th edition, New York, 1929.

Encyclopedia of Canada, 6 vols., Toronto, 1935.

English, Captain R. A. J. (prepared by): *Sailing Directions for Antarctica,* Washington, 1943.

Falk, Emil A.: *See* McClellan.

Farrow, Edward S.: *Military Encyclopaedia,* 2nd ed., New York, 1895.

Flandrau, Grace: *Red River Trails,* published by the Great Northern Railway, no date.

Franchere, Gabriel: *Narrative of a Voyage to the North-West Coast of America,* New York, 1854.

Franklin, Sir John: *Narrative of a Journey to the Shores of the Polar Sea,* London, 1824.

———: *Narrative of a Second Expedition to the Shores of the Polar Sea,* London, 1828.

Gates, Charles M.: *See* McLeod.

Ghent, W. J.: *The Road to Oregon,* New York, 1934.

Gibson, Colonel A.: Librarian of the Army War College. Letters of February 19 and June 8, 1944.

Gibson, R. A.: Letter of April 26, 1944.

Goodspeed, Edgar Johnson: Letter of December 12, 1936.

Gordon, Daniel Minor: *Mountain and Prairie,* Montreal, 1880.

Gosch, C. C. A.: *See* Munk.

Grant, George Monro: *Ocean to Ocean,* Toronto, 1873.

Greene, F. V.: Section of his report in "Reports upon the survey of the boundary between the territory of the United States and the possessions of Great Britain, etc." U.S. State Department, 1878.

Grenfell, Sir Wilfred: *Labrador: The Country and the People,* New York, 1912.

Grinnell, George Bird: *See* Whitney.

Hale, Ralph T.: *See* Bartlett.

Hambidge, Gove (Editor): *Climate and Man: Yearbook of Agriculture,* U.S. Dept. of Agriculture, Washington, 1941.

Handbook of Indians of Canada, Ottawa, 1912.

Hanson, Earl Parker: *Journey to Manaos,* New York, 1938.

———: Letter of February 29, 1944.

Hargrave, Joseph James: *Red River*, Montreal, 1871.

Harley, G. W.: Letters of August 31 and September 25, 1944.

Harmon, Daniel Williams: *A Journal of Voyages and Travels in the Interior of North America*, New York, 1922.

Hawkes, John: *The Story of Saskatchewan and Its People*, Chicago and Regina, 1924.

Hearne, Samuel: *A Journey from Prince of Wales' Fort in Hudson's Bay to the Northern Ocean*, London, 1795.

Henry, Alexander (the younger): Journal of, in *New Light on the Early History of the Greater Northwest*, edited by Elliott Coues, 3 vols., New York, 1897.

Hind, Henry Youle: *Narrative of the Canadian Red River exploring expedition of 1857, and of the Assiniboine and Saskatchewan exploring expedition of 1858*, Toronto, 1859, London, 1860.

Hodge, Frederick Webb (Editor): *Handbook of American Indians North of Mexico* (Bureau of American Ethnology of the Smithsonian Institution), Washington, 1910.

Hornaday, William Temple: "The Extermination of the American Bison, With a Sketch of Its Discovery and Life History," United States National Museum, *Report* for 1887, Washington.

Hunter, Martin: *Canadian Wilds*, Columbus, Ohio, 1907.

Huntington, Ellsworth: *Mainsprings of Civilization*, New York, 1945.

Ingstad, Helge: *The Land of Feast and Famine*, New York, 1933.

Inman, Henry: *Buffalo Jones' Forty Years of Adventure*, Topeka, Kansas, 1899.

Innis, Harold A.: *The Fur Trade in Canada*, Yale University Press, 1930.

———: *Peter Pond: Fur Trader and Adventurer*, Toronto, 1930.

James, Edwin (Editor): *A Narrative of the Captivity and Adventures of John Tanner*, London, 1830.

Jenness, Diamond: *The Indians of Canada*, Ottawa, 1932.

Jolliffe, Norman: Letter of March 20, 1944.

Johnson, R. E.: *See* Kark.

Jones, Buffalo: *See* Inman.

Kane, Paul, *Wanderings of an Artist,* London, 1859, and Toronto, 1925.

Kark, Major R. M., R. E. Johnson, and Captain J. S. Lewis: "Defects of Pemmican as an Emergency Ration for Infantry Troops," *War Medicine,* June, 1945.

Keating, Wm. H.: *Narrative of an Expedition to the Source of St. Peter's River, Lake Winnepeek, Lake of the Woods, &c. &c. Performed in 1823,* Philadelphia, 1824.

Kelsey, Henry: *The Journal of Henry Kelsey,* edited by Charles Napier Bell, Historical and Scientific Society of Manitoba, 24th May, 1928, Winnipeg, 1928.

———: *The Kelsey Papers,* with an introduction by Arthur G. Doughty and Chester Martin, Ottawa, 1929.

Kennicott, Robert: *The First Scientific Exploration of Russian America and the Purchase of Alaska, The Journal of Robert Kennicott, May 19, 1859-Feb. 11, 1862.* Edited by James J. Alton, Evanston, Ill., 1942.

Kephart, Horace: *The Book of Camping and Woodcraft,* Second Edition, Toronto, 1908.

King, Richard: *Narrative of a Journey to the Shores of the Arctic Ocean,* London, 1836.

Knox, Mrs. Olive Elsie: *By Paddle and Saddle,* Toronto, 1943.

Larpenteur, Charles: *Forty Years a Fur Trader on the Upper Missouri,* edited by Milo Milton Quaife, Chicago, 1933.

Lewis, J. S.: *See* Kark.

Lewis, Meriwether, and William Clark: *Travels to the Source of the Missouri River,* London, 1814.

Lieb, Clarence W.: Comments on Karsten Andersen, published as a note to an earlier paper on Stefansson, with the heading "Statement," *American Journal* of Digestive Diseases and Nutrition, Vol. II, No. 12, February, 1936.

———: "The Effects of an Exclusive Long-Continued Meat Diet, Based on the History, Experience and Clinical Survey of Vilhjalmur Stefansson, Arctic Explorer," *Journal* of the American Medical Association, July 3, 1926.

———: "The Effects on Human Beings of a Twelve Months' Exclusive Meat Diet," *Journal* of the American Medical Association, July 6, 1929.

Lieb, Clarence W.: "A Year's Exclusive Meat Diet and Seven Years Later," *American Journal* of Digestive Diseases and Nutrition, Vol. II, No. 8.

—— and Edward Tolstoi: "Effect of an Exclusive Meat Diet on Chemical Constituents of the Blood," *Proceedings* of Society for Experimental Biology and Medicine, 1929.

——, Vilhjalmur Stefansson, and William A. Thomas: "Meat Diet in Health and in Disease," American Medical Association reprint, 1927.

Lindsay, Martin Alexander: *The Epic of Captain Scott,* New York, 1934.

——: *Sledge,* London, 1935.

Lund, Charles E., Acting Chief, Foodstuffs Unit, Department of Commerce: Letter of June 14, 1944.

MacKay, Douglas: *The Honourable Company,* Indianapolis and New York, 1936.

Mackenzie, Alexander: *Voyages from Montreal, on the River St.·Lawrence, through the Continent of North America, to the Frozen and Pacific Oceans: In the Years 1789 and 1793. With a Preliminary Account of the Rise, Progress and Present State of the Fur Trade of that Country,* London, 1801.

MacLeod, Mrs. A. N.: Letter of June 22, 1944.

Mair, Charles: *The American Bison,* Toronto, 1926.

Manning, T. H.: Letter of May 18, 1944.

Marcy, Randolph B.: *The Prairie Traveler, and Handbook for Overland Expeditions,* New York, 1859.

Markham, Sir Clements Robert: *Lands of Silence,* London, 1921.

Martin, Chester: *Lord Selkirk's Work in Canada,* Toronto, 1916.

——: *See* Kelsey.

Mason, Michael Henry: *The Arctic Forests,* London, 1924.

Matthews, Washington: *Ethnography and Philology of the Hidatsa Indians,* Washington, 1877.

Mawson, Sir Douglas: *The Home of the Blizzard,* London and Philadelphia, 1915.

McClellan, Walter S.: "The Effect of the Prolonged Use of Exclusive Meat Diets on Two Men," *Journal* of the American Dietetic Association, December, 1930.

—— and Eugene F. Du Bois: "Prolonged Meat Diets with a

Study of Kidney Function and Ketosis," *Journal* of Biological Chemistry, July, 1930.

McClellan, Walter S., Virgil R. Rupp, and Vincent Toscani: "Prolonged Meat Diets with a Study of the Metabolism of Nitrogen, Calcium, and Phosphorus," *Journal* of Biological Chemistry, July, 1930.

———, Henry J. Spencer, and Emil A. Falk: "Prolonged Meat Diets with a Study of the Respiratory Metabolism," *Journal* of Biological Chemistry, October, 1931.

———, Henry J. Spencer, Emil A. Falk, and Eugene F. Du Bois: "A Comparison of the Thresholds of Ketosis in Diabetes, Epilepsy, and Obesity," *Journal* of Biological Chemistry, December, 1928.

——— and Vincent Toscani: "Changes in the Rate of Excretion of Acetone Bodies During the Twenty-four Hours," *Journal* of Biological Chemistry, December, 1928.

McClintock, Admiral Sir Francis Leopold: "On Arctic Sledge-Travelling," *The Antarctic Manual*, London, 1901.

McIntire, Vice Admiral Ross T., Surgeon General of the Navy: Letter of March 16, 1944.

McLeod, Archibald Norman: Journal of, for the years 1800-01, in *Five Fur Traders of the Northwest*, edited by Charles M. Gates, Minneapolis, 1933.

Merk, Frederick (Editor): *Fur Trade and Empire: George Simpson's Journal*, Cambridge, Mass., 1931.

Merriman, Robert Owen: "The Bison and the Fur Trade," *Bulletin* of the Department of History and Political and Economic Science in Queen's University, Kingston, Ont., 1926.

Mikkelsen, Captain Ejnar: *Conquering the Arctic Ice*, London and Philadelphia, 1909.

Milton, Viscount, and W. B. Cheadle: *The Northwest Passage by Land*, London, 1865.

Mitchell, Ross: Letter of March 10, 1944.

Moberly, Henry John, and William Bleasdell Cameron: *When Fur Was King*, New York, 1929.

Montu, Elizabeth: *See* Torrey.

Morice, Father A. J.: "The Great Dene Race," *Anthropos*, Salz-
burg, Austria, Vol. I, 1906.
Morton, Arthur S.: *A History of the Canadian West to 1870-71*,
Toronto and New York, 1939.
————: "The Place of the Red River Settlement in the Plans of
the Hudson's Bay Co., 1812-1825," pp. 103-110, of the *Report*
of the 1929 Meeting of the Canadian Historical Association,
Ottawa, 1930.
Munk, Jens: "Navigatio Septentrionalis: That is, a Relation or
Description of a Voyage in Search of the North-West Pas-
sage . . . ," *Danish Arctic Expeditions, 1605 to 1620*, edited
by C. C. A. Gosch. 2 vols. The Hakluyt Society, London, 1897.
Murray, Alexander Hunter: *Journal of the Yukon*, edited by
L. J. Burpee, Ottawa, 1910.
Murray, George (Editor): *The Antarctic Manual for the Use of
the Expedition of 1901*, London, 1901.
Nansen, Fridtjof: *First Crossing of Greenland*, London, 1890.
National Archives, Washington: Letters signed by P. M. Hamer,
Director of Reference Service, dated May 11 and May 24, 1944.
Neihardt, John G., Office of Indian Affairs, Washington: Letter
of March 22, 1944.
Nute, Grace Lee: *The Voyageur*, New York and London, 1931.
Oberholtzer, Ernest C.: Letter of May 31, 1944.
Oxford English Dictionary, 13 vols., Oxford, 1933.
Paden, Irene D.: *The Wake of the Prairie Schooner*, New York,
1943.
Parkman, Francis: *The Oregon Trail*, 4th edition, Boston, 1872.
Peary, Robert E.: *Secrets of Polar Travel*, New York, 1917.
The Polar Book (published for the British Polar Exhibition,
1930, by a committee of British Arctic and Antarctic explorers,
under direction of L. C. Bernacchi), London, 1930.
Pond, Peter: *See* Innis.
Pope, John: "Report on an exploration of the Territory of
Minnesota by Brevet Captain Pope," Senate Executive Docu-
ment 42, 31st Cong. 1st Session.
Post, Augustus: Letter of March 9, 1944.
Powell, John Wesley: 23rd annual report of the Bureau of
American Ethnology, Washington.

Priestley, Raymond E.: *Antarctic Adventure,* London and New York, 1915.

Pritchett, John Perry: *The Red River Valley, 1811-1849,* New Haven, Toronto and London, 1942.

Quaife, Milo Milton: *See* Larpenteur.

Reid, A. P.: "Half-breed Races of North-Western Canada," *Journal* of the Royal Anthropological Institute of Great Britain and Ireland. 4:49, 1875.

Rice, Henry M.: Letter to J. E. Fletcher, contained in House Executive Document 51, 31st Congress, 1st Session, "Report of Major Wood."

Richardson, A. J. H.: Letter of April 8, 1944.

Richardson, Albert D.: *Beyond the Mississippi,* New York, 1867.

Richardson, John: *Arctic Searching Expedition,* 2 vols., London, 1851.

Ridge, John: Letter written about June 1, 1944, to Ross Mitchell.

Ritchie, Stephen G.: "The Dentition of the Western and Central Eskimos," Vol. XII, Report of the Canadian Arctic Expedition 1913-18, *The Copper Eskimos,* Ottawa, 1923.

Robinson, H. M.: *The Great Fur Land, Or Sketches of Life in the Hudson's Bay Territory,* London, n.d. (ca. 1879).

Roe, F. G.: Letters of April 28, May 25, and June 21, 1944.

Rupp, Virgil R.: *See* McClellan.

Russell, Frank: *Explorations in the Far North,* Iowa City, Iowa, 1898.

Sage, Walter N.: "John Work's First Journal, 1823-1824," *Report* of the Annual Meeting of the Canadian Historical Association, held at Ottawa, 1929, Department of Public Archives, Ottawa, 1930.

Schley, Rear Admiral Winfield Scott, and J. R. Soley: *The Rescue of Greely,* New York, 1885.

Schoolcraft, H. R.: *Indian Tribes of the United States,* Vol. IV, Philadelphia, 1854.

Scott, Robert Falcon: *Scott's Last Expedition,* London and New York, 1913.

———: *The Voyage of the Discovery,* London and New York, 1905.

———: *See* Lindsay.

Selkirk Papers: Unpublished documents in Public Archives of Canada.

Seltzer, Carl C.: "The Anthropometry of the Western and Copper Eskimos, based on Data of Vilhjalmur Stefansson, *Human Biology,* Vol. 5, No. 3, September, 1933.

Shackleton, Sir Ernest Henry: *The Heart of the Antarctic,* London, 1909.

Simpson, Thomas: *Narrative of the Discoveries on the North Coast of America,* London, 1843.

Simpson, Sir George: *Narrative of an Overland Journey Around the World,* London, 1847.

———: *See* Merk.

Skinner, Constance Lindsay: *Beaver Kings and Cabins,* New York, 1933.

Slaughter, Linda M. "Leaves from Northwestern History," *Collections* of State Historical Society of North Dakota, Vol. I, Bismarck, N. D., 1906.

Smithsonian Institution: Letter of March 2, 1944, signed by J. E. Graf, Associate Director.

Soley, J. R.: *See* Schley.

Spencer, Henry J.: *See* McClellan.

Spilsbury, Francis: *Free Observations on the Scurvy, Gout, Diet and Remedy,* London, 1780.

Steele, Major General Sir Samuel Benfield: *Forty Years in Canada,* Toronto, 1915.

Stefansson, Vilhjalmur: "Adventures in Diet," *Harper's Magazine,* November, December, 1935, January, 1936.

———: *Anthropological Papers,* New York, 1913.

———: *Arctic Manual,* New York, 1944.

———: "The Diet of Eskimos," *Medical Record,* August 16, 1939.

———: "The Diets of Explorers," *The Military Surgeon,* Vol. 95, No. 1, July, 1944.

———: "The Dilemma in Vitamins," *Science,* May 26, 1939.

———: "Food of the Ancient and Modern Stone Age Man," *Journal* of the American Dietetic Association, Vol. 13, No. 2, July, 1937.

———: *The Friendly Arctic,* New York, 1921.

Stefansson, Vilhjalmur: *Greenland,* New York, 1942.

————: *Hunters of the Great North,* New York, 1922.

————: "Living on the Fat of the Land," *Harper's Magazine,* July, 1945.

————: *My Life with the Eskimo,* New York, 1913.

————: "Observations on Three Cases of Scurvy," *Journal* of the American Medical Association, November 23, 1918.

————: "Pemmican," *The Military Surgeon,* Vol. 95, No. 2, August, 1944.

————: "See Your Dentist Twice a Year," *Atlantic Monthly,* November, 1945.

————: *Unsolved Mysteries of the Arctic,* New York, 1938.

————: *See* Lieb.

————: *See* Seltzer.

Stelfox, Henry: Letters of June 15 and July 2, 1944.

Stirling, Matthew Williams: "Indians of Our Western Plains," *National Geographic Magazine,* July, 1944.

Tache, Alexandre Antonin: *Esquisse sur le Nord-Ouest de l'Amerique,* Montreal, 1869.

————: *Sketch of the North-West of America,* Translated into English by Capt. D. R. Cameron, Montreal, 1870.

Tanner, John: *See* James.

Thomas, William A.: *See* Lieb.

Thompson, David: *David Thompson's Narrative of his Explorations in Western America,* 1784-1812, edited by J. B. Tyrrell, Toronto, 1916.

Thwaites, Reuben Gold: *Jesuit Relations and Allied Documents,* 72 vols., Cleveland, 1896-1901.

Tolstoi: Edward: "The Effect of an Exclusive Meat Diet on the Chemical Constituents of the Blood, *Journal* of Biological Chemistry, September, 1929.

————: "The Effects of an Exclusive Meat Diet Lasting One Year on the Carbohydrate Tolerance of Two Normal Men," *Journal* of Biological Chemistry, September, 1929.

————: *See* Lieb.

Torrey, John C., and Elizabeth Montu: "The Influence of an Exclusive Meat Diet on the Flora of the Human Colon," *Journal* of Infectious Diseases, August, 1931.

Toscani, Vincent: *See* McClellan.

Trobriand: *See* de Trobriand.

Turner, Lucien M.: "Ethnology of the Ungava District," *11th Annual Report* of the Bureau of Ethnology, for 1889-90, Washington, 1894.

Tyrrell, J. B.: *See* Thompson.

Umfreville, Edward: *The Present State of Hudson's Bay*, London, 1790.

Wade, Mason: Letter of May 12, 1944.

Webster's New International Dictionary, Springfield, Mass., 1939.

West, John: *A Substance of a Journal During a Residence at the Red River Colony, British North America*, London, 1824.

Whitney, Caspar: *On Snow-Shoes to the Barren Grounds, Twenty-Eight Hundred Miles After Musk-Oxen and Wood-Bison*, New York, 1896.

———, George Bird Grinnell and Owen Wister: *Musk-Ox, Bison, Sheep and Goat*, New York, 1904.

Wilkins, Sir Hubert, *Undiscovered Australia*, London, 1928.

Will, George Francis: Letters of March 22 and May 12, 1944.

———: *See* de Trobriand.

Winship, George Parker: "The Coronado Expedition 1540-1542," *14th Annual Report*, Bureau of Ethnology, Smithsonian Institution.

Wissler, Clark: *The American Indian: An Introduction to the Anthropology of the New World*, New York, 1917.

Wood (Major): *See* Rice.

Wood, Stewart Taylor, Commissioner, Royal Canadian Mounted Police: Letter of March 22, 1944.

Work, John: *See* Sage.

Index

CPSIA information can be obtained
at www.ICGtesting.com
Printed in the USA
BVHW050015091221
623543BV00002B/215